IOWA
GEOLOGICAL SURVEY

Bulletin No. 4
Revised Edition

THE WEED FLORA
OF IOWA

By L. H. PAMMEL and CHARLOTTE M. KING
WITH THE COLLABORATION OF
J. N. MARTIN, J. C. GILMAN, J. C. CUNNINGHAM,
ADA HAYDEN, F. D. BUTCHER, D. PORTER,
R. R. ROTHACKER

GEORGE F. KAY, Ph. D., State Geologist
JAMES H. LEES, Ph. D., Assistant State Geologist

DES MOINES:
PUBLISHED FOR THE IOWA GEOLOGICAL SURVEY
BY THE STATE OF IOWA
1926

LETTER OF TRANSMITTAL

Iowa Geological Survey

To Governor John Hammill and Members of the Geological Board:

Gentlemen: I submit herewith a revision of the bulletin on the Weed Flora of Iowa and recommend that it be published for distribution among the people of the state.

The thanks of the whole state are due Dr. L. H. Pammel and Miss Charlotte M. King of the Iowa State College of Agriculture and Mechanic Arts for the preparation of a comprehensive and thorough report, representing many years of careful and painstaking scientific work, on a subject that is most intimately related to agriculture, the industry that far exceeds all other industries of our great state.

The Survey wishes to express its thanks to Dean Curtiss, Director of the Iowa Agricultural Experiment Station, for his co-operation, and for his kindness in permitting the Survey to include in the bulletin on weeds results of investigations which were carried forward by Doctor Pammel in connection with the Experiment Station.

The Iowa Geological Survey had the honor, about twelve years ago, to publish a complete monograph by Doctor Pammel on the Weed Flora of Iowa. This publication has proved to be of great value, and has been very popular with all classes of workers with this group of plants. It is with the fullest confidence that this revision of that monograph will be of equal if not of greater service to the agricultural and related interests of the state that it is now presented for publication as a revised edition of Bulletin 4 of the Iowa Geological Survey.

In addition to the first edition of the Weed Flora of Iowa the Survey has published in its series of Bulletins an extensive discussion of the Grasses of Iowa by Doctor Pammel and others, a study of Iowa Birds of Prey by Bert H. Bailey and Miss Clementina S. Spencer and a report on Iowa Rodents by Dayton Stoner. All of these have been extensively used and of much value to the people of Iowa.

I have the honor to be,

Yours very sincerely,

George F. Kay,

State Geologist.

Des Moines, May 1, 1925.   12 465

PREFACE

Weeds do an enormous damage to the crops of Iowa. A conservative estimate places the amount of this annual injury at $50,000,000, a loss which could be largely avoided if we had sufficient information on the subject of weed control to enable us to keep the weeds down. On account of the lack of available information about weeds it seems appropriate to publish at this time a volume of the Weed Flora of the state.

The need of a volume dealing with weeds as a feature of the flora of the state has long been felt by the public schools of Iowa. Many papers touching upon this subject have been published by the Iowa Agricultural Experiment Station, but these papers are mostly out of print. The present work is much more comprehensive than anything heretofore published in this state. As the title indicates, it is not exclusively a book about weeds, but rather a weed flora. Information relating to the geographical distribution of weeds makes it a contribution to the local flora of the United States. The chapter on morphology of weeds will greatly help the student to understand the changes occurring in the development of the flower and the formation of the seed. The chapter on seeds describes a large number of weed seeds; this will be found of value to those engaged in a study of seeds.

In the preparation of this Weed Flora we have been greatly assisted by Messrs. R. I. Cratty, F. W. Paige, O. M. Olson, J. P. Anderson and Prof. B. Shimek, who have aided in giving the geographical distribution of Iowa weeds. In most cases this is indicated in a general way, rather than by specific localities. We were assisted also by Professor J. N. Martin, who has written the chapter on morphology of the plant; by Dr. Ada Hayden, who has written the chapter on dissemination; by Professor J. C. Cunningham, who has written the chapter on roots and underground organs; Dr. J. C. Gilman and others who have contributed the papers to which their names are attached. The bibliography was prepared by Miss King. It is not complete but enough papers are given to enable the student to find the important literature. We are indebted to Dr. Clark, of the Canadian Seed Laboratory, for

the privilege of using some of the admirable illustrations of the
Canadian work on weeds, to Dr. Ernst Bessey for illustrations
from Beal's Weeds of Michigan, also to the Michigan Station
for the classic Hillman seed figures in the Michigan bulletin, to
the Nevada Station for the use of the Hillman cuts, and to the
Connecticut Experiment Station for the use of some figures.
Some of the Hillman figures and a few other figures have been
taken from government publications. We are also indebted to
various publishers for figures which have been taken from several
textbooks of botany, as the Bergen and Davis book published by
Ginn & Co. Others have been taken from several botanical works,
including Thome's, published in German. A few figures have been
taken from the Botanical Gazette, for which credit is given under
each figure. Many of the drawings were prepared by Doctor Hayden. The photographs were made by F. E. Colburn and E. H.
Richardson, photographers at the Iowa Agricultural Experiment
Station; also by Oliver Miller, G. T. Hart, C. R. Quade and Dr. Ada
Hayden. We are also much indebted to Dr. James H. Lees for
assistance in proof reading and critical editorial work. To all who
have assisted in the preparation of ''The Weed Flora of Iowa'' we
wish to express our sincere thanks.

L. H. PAMMEL,
CHARLOTTE M. KING.

Ames, Iowa, February 9, 1925.

TABLE OF CONTENTS

CHAPTER I.

DESCRIPTIVE MANUAL

L. H. PAMMEL and CHARLOTTE M. KING

KEY TO FAMILIES

I. Plants without true flowers; not producing seeds............*Pteridophyta.*
  Stems jointed, rushlike ....*Equisetaceae.*

I. Plants with true flowers, stamens and pistils and producing seeds..........
  Spermatophyta.
  II. Ovules not borne in a closed ovary (Pine, Spruce).....*Gymnospermae.*
  II. Ovules borne in a closed ovary (Rose, Willow, Corn, etc.)..........
  Angiospermae.
    III. Stems endogenous without central pith; no annual rings; parts
      of the flower usually in threes; single cotyledon..............
      Monocotyledoneae.
      1. Grasslike plants 2.
        2. Flowers enclosed by chaff-like scales.
          Stems hollow; sheaths of leaves split............*Gramineae.*
          Stems solid; sheaths of leaves not split.........*Cyperaceae.*
        2. Flowers not inclosed by chaff-like scales..........*Juncaceae.*
      1. Plants not grasslike; flowers with a perianth of 6 pieces;
        stamens 6 ....*Liliaceae.*
    III. Stem formed of bark, wood, and pith, exogenous; leaves netted-
      veined; embryo with a pair of cotyledons........*Dicotyledoneae.*
      1. Corolla absent
        2. Plants fleshy or scurfy...................*Chenopodiaceae.*
        2. Plants not fleshy or scurfy 3.
          3. Ovary free 4.
            4. Flowers unisexual.
              Ovary 1-celled ....*Urticaceae.*
              Ovary 3-celled ....*Euphorbiaceae.*
            4. Flowers perfect.
              Calyx and bracts greenish and scarious...........
              Amaranthaceae.
              Calyx generally corolla-like.
                1. Fruit a 1-seeded achene............*Polygonaceae.*
                1. Fruit a 5-12 seeded berry.........*Phytolaccaceae.*
          3. Ovary inferior ....*Nyctaginaceae.*
      1. Calyx and corolla present.
        2. Corolla of separate petals 3.
          3. Plants fleshy, flowers yellow..............*Portulacaceae.*

3. Plants not fleshy 4.
    4. Pistil single 5.
        5. Flowers regular.
            Stamens numerous, free...........*Ranunculaceae.*
            Stamens numerous; sepals and petals present, inserted on calyx......................*Rosaceae.*
            Stamens 10; fruit a legume.......*Leguminosae.*
    4. Pistil compound 6.

        6. Ovary free.
            Ovary 1-celled ....*Caryophyllaceae.*
            Ovary more than 1-celled 7.
            7. Ovaries united into a ring.........*Malvaceae.*
            7. Ovaries not united into a ring 8.
                8. Leaves simple.
                    With punctate dots; stamens numerous....
                            Hypericaceae.
                    Leaves not with punctate dots; stamens 6..
                            Cruciferae.
                    Leaves compound, pinnately 3-foliate......
                            Anacardiaceae.
                    Leaflets 3, obcordate..........*Oxalidaceae.*
                    Leaflets, 5-7 pairs..........*Zygophyllaceae.*
                    Leaflets 3, viscid or fetid herbs...........
                            Capparidaceae.
        6. Ovary adherent; flowers in umbels..*Umbelliferae.*
        6. Flowers not in umbels..............*Onagraceae.*

1. Calyx and corolla present, petals more or less united.
    2. Flowers regular 3.
        3. Plants with milky juice.
        Stamens united ....*Asclepiadaceae.*
        Stamens distinct ....*Apocynaceae.*
        3. Plants without milky juice.
            4. Plants twining ....*Convolvulaceae.*
            4. Plants not twining 5.
                5. Stamens 5 or more 6.
                    6. Style 2-cleft; flowers not in heads; fruit 2-4 seed-like nutlets ....*Boraginaceae.*
                    Fruit many seeded pod.........*Hydrophyllaceae.*
                    Flowers in heads; anthers in ring or tube about the style ....*Compositae.*
                6. Style 1; fruit many seeded.........*Solanaceae.*
            5. Stamens fewer than corolla lobes.
            Caulescent, flowers blue..............*Verbenaceae*
            Acaulescent, flowers greenish........*Plantaginaceae.*
    2. Flowers irregular.
    Stems 4-angled; ovary deeply 4-lobed.............*Labiatae.*
    Stems not 4-angled; ovary 2-celled........*Scrophulariaceae.*

PTERIDOPHYTA, FERNS AND THEIR ALLIES.

This group of plants, sometimes called vascular cryptogams, is represented in our flora by the maidenhair fern, brake, spleenwort, shield fern, horsetail, etc. The Boston fern is frequently culti-vated.

FIG. 1. Common Horsetail (*Equisetum arvense*). Roadsides, fields, common everywhere in Iowa.
(*Photographed by Colburn.*)

FIG. 1-A. Distribution of Common Horsetail.

EQUISETACEAE, HORSETAIL FAMILY.

This small family of rushlike plants contains a few species only and but one that is weedy.

Common Horsetail (*Equisetum arvense* L.).

Description.—A rushlike perennial with running rootstocks and annual stems; with fertile and sterile plants, the fertile appearing early in spring with a terminal cone, yellowish in color, bearing the spore cases (sporangia) underneath a scale; spores provided with hygroscopic bands; sterile stem with whorled branches.

Distribution.—Widely distributed in North America, common in sandy moist fields and on railroad embankments; common in Story, Boone, Carroll, Crawford, Harrison, Woodbury, Clinton, Dubuque, Lee, Page, Polk, Cerro Gordo, Emmet, Webster, Marshall, Johnson, Winneshiek and Allamakee counties.

Extermination.—This perennial is very persistent in fields; it can be kept in check only by giving frequent shallow cultivation during the summer after the small grain is removed.

SPERMATOPHYTA, FLOWERING PLANTS.

These plants have stamens and pistils and reproduce by seeds. The group is represented by the pine, spruce, hemlock, wheat, rye, corn, rose, maple, ash, aster, goldenrod, squash, etc.

GYMNOSPERMAE, GYMNOSPERMS.

Seeds not inclosed in an ovary. Trees or shrubs generally with needlelike or scalelike leaves; represented in Iowa by the red cedar, white pine, etc. None are weedy.

ANGIOSPERMAE, ANGIOSPERMS.

Ovules borne in a closed ovary. Represented by a large number of our native and cultivated plants, like wheat, corn, lily, rose, clover, tomato, etc.

MONOCOTYLEDONEAE, MONOCOTS.

Plants with endogenous stem, the woody fibers in bundles distributed through the pith. Annual ring absent. Flowers generally on the plan of three; embryo with a single cotyledon. Corn, lily, onion, asparagus, blue grass, switch grass are representatives.

GRAMINEAE, GRASS FAMILY.

This large family is of great economic importance, since it contains many of our food plants, including the well known cereals,

FIG. 2. Johnson Grass (*Sorghum halepense*); *a*, sessile spikelets. A most troublesome weed.
(*Lamson-Scribner, U. S. Dept. Agr.*)

FIG. 2-A. Distribution of Johnson Grass. Reported recently from southwestern Iowa.

rye, wheat, oats, barley, corn, kaffir corn and millet, besides such forage grasses as blue grass, timothy, brome grass, foxtail, and a few ornamental plants, like pampas grass, ribbon grass, etc.

Johnson Grass (*Sorghum halepense* (L.) Pers.).

Description.—A stout perennial, with smooth, erect, simple cu'ms, 3 to 5 feet high, and strong, creeping root-stocks; leaves elongated, one-fourth to three-fourths inch wide, acute; ligule ciliate, and on the back where leaf-blade joins the sheath there is more or less pubescence; panicle open, 6 to 12 inches long, the whorled branches naked below, the 3 to 5-flowered racemes clustered towards their extremities; pedicels of the staminate (rarely neutral) spikelets pilose with stout hairs; sessile spikelet broadly lanceolate, acute, 2 to 3 lines long, pale green or violet, becoming dark or nearly black at maturity; callus small, obtuse, shortly and sparsely barbate; first glume coriaceous, sparingly pubescent on the flattened back, 5 to 7-nerved; second glume similar and equaling the first, convex below, subcarinate above, acute, the hyaline inflexed margins ciliate; third glume a little shorter than the outer ones, membranous, faintly 2-nerved, the infolded margins ciliate; fourth glume broadly oval, obtuse, nearly one-half shorter than the second, 2-lobed or bidentate at the apex, ciliate awned; awn 5 to 8 lines long; palea a little shorter than the glumes, nerveless, ciliate. Introduced and cultivated in many southern states for hay; in many places it has become a dangerous weed, difficult to exterminate.

Distribution.—The weed is common in the south, often a most troublesome weed. It has been reported as persisting in the vicinity of Hamburg, Fremont county, Iowa.

Extermination.—Use the same methods as for quack grass. This may become a most troublesome weed in southern Iowa.

Smooth Crab Grass (*Digitaria humifusa* Pers.).

Description.—An annual 6 inches to 2 feet high, closely resembling *D. sanguinalis* in habit, but smooth throughout, excepting for a few hairs at the throat of the sheaths; spikelets 2 to 7, smaller than in *D. sanguinalis,* about 1 line in length; first glume very minute or obsolete; second and third glumes nearly equal in length, or the second a little shorter than the fourth, pubescent at the beak.

Distribution.—Smooth crab grass is native to Europe but is now cosmopolitan; in eastern North America from New England to Texas and Mexico, Rocky mountains and Pacific coast; less com-

Figure 3   Figure 3-A

FIG. 3.   Common Crab Grass (*Digitaria sanguinalis*).   Common in cultivated fields.
FIG. 3-A.   Smooth Crab Grass (*Digitaria humifusa*); *a*, leaf with sheath; *b*,
spikelet; *c*, *d*, scales, stamens and pistils.   Common in gardens and lawns.
(*Drawn by C. M. King.*)

mon in Iowa than common crab grass; rapidly spreading in the state, particularly in gardens; common in lawns and pastures of Story, Marshall, Linn, Polk, Boone, Pottawattamie and other counties.

FIG. 3-B.   Distribution of Smooth Crab Grass.

Extermination.—This weed is somewhat more difficult to exterminate than the foxtail, especially in lawns where it is common. Here it produces seed so close to the ground that the heads escape the lawn mower. It may, however, be easily destroyed in fields which are cultivated. The soil should be stirred with a cultivator or hoe, exposing the roots to the sun.

Common Crab Grass.   Finger Grass (*Digitaria sanguinalis* (L.) Scop.).

Description.—A much branched, leafy annual, 1 foot to 3 feet high, spreading on the ground, with erect, smooth, spreading culms, frequently rooting at the lower joints, joints sometimes smooth, though more frequently bearded with deflexed hairs; sheaths loose, generally pilose, hairy, ciliate on the margins, with a membranaceous ligule; leaves 2 to 4 inches long with rough margins, occasionally pilose at the base; flowers produced in digitate spikes, hence the common name finger grass; spikelets less than one-eighth inch long in pairs, one nearly sessile, the other with a stalk, each flower consisting of 2 sterile glumes and the flower proper; the first glume very small, the second about one-half to two-thirds as long as the spikelet, usually hairy on the margin, the third glume somewhat longer than the fourth, which is 5-nerved and usually silky-villous along the marginal nerves, fourth glume smooth and

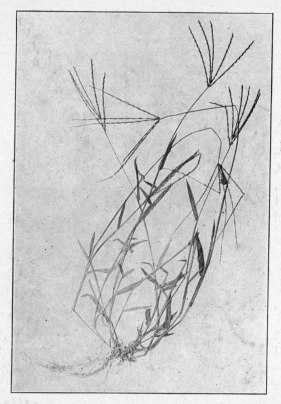

FIG 3-C. Common Crab Grass (*Digitaria sanguinalis*). Common in fields, gardens, meadows. Rooting at the joints.
(*Photographed by Colburn.*)

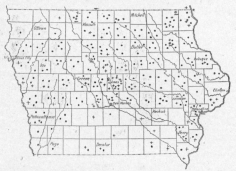

FIG. 3-D. Distribution of Common Crab Grass.

acute; fruit minute, pitted and cross-striated, light straw color except where the sterile glumes remain attached. These areas are gray in color and minutely hairy.

Distribution.—This European grass is cosmopolitan; abundant in the eastern and southern states and in California; common in all parts of Iowa, particularly in gardens, corn fields, and streets. It is abundant in Story, Polk, Carroll, Woodbury, Webster, Marshall, Linn and Clayton counties.

Extermination.—This grass is much more difficult to remove than the foxtails because it roots so readily at the joints. Thorough cultivation will remove the weed. Do not allow it to go to seed.

Chemical Composition.—Common crab grass (*Digitaria sanguinalis*) has been used as a forage plant in many parts of the United States. Many chemical analyses of this grass have been made. Analyses are reported from Mississippi, Tennessee and Iowa. The Iowa analysis reported by Weems is as follows:

NATURAL CONDITION

Sample	Water	Fat	Protein	Albuminoids	Crude fiber	Ash	Nitrogen free extract
1	66.95	1 11	2.52	(1.98)	8.62	4.10	16.70

WATER FREE SUBSTANCE

1		3.34	7.61	(5.98)	26.11	12.41	50.53

Old Witch Grass. Tickle Grass (*Panicum capillare* L.).

Description.—An annual with usually coarse, branching stems 1 foot to 3 feet long, with very hairy leaf-sheaths and capillary, widely spreading panicles, terminal on the culm or its branches; culm geniculate and branching near the base, rarely simple, generally pilose or pubescent below the bearded nodes; sheaths pilose to densely hirsute, with spreading hairs; ligule very short, densely ciliate; leaf-blade flat, lanceolate or linear, acute, usually thinly hairy on both sides, margins scabrous and ciliate near the base; the hairs throughout spring from small papillæ, those on the leaf-blade being confined chiefly to the principal nerves; panicle diffuse, 3 to 12 inches long, the branches solitary, in pairs, or rarely whorled, the ultimate branches and pedicels strongly hispid; spikelets 1 line long, ovate, acute, or abruptly acuminate-pointed, smooth; first glume clasping the base of the spikelet, obtuse or acute, 1 to 3-nerved, about one-third the length of the 5 to 7-nerved and nearly equal second and third glumes, the acute tips of which are sometimes minutely pubescent; flowering glume smooth and shining, elliptical, obtuse, or subacute, a little shorter than the larger outer glumes. Variable. July to October.

FIG. 4. Old Witch Grass (*Panicum capillare*). Common in fields and gardens, etc.
(*Photographed by Hart.*)

FIG. 4-A. Distribution of Old Witch Grass.

Distribution.—Old witch grass is a common weed throughout the state. It is variable, the form occurring in cultivated fields being stout and hispid; but when growing in moist meadows and old lake beds it has slender and somewhat capillary branches. In Iowa it is quite common in Plymouth, Woodbury, Muscatine, Story, Emmet, Franklin, Clinton, Carroll, Crawford, Pottawattamie, Scott and other counties.

Extermination.—This annual grass is easily exterminated by cultivation, and seldom gives trouble in well cultivated corn fields. When the weed is abundant, it might be well to rotate corn with some leguminous crop.

Sprouting Crab Grass (*Panicum dichotomiflorum* Michx.).

Description.—A smooth, usually much-branched annual with stems 2 to 6 feet tall, rather coarsely spreading or ascending (rarely erect); long, flat leaves and diffuse terminal and lateral panicles; sheaths smooth, lax, somewhat flattened; ligule ciliate; leaf-blade 6 to 24 inches long, 2 to 10 lines wide, acute, scabrous on the margins and sometimes also on the prominent nerves, rarely pilose on the upper surface; panicles pyramidal, 4 or 5 to 12 or 15 inches long, the primary and secondary branches spreading, scabrous; spikelets rather crowded upon short, appressed and scabrous pedicels, lanceolate-ovate; acute, 1 line to 1½ lines long, smooth, green or purplish; lowest glume embracing the base of the spikelet, usually obtuse and nerveless, rarely 1 to 3-nerved, one-fourth to one-third as long as the nearly acute 5 to 7-nerved second and third glumes, the latter having sometimes a hyaline palea in its axil; floral glume elliptical, subacute, smooth and shining, a little shorter than the larger outer glumes; anthers saffron yellow.

Distribution.—Widely distributed in eastern North America, common in many parts of Iowa, including Ames, Des Moines, Sioux City, Council Bluffs, Davenport, Eddyville. Frequent in Woodbury, Linn, Polk, Marshall and Carroll counties.

Extermination.—This plant may be controlled by preventing the formation of seeds. The field should have thorough cultivation.

Fig 5.   Sprouting Crab Grass (*Panicum dichotomiflorum*); *a, b, c,* spikelets;
d, e, flowering glume.   Widely distributed in the state.
(*U. S. Dept. of Agr.*)

Fig. 5-A.   Distribution of Sprouting Crab Grass.

Barnyard Grass (*Echinochloa crusgalli* (L.) Beauv.).

Description.—A coarse, ascending, leafy annual 1 to 5 feet high, with wide leaves; spike 1 inch to 3 inches long, crowded in a

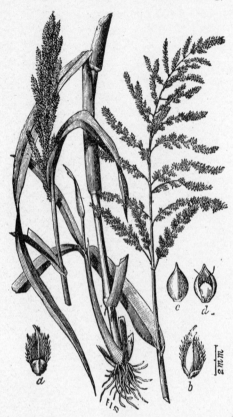

Fig. 6. Barnyard Grass (*Echinochloa crusgalli*). Fields, barnyards and roadsides.
(*U. S. Dept. of Agr.*)

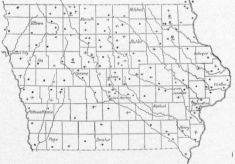

Fig 6-A. Distribution of Barnyard Grass.

dense panicle; culms frequently branched near the base; sheaths
loose, smooth or sometimes hispid; leaves broad and flat, 6 inches
to 1 foot or more long; smooth or roughened, margin roughened;
spikelets densely and irregularly crowded in several rows along
one side of the spikelike branches of the panicle, 1½ lines long,
outer glume or bract from one-fourth to one-half the length of the
spikelets, second and third glumes smooth, pubescent or hispid
along the nerves, fourth glume smooth, awnless or short awn-
pointed.

Distribution.—Barnyard grass is native to Iowa, also to other
parts of North America, and is quite generally distributed, particularly in barnyards, on shores of lakes, streams and in gardens,
but is most abundant in low places. It is common in Story, Boone,
Clinton, Cerro Gordo, Winnebago, Polk, Johnson, Iowa, Scott,
Muscatine, Lee, Keokuk, Fremont, Clayton and Emmet counties.

Extermination.—This plant may be eradicated by thorough cultivation and by preventing the formation of seeds.

Chemical Composition.—Chemical analyses of this grass have
been reported from Iowa, North Carolina and South Dakota.
Weems in a paper on Iowa grasses reports the following composition from Iowa material.

NATURAL CONDITION

Sample	Water	Fat	Protein	Albu-minoids	Crude fiber	Ash	Nitrogen free extract
1	76.34	0.73	1.43	(1.35)	9.44	2.47	9.59

WATER FREE SUBSTANCE

1		3.09	6.07	(5.73)	39.90	10.46	40.48

Yellow Foxtail or Pigeon Grass (*Setaria glauca* (L.) Beauv.).

Description.—An erect annual 1 foot to 2½ feet high; with flat
leaves; bristly cylindrical spike, from 1 inch to 3 inches long; heads
slender; bristles tawny yellow; small seeds conspicuously cross-
striated and distinguished from the next species because of their
larger size and by the cross-striation.

Distribution.—This weed is quite generally distributed in the
United States, particularly in eastern states. It occurs everywhere
in the state of Iowa, particularly in corn fields, where it comes up
abundantly, after the corn is laid by; also in gardens and in pastures, especially in the fall. It is common in grain fields, especially

in Story, Calhoun, Boone, Linn, Marshall, Cerro Gordo, Jasper, Winnebago, Emmet, Lyon, Johnson, Woodbury, Clayton and Winneshiek counties.

Extermination.—It is not generally recognized, but it is probably true, that more money is spent in the extermination of foxtails than of any other class of weeds we have in the state of Iowa, yet they are all easily destroyed. One of the best and most effective methods of destroying the foxtail is by plowing the small grain field as soon as the grain is removed. If this is not done a large amount of seed is produced. After this plowing in the fall the field should be disked and harrowed in the spring and then planted to corn. The corn should be cultivated as frequently as possible, at least four or five times. This method should prove effective for the destruction of foxtail and pigeon grass.

FIG. 7. Pigeon Grass (*Setaria glauca*); *a*, spikelet showing the second glume, the upper portion of the flowering glume and bristles; *b*, spikelet showing the back of the first and third glumes. (*U. S. Dept. Agr.*)

FIG. 7-A. Distribution of Pigeon Grass.

Chemical Composition.—Various analyses have been reported from Washington, D. C., Mississippi, South Dakota and Iowa. The following analyses are given by Dr. Weems:

NATURAL CONDITION

Date	Water	Fat	Protein	Albu-minoids	Crude fiber	Ash	Nitrogen free extract
Sept. 11, 1897	80.53	.50	2.05	(1.91)	6.86	2.92	7.14

WATER FREE SUBSTANCE

	Water	Fat	Protein	Albu-minoids	Crude fiber	Ash	Nitrogen free extract
		2.55	10.53	(9.85)	35.30	14.49	37.13

FRESH OR AIR DRY SUBSTANCE

	Water	Ash	Fat	Crude fiber	Protein	Nitrogen free extract	Albu-minoids
South Dakota (7)	8.17	13.40	1.88	31.25	10.53	34.77	6.94
Tennessee (2):							
Nearly ripe	3.20	7.75	3.80	31.77	5.00	47.48	
Washington, D. C. (3):							
Cut July 1, very young	74.20	2.80	.60	5.59	4.39	12.42	
Cut July 24, early bloom	68.40	2.29	.84	8.14	2.86	17.47	

WATER FREE SUBSTANCE

	Water	Ash	Fat	Crude fiber	Protein	Nitrogen free extract	Albu-minoids
South Dakota (1):							
Aug. 8. 1898		14.59	2.05	34.03	11.47	37.86	
Tennessee (2)		9.04	3.93	32.82	5.16	49.05	
Washington, D. C. (3):							
Cut July 1, very young		10.80	2.30	21.70	17.00	48.10	
Cut July 24, early bloom		7.30	2.70	25.80	9.00	55.30	
Mississippi		16.74	2.71	35.04	9.20	34.31	

Bristly Foxtail (*Setaria verticillata* (L.) Beauv.).

Description.—An annual from 1 foot to 2½ feet high with leaves from 2 to 7 inches long, somewhat narrower than in the preceding, from one-fourth to one-half inch wide; sheaths smooth, rough on the margins and veins; spike cylindrical, from 1 inch to 4½ or 5 inches long, composed of short cylindrical clusters; bristles short, a little longer than the spike, single or in pairs, barbed downward; seeds small, greenish, one-eighth line long, minutely cross-striated and wrinkled.

Distribution.—This European grass is more common in the eastern and southeastern parts of the United States. It is of compara-

Fig. 8. Bristly Foxtail (*Setaria verticillata*); *a*, spikelet showing bristle and glume; *b*, spikelet.
(*U. S. Dept. Agr.*)

tively recent introduction in Iowa and first appeared near green-houses. It is most abundant in the southeastern part, though occurring also at such points as Marshalltown, Ames, Sioux City and Council Bluffs, and elsewhere in Woodbury, Linn, Clayton, Johnson and Polk counties. It is found in gardens and in the streets. It is commonly spread by cattle and sheep. The bristles enable the fruit to cling to animals.

FIG. 8-A. Distribution of Bristly Foxtail.

Green Foxtail (*Setaria viridis* (L.) Beauv.).

Description.—An erect annual from 1 foot to 3 feet high; leaves 4 to 12 inches long, with rough margins; greenish, more or less compound cylindrical spikes from 1 inch to 5 or even in some cases 6 inches long; bristles few, much longer than the spikelets; spikelets one-half inch long, the chaff of second and third glumes as long as the minute chaff of the fourth glume, the latter being dotted and striate. A single head produces an enormous number of seeds.

Distribution.—This European grass is common in North America, especially in the eastern part. It is found everywhere in this state, particularly in corn fields, gardens and vacant places, and has been noted especially in Story, Boone, Polk, Linn, Lee, Appanoose, Madison, Johnson, Fremont, Woodbury, Cerro Gordo, Clayton and Dubuque counties.

Extermination.—The foxtails are annuals and hence it ought to be an easy matter to destroy them. They produce an enormous amount of seed. Mr. G. M. Lummis estimated that a good sized plant of *Setaria viridis* had 2,500 to 5,000 seeds, and *Setaria glauca* 1,000 to 5,000; this being the progeny of a single seed.

Chemical Composition.—Green foxtail grown in Pennsylvania

and cut August 11, 1880, analyzed as follows, according to the U. S. Department of Agriculture.*

Plate 1

GREEN FOXTAIL
(Setaria viridis (L.) Beauv.)

FIG. 9. Green Foxtail (*Setaria viridis*). Common in corn fields and waste places. (*After Clark and Fletcher.*)

*Jenkins and Winton: Bull. Off. Exp. Sta. 11: 71.   Chem. Comp. Am. Grasses, 1884, p. 125:

FRESH AIR DRY MATERIAL

Water	Ash	Protein	Fiber	Nitrogen free extract	Fat
14.30	6.80	7.30	18.80	50.18	2.62

WATER FREE SUBSTANCE

	7.9	8.6	21.9	58.5	3.1

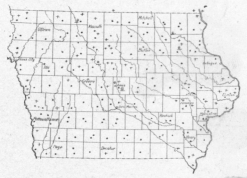

FIG. 9-A. Distribution of Green Foxtail.

Fig. 9-B. Foxtail and other weeds in a back dooryard. There are many such places
in Iowa.
(*Photograph by Charlotte M. King.*)

Where these grasses are so abundant the ground becomes thickly covered. Dr. Beal of the Michigan Agricultural College has found that the seed retains its vitality for a considerable length of time. After six years twenty-one seeds out of fifty germinated. The seeds of all three species are much more tenacious when young than when older. The ground is covered so thickly that only a part of the plants are destroyed by the cultivator. Covering the plants with soil or exposing the roots to the sun are effective measures for destroying these weeds.

FIG. 9-C. A weedy cornfield: Foxtail, smartweed, etc. Such a weedy field materially decreases the yield of corn. The weeds have crowded out the corn.
(Photograph by Pammel.)

Clark and Fletcher recommend as follows: "The only way to eradicate this weed is to mow it or hoe it out before it goes to seed. Anything which prevents it from going to seed for a number of years will eradicate it in time. Most ground, however, is so full of the seed that it takes a number of years of conscientious work to exterminate it."

Sandbur *(Cenchrus pauciflorus* Benth).

Description.—Annual, with spreading or ascending, much-branched culms, rarely 1 foot high, somewhat compressed; leaves flat or simply folded, about 6 inches long, acute, finely serrulate along the margins; sheaths generally much exceeding the internodes, hairy along the margins and at the throat; burs containing the spikelets, 6 to 20, nearly globose, covered with strong and more or less pubescent, barbed spines, which become very hard at maturity and readily fall off.

Distribution.—Common in eastern North America, sandy shores of lakes, streams, and sandy soil. In Iowa, common on Muscatine Island, railroad embankments, gravel knolls, and in Polk, Clinton, Muscatine, Scott, Woodbury, Linn, Jackson, Johnson, Dubuque, Webster and Black Hawk counties.

Extermination.—This weed is easily exterminated by cultivation. The roots are fibrous and exposing them to the sun for a short time will destroy the weed.

FIG. 10. Sandbur (*Cenchrus pauciflorus*). Common on sandy soils, gravel knolls, etc.
(*Photographed by Hart.*)

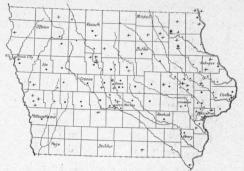

FIG. 10-A. Distribution of Sandbur.

Vanilla or Holy Grass (*Hierochloe odorata* (L.) Wahlenb.).

Description.—A perennial grass with creeping, fragrant yellow-

FIG. 11. Holy Grass, Vanilla Grass (*Hierochloe odorata*). Common in northwestern and northern Iowa in low grounds. Creeping "roots" something like those of Quack Grass, but with the odor of vanilla.

(Photographed by Colburn.)

ish root-stocks, one-half foot high; panicle somewhat one-sided, 2 to 5 inches long; spikelets chestnut colored, 3-flowered; the two lower flowers staminate with 3 stamens; the upper flower perfect, short pedicelled, awnless, with 2 stamens.

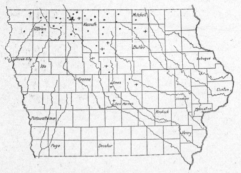

FIG. 11-A. Distribution of Holy Grass.

Distribution.—Common in the north. Frequently a troublesome weed in Minnesota and northwest territory. Common only as a weed in a few of the northwestern counties of Iowa.

Extermination.—This weed can be exterminated by giving a shallow plowing after the crop has been removed and stirring the soil, thus exposing the root-stocks to the action of the sun.

Poverty Grass (*Aristida dichotoma* Michx.).

Description.—A slender, tufted, branched annual from 12 to 24 inches tall; spikelets in narrow, striate, simple or compound spikes; empty glumes nearly equal, longer than the flowering glume, equaling the small lateral awns; the awns unequal, the long middle awn horizontal, but soon becoming reflexed.

Distribution.—Poverty grass is common in dry, sterile, or clay soil in southeastern Iowa.

Extermination.—The fibrous roots of the plant are easily killed by cultivation.

Long-awned Poverty Grass (*Aristida tuberculosa* Nutt.).

Description.—A rigid, much-branched perennial, 12 to 18 inches tall; panicles simple, 4 to 7 inches long; erect, rather distant branches, the lower in pairs of which one is short and few-flowered, the other elongated and many-flowered; empty glumes, nearly equal, awn-pointed, flowering glume, twisted above to division of awns; awns nearly equal, articulated with glume.

Fig. 12. Poverty Grass (*Aristida dichotoma*). Common in dry, sterile soil, *a*, lower or empty glumes of a spikelet; *b*, a floret showing awns, middle one coiled.
(*U. S. Dept. of Agr.*)

Fig. 12-A. Distribution of Poverty Grass.

Distribution.—Common on gravelly knolls and sandy soil in northeastern and eastern Iowa.

Extermination.—This plant succumbs readily to cultivation.

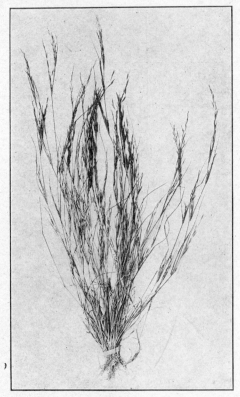

Fig. 13.   Long-awned Poverty Grass (*Aristida tuberculosa*).   Common in gravelly and
sandy fields.
(*Photographed by Colburn.*)

Mexican Drop-seed Grass (*Muhlenbergia mexicana* (L.) Trin.).

Description.—An upright or ascending, usually much-branched
perennial 1 foot to 3 feet high, with a scaly, creeping root-stock;
numerous flat leaves and contracted, densely-flowered panicles;
sheaths longer or shorter than the internodes, smooth; ligule one-
half line or less long; leaf-blades 1 line to 3 lines wide, 2 to 7 inches
long; spikelets about 1 line long on very short pedicels; empty
glumes nearly equal, acuminate-pointed, about the length of the
floral glume (a little shorter or sometimes a little longer), scabrous
on the keel; flowering glume lanceolate, acute or mucronate-
pointed, 3-nerved, pilose near the base and on the callus; palea a
little shorter than its glume, very acute.

Distribution.—Widely distributed in eastern North America,
from Canada to Minnesota, South Dakota, Iowa, Nebraska and

Missouri. Common everywhere in waste ground in Iowa, especially Calhoun, Clinton, Linn, Jasper, Lee, Fremont and Dubuque counties.

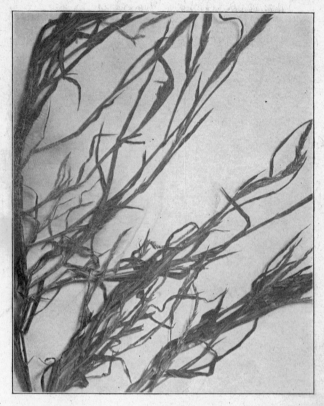

Fig. 14. Mexican Drop-seed Grass or Nimble Will (*Muhlenbergia mexicana*). Common in orchards, gardens and fields; sometimes incorrectly called Orchard Grass, also called Turkey Grass because of the thickened clustered "roots."
(*Photographed by Hart.*)

Fig. 14-A. Distribution of Mexican Drop-seed Grass.

Extermination.—The "roots" of this grass are different from those of quack grass and other perennial weeds and they are less difficult to exterminate. The "roots" of this weed and the allied species are more or less clustered. In an experiment conducted to exterminate it we found that by giving a shallow plowing of four or five inches and harrowing to expose the "roots" to the sun, they were killed, no growth making its appearance during the rest of the season. Of course this is not effective during rainy weather.

FIG. 14-B. Mexican Drop-seed Grass (*Muhlenbergia mexicana*); *a, b,* spikelets.
(*U. S. Dept. of Agr.*)

Chemical Composition.—Mexican drop-seed grass has been chemically investigated by the Dakota, Tennessee and Iowa stations. The Iowa analyses* were made at seven different times between April 29 and July 20 with the following results. The water content varies greatly as does the protein content.

*Grasses of Iowa. Iowa Geol. Surv. Bull. 1. 408.

NATURAL CONDITION

Sample	Date	Height inches	Water	Fat	Protein	Albu-minoids	Crude fiber	Ash	Nitrogen free extract
1	4–29–1896	4–12	84.82	.88	3.51	(2.73)	3.70	2.04	5.05
2	5–14–1896	20–23	73.28	1.21	5.12	(3.78)	7.72	2.77	9.90
3	5–28–1896	26–29	82.95	.54	2.86	(1.96)	6.13	1.95	5.27
4	6– 8–1896	36–38	77.46	.79	2.41	(2.14)	8.10	2.08	9.16
5	6–18–1896	38–39	73.37	.81	2.13	(2.10)	9.01	2.57	12.11
6	6–29–1896	39–40	58.77	1.49	3.22	(2.60)	13.32	2.61	20.56
7	7–20–1896	48–49	81.98	.53	1.48	(1.09)	5.82	1.10	9.09

WATER FREE SUBSTANCE

Sample	Date	Height inches	Water	Fat	Protein	Albu-minoids	Crude fiber	Ash	Nitrogen free extract
1				5.81	23.16	(17.09)	24.36	13.41	33.26
2				4.52	19.17	(14.17)	28.90	10.38	37.03
3				3.14	16.77	(11.46)	37.72	11.43	30.94
4				3.49	10.70	(9.52)	35.94	9.27	40.60
5				3.03	8.00	(7.88)	33.83	9.67	45.47
6				3.62	7.81	(6.30)	32.31	6.40	49.86
7				2.95	8.26	(6.11)	32.48	6.16	50.15

Marsh Muhlenberg (*Muhlenbergia racemosa* (Michx.) B. S. P.)

Description.—A rather stout, upright perennial, with very tough and densely scaly root-stocks, nearly simple culms, 2 to 3 feet high, and densely flowered panicles, 2 to 4 inches long; spikelets 2 to 3 lines long, the long, acuminate-pointed outer glumes nearly equal and exceeding the very acute flowering glume, which is densely bearded at the base.

Distribution.—Widely distributed in eastern North America, especially in meadows, from Canada and New England to New Jersey, west to the Rocky mountains, Iowa to Missouri.

Extermination.—The clustered root-stocks are easily destroyed by exposing to the sun. Use the same methods as those given for the Mexican drop-seed grass.

FIG. 15.   Marsh Muhlenberg, Drop-seed Grass, Wild Timothy, frequently called Orchard Grass (*Muhlenbergia racemosa*).   Common in gardens, orchards, and especially in grain fields in low grounds.

(Photographed by Hart.)

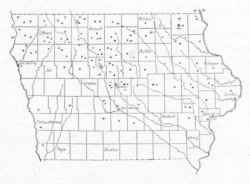

FIG. 15-A.   Distribution of Marsh Muhlenberg.

FIG. 15-B. Marsh Muhlenberg (*Muhlenbergia racemosa*); *a,* spikelet with long acuminate-pointed outer glumes; *b,* flowering glume, bearded.
(*U. S. Dept. of Agr.*)

Nimble Will (*Muhlenbergia Schreberi* J. F. Gmel.).

Description.—A low, ascending perennial with slender, much-
branched, wiry culms, 1 foot to 2 feet long; sheaths smooth, pilose
at the throat; ligule very short; leaf-blade 1 line to 2 lines wide,
1 inch to 4 inches long, scabrous on both sides; panicles 3 to 7 inches
long, slender, branches erect, rather densely flowered; spikelets 1
line long, equaling or exceeding the pedicels; empty glumes minute,
unequal, the lower sometimes obsolete; flowering glume narrowly
lanceolate, pilose near the base, scabrous on the nerves above, terminating in a slender straight awn, 1 line to 2 lines long; palea
equaling the glume.

Distribution.—Nimble Will was originally confined to southeastern Iowa. It has spread northward along the Mississippi, where it

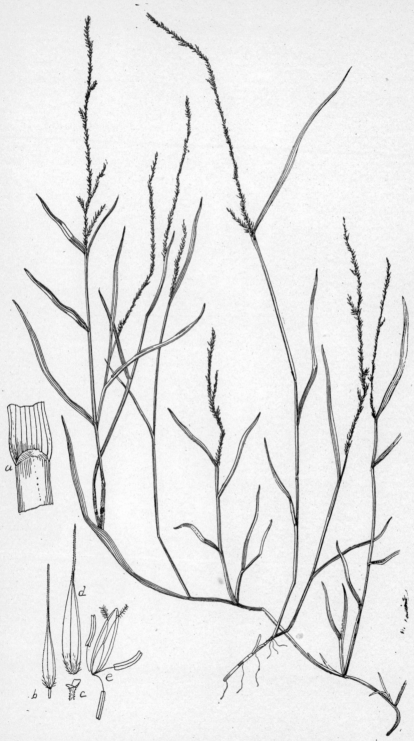

FIG. 16. Nimble Will (*Muhlenbergia Schreberi*); *a*, sheath and base of leaf; *b, d,* glumes; *c*, lower part of rachilla; *e*, flower. In southern Iowa. (*Drawn by C. M. King.*)

is now abundant as far north as Dubuque and McGregor. It occurs also in central Iowa in Story, Boone and Webster counties and is spreading, especially in woodland pastures. The grass is of little economic importance.

Extermination.—This weed is much more difficult to destroy than the other nimble wills herein described. The root-stocks spread somewhat horizontally and are large and fibrous. They should be given thorough cultivation, exposing the roots to the sun, and followed by some leguminous crop. This weed is apt to be abundant in pastures. In this case there is no more satisfactory method of treatment than to get blue grass and white clover into the pasture.

Sheathed Rush Grass (*Sporobolus vaginiflorus* (Torr.) Wood.).
Description.—A slender, caespitose annual, 1 foot to three feet

FIG. 17. Drop-seed or Sheathed Rush Grass (*Sporobolus vaginiflorus*). Common in sandy fields, lawns and gravelly soil.
(*Photographed by Hart.*)

high, with narrow, short leaves, and simple, few-flowered, terminal
and axillary, spikelike panicles which are about 1 inch long, and
mostly enclosed in the somewhat inflated leaf-sheaths; spikelets
1 line to 2 lines long.

FIG. 17-A.   Distribution of Sheathed Rush Grass.

Distribution.—Common in sterile fields and waste places from
New England to Wisconsin, South Dakota, and Iowa, and southward. Especially common in pastures, lawns, and along roadsides
in Iowa, particularly in Story, Polk, Boone, Clinton, Crawford,
Carroll, Webster and Emmet counties.

Extermination.—This annual is easily exterminated by cultivation, for the small fibrous roots succumb readily when exposed
to the sun. The plant should not be permitted to form seed.

Small Rush Grass, Drop-seed (*Sporobolus neglectus* Nash).

Description.—Culms 6 to 12 inches high, erect, from a usually
decumbent base, slender, often much-branched, smooth and glabrous; sheaths about half as long as the internodes, inflated; ligule
very short; leaves 1 line wide or less at the base, smooth and
glabrous beneath, scabrous and hairy near the base above, attenuate
into a slender point, the lower elongated, the upper 1 inch to 3
inches long, setaceous; terminal panicle 1 inch to 2½ inches in
length, usually more or less included in the upper sheath, striate;
lateral panicles enclosed in the sheaths; spikelets about 1½ lines
long, the outer scales acute, the lower one slightly shorter, third
scale acute, glabrous, a little longer than the second, and about
equaling the acute palet.

Distribution.—Small rush grass occurs from New Brunswick to
Virginia, Wisconsin, Iowa, South Dakota and Texas, in situations
similar to those where the preceding species is found. It grows
especially along beaten paths, pastures and roadsides.

FIG. 18. Small Rush Grass or Drop-seed (*Sporobolus neglectus*). Pastures, sandy fields.
(*Photographed by Hart.*)

FIG. 18-A. Distribution of Small Rush Grass.

Extermination. This weed should be treated in the same manner as the preceding species.

Wild Oats (*Avena fatua* L.).

Description.—An erect, glabrous annual, 3 to 5 feet high, with flat leaves and spreading panicles of large, oatlike, nodding

Plate 3

WILD OATS
(*Avena fatua* z.)

FIG. 19.   Wild Oats (*Avena fatua*).   In oat and grain fields, northeastern Iowa.
(*After Clark and Fletcher.*)

FIG. 19-A. Distribution of Wild Oats.

spikelets; spikelets 2 to 4-flowered, with empty glumes three-fourths to 1 inch long, and pubescent, flowering glumes 6 to 9 lines long, awns nearly twice as long as the spikelets.

Distribution.—Common in Canada, rare in eastern North America, abundant in the northwest, Wisconsin, Minnesota, Dakotas, Rocky mountains and Pacific coast. In a few counties in northern and northeastern Iowa it is found commonly in oat fields and sometimes in waste places.

Extermination.—Wild oats has been largely spread with oat seed. Only clean oat seed should be sown. It succumbs readily to cultivation. Rotation of crops should be practiced. Corn or some other cultivated crop may follow oats, or the oat field may be brought into meadow. Clover and timothy are good rotations, with corn and oats, to subdue wild oats.

Crowfoot Grass, Wire Grass (*Eleusine indica* Gaertn.).

Description.—A coarse, tufted annual, with erect or spreading stems, 6 to 24 inches high, and digitate spikes; sheaths compressed and sparingly ciliate; leaf-blade long and narrow, both surfaces glabrous, or the upper scabrous and thinly hairy; spikes 5 to 7, 2 to 4 inches long, digitate at the apex of the culm, often with 1 or 2 lower down, widely spreading; spikelets closely imbricated, 1½ to 2 lines long, 3 to 6-flowered; glumes obtuse, the first small and 1-nerved; seeds rugose, enclosed within a thin, loose pericarp.

Distribution.—Wire grass is naturalized from the Old World. It is found in waste ground, streets, yards, from New England to Iowa, and commonly southward. In Iowa it occurs particularly in Marshall, Scott, Story, Pottawattamie, Lee, Appanoose and Clinton counties.

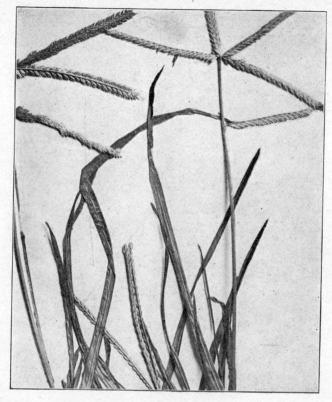

FIG. 20.   Crowfoot Grass (*Eleusine indica*).   Streets, roadsides, southern and southeastern Iowa.
(*Photographed by Hart.*)

FIG. 20-A.   Distribution of Crowfoot Grass.

Extermination.—Cultivation readily destroys the weed.   When
it appears in the lawn it must be pulled up or the grass cut close
to the ground.

Chemical Composition.—The chemical composition of Yard grass, Crowfoot, Crab grass, Wire grass (*Eleusine indica*) (cut August 11, 1880; grown in Pennsylvania) according to U. S. Department of Agriculture, (Chem. Comp. Am. Grasses, 1884, p. 125) is as follows:

FRESH OR AIR DRY MATERIAL

Water	Ash	Protein	Fiber	Nitrogen free extract	Fat
14.30	19.81	10.14	19.63	43.33	2.79

WATER FREE SUBSTANCE					
	11.5	11.8	22.9	50 5	3.3

Southern Spear Grass (*Eragrostis pilosa* (L.) Beauv.).

Description.—An annual, 5 to 18 inches high, with erect or ascending stems diffusely branching near the base; sheaths pilose

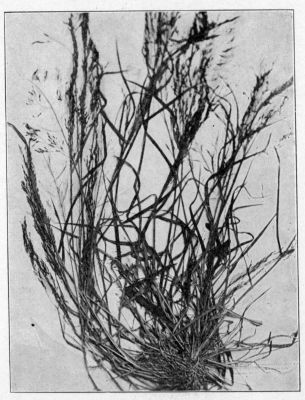

FIG 21.   Southern Spear Grass (*Eragrostis pilosa*).   Roadsides, streets, fields, etc.
(Photographed by Quade.)

at the throat, otherwise smooth, leaf-blade 1 to 7 lines long, one-half line to 1½ lines wide, conduplicate when dry; panicle oblong-lanceolate to pyramidal, 3 to 8 or 12 inches long, the widely spreading primary branches solitary, or 2 to 3 together, the axils not pilose; spikelets narrow-lanceolate, 2 to 4½ lines long, 3 to 15-flowered, appressed to the branches, nearly equaling or exceeding their capillary pedicels; empty glumes ovate, acute, scabrous on the keel, the longer one about one-half line in length; flowering glume broadly ovate, obtuse, distinctly 3-nerved, scabrous on the keel, about three-fourths line long; palea scabrous on the keels; grain oblong.

FIG. 21-A. Distribution of Southern Spear Grass..

Distribution.—This grass is widely distributed in eastern North America in waste places, roadsides, and sometimes in fields, especially in sandy soil, New England to Wisconsin, Minnesota and southward. It is common in Story, Polk, Johnson, Marshall, Linn, Clayton, Cerro Gordo, Fremont and Woodbury counties.

Extermination.—The southern spear grass succumbs readily to cultivation.

Candy Grass (*Eragrostis megastachya* (Koeler) Link).

Description.—A rather showy, much-branched annual, with erect or ascending stems, 6 inches to 2 or 3 feet high; sheaths striate, smooth, hairy at the throat; ligule a fringe of short hairs; leaf-blade flat, 3 to 10 inches long, 1 to 3 lines wide, somewhat scabrous on the upper surface; panicle elliptical or oblong, the branches usually spreading, flowered, 2 to 8 lines long, 1½ to 2 lines broad, spikelets ovate to linear, 7 to 40 empty glumes nearly equal, ovate, obtuse, prominently nerved, and scabrous on the keel; palea ciliate on the keels.

Distribution.—*Eragrostis megastachya* is a weedy grass introduced by the earliest settlers. It is common in all parts of the state, especially in Story, Boone, Clinton, Lee, Marshall, Scott, Polk, Linn, Cerro Gordo, Clayton, Johnson, Lyon, O'Brien and Woodbury counties.

Extermination.—This weed is easily exterminated by cultivation. The best way to kill it is to cultivate corn in the infested soil and follow with small grain.

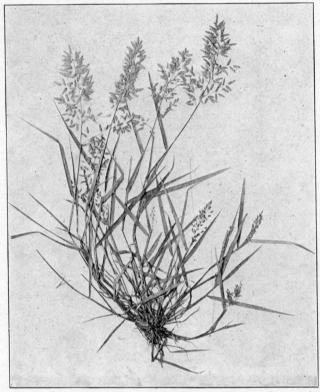

FIG. 22.   Candy Grass, Stink Grass (*Eragrostis megastachya*).   Common in gardens, fields and roadsides.   (*Photographed by Colburn.*)

FIG. 22-A. Distribution of Candy Grass.

Chess, Cheat (*Bromus secalinus* L.).

Description.—An erect annual, 2 to 3 feet high; culms smooth or pubescent at the nodes; sheaths striate smooth, scabrous or in some cases pilose; ligule short, blunt; leaf-blade 6 to 12 inches long,

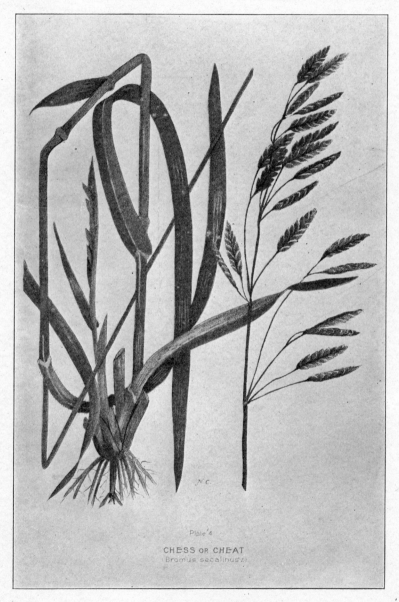

FIG. 23. Chess or Cheat (*Bromus secalinus*). In grain fields. (*After Clark and Fletcher.*)

rather broadly linear, smooth beneath, more or less rough and
pilose on the upper surface; panicle 4 to 8 inches long, erect, the
more or less compound branches spreading, even in fruits; spikelets 6 to 10 lines long, oblong ovate, turgid, 6 to 12-flowered,
pendulous in fruit, empty glumes oblong lanceolate, acute, the first
3 to 5, the second 7-nerved; flowering glumes ovate-oblong, obscurely 7-nerved, smooth or minutely downy along the margins
and toward the apex, becoming nearly cylindrical in fruit; palea
obtuse, strongly nerved; nerves toothed or fringed with distant
bristles.

Distribution.—Cheat is common wherever wheat is cultivated
and sometimes in waste places, from the Atlantic to the Pacific.
At one time common in many parts of Iowa, it now occurs
sparingly except where wheat is cultivated, in southern and western
Iowa, in Madison, Woodbury, Monona and Pottawattamie counties.

Extermination.—Clean seed should be sown in clean soil. The
weed succumbs readily to cultivation.

Chemical Composition.—The common *Bromus secalinus* analyzed
at the Iowa station by Weems shows the following analysis:

NATURAL CONDITION

Sample	Date	Height inches	Water	Fat	Protein	Albu-minoids	Crude fiber	Ash	Nitrogen free extract
1	5-20-1896	25-30	79.22	1.99	2.74	(1.96)	9.15	2.21	4.59
2	6-15-1896	28-29	66.55	1.19	3.23	(2.49)	12.38	2.64	14.01

WATER FREE SUBSTANCE

Sample	Date	Height inches	Water	Fat	Protein	Albu-minoids	Crude fiber	Ash	Nitrogen free extract
1					9.59	13.17	(9.42)	44.04	10.63	22.57
2					3.57	9.66	(7.44)	37.03	7.91	41.83

FIG. 23-A.   Distribution of Cheat or Chess.

There is considerable nourishment in the nutritive substance when the plant is young, but when old it can not be considered very nutritious.

Soft Chess (*Bromus hordeaceus* L.).

Description.—An erect, usually slender, pubescent annual, 1 to 3 feet high, with flat leaves, and contracted panicles, 1 to 3 inches long; spikelets 3 to 8-flowered, ½ to 1 inch long, with pubescent glumes, the flowering ones 3½ to 4½ lines long, obtuse and awned; awns 3 to 4 lines long.

Distribution.—Soft chess is frequent in waste places, roadsides, and fields, from Canada to Virginia and Rocky mountains. It is the most abundant of the brome grasses in Iowa, Story, Boone and Polk counties, and is becoming common in Cerro Gordo, Clayton, Johnson, Woodbury, Ida, Marshall and Linn counties.

Extermination.—This weedy grass succumbs readily to cultivation. Fields are largely infested from plants growing in waste places. Therefore, the soft chess along roadsides and in waste places should be cut.

Chemical Composition.—Chemical analysis made at the experiment station at Ames by Dr. Weems shows the following results:

NATURAL CONDITION

Sample	Date	Height inches	Water	Fat	Protein	Albuminoids	Crude fiber	Ash	Nitrogen free extract
1	4-24-1896	5.10	85.07	1.41	4.19	(3.23)	3.18	1.92	4.23
2	5- 4-1896	18-18	87.29	.94	2.14	(1.38)	3.38	1.83	4.45
3	5-11-1896	18-24	79.37	.85	2.62	(2.50)	5.47	2.19	9.50
4	5-20-1896		80.63	.78	2.96	(2.10)	6.42	2.05	7.16
5	6- 1-1896	30.32	71.41	.85	3.52	(3.08)	10.01	2.54	11.67

WATER FREE SUBSTANCE

Sample	Date	Height inches	Water	Fat	Protein	Albuminoids	Crude fiber	Ash	Nitrogen free extract
1				9.46	28.05	(26.61)	21.31	12.89	28.26
2				7.43	16.83	(14.80)	26.61	14.38	34.75
3				4.10	12.71	(12.12)	26.54	10.64	46.01
4				4.08	15.30	(10.88)	33.18	10.61	36.83
5				2.95	12.30	(10.76)	35.01	8.91	40.83

This grass is very nutritious in its young condition. The protein varies from 2.14 per cent to 4.19 per cent, but there is a seeming variation with individual plants found under differing conditions.

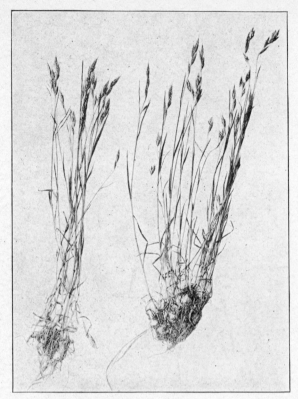

FIG. 24. Soft Chess, Annual Brome Grass (*Bromus hordeaceus*). Common in fields and waste places.

(*Photographed by Colburn.*)

FIG. 24-A. Distribution of Soft Chess.

Downy Brome Grass (*Bromus tectorum* L.).
Description.—A slender, erect, leafy annual, 7 to 25 inches

high, with narrow, softly pubescent leaves, and open, nodding panicles, 3 to 7½ inches long; spikelets 5 to 8-flowered, with unequal, acuminate-pointed, hirsute, empty glumes, and rough or hirsute flowering glumes, 4 to 6 lines long; awns 6 to 8 lines long.

Distribution.—This grass is common in waste places in regions of the Rocky mountains and the Pacific coast, Atlantic states, Maine to Iowa. It has been noted as especially prevalent in Story, Marshall, Ida, Lyon, Linn, Polk, Clinton, Madison, Woodbury, Fremont and Cerro Gordo counties. Becoming abundant in Iowa.

Fig. 25. Downy or Awned Brome Grass (*Bromus tectorum*). An annual grass, in streets of our larger cities. (*Photographed by Quade.*)

Extermination.—Care should be used in destroying packing material, for in the few localities in which this weed occurs in Iowa, it has come from packing material. It succumbs readily to cultivation.

FIG. 25-A.—Distribution of Downy Brome Grass.

Poison Darnel (*Lolium temulentum* L.).

Description.—An annual, with smooth, stout culm, 2 to 3 feet high; sheaths scabrous; ligule short, spike 6 to 12 inches long;

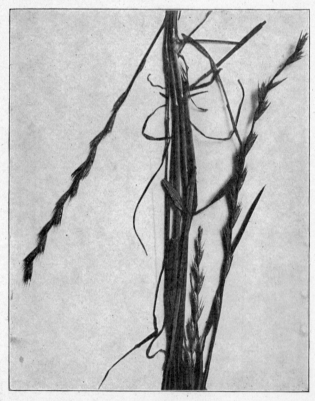

FIG. 26. Poison Darnel (*Lolium temulentum*). Common in oat and wheat fields in northern Iowa.
(*Photographed by Hart.*)

spikelets 5 to 7-flowered; empty glumes sharp pointed, as long as the spikelet, flowering glumes turgid, awned or awnless, shorter and broader than in *L. perenne*.

Distribution.—Poison darnel was introduced from Europe; it has become naturalized in eastern North America and is quite abundant on the Pacific coast. It is found in many counties in Iowa.

FIG. 26-A. Distribution of Poison Darnel.

Extermination.—Only clean oats or wheat should be sown. The weed succumbs readily to cultivation.

Quack Grass (*Agropyron repens* (L.) Beauv.).

Description.—A perennial with a many-jointed, creeping rhizome (root-stock); culm from 18 inches to 4 feet high, bearing numerous leaves from 5 to 12 inches long, and from one-third to one-fourth inch wide; margins rough, very smooth beneath, slightly hirsute above; spikes 6 to 12 inches long, erect; spikelets on opposite sides of a jointed and channeled rachis, pubescent on the margin, erect, 4 to 8-flowered; lower or sterile glumes acute or short-awned, prominently 5 to 7-nerved, flowering glumes smooth; palet acute or somewhat rounded, smooth or slightly pubescent.

The western wheat grass (*Agropyron Smithii* Rydb.) is closely related to quack grass. The plant is glaucous; leaves are rigid, bluish green in color, scabrous on the margin, edges rolling in; spikelets 7 to 13-flowered, in a thicker spike ("head") than quack grass; running root-stocks ("roots"). Common along railways and in northwestern Iowa. This plant is not considered a weed. It may be used to plant railway embankments.

The slender wheat grass (*Agropyron tenerum* Vasey) which also resembles quack grass, produces a slender long head, greenish in color; running root-stocks are absent.

Distribution.—Quack grass is common and widely distributed from Manitoba, Minnesota, and western Iowa to Arkansas and Texas. In Iowa it has been found in Clayton, Cerro Gordo, John-

COUCH QUACK or SCUTCH GRASS
(Agropyron repens Linn.)

FIG. 27. Quack Grass, Quick Grass, Scutch Grass (*Agropyron repens*). Fields, waste places, around elevators, meadows, roadsides and pastures, especially in northern Iowa.

(After Clark and Fletcher.)

son, Winneshiek, Allamakee, Jones, Emmet, Marshall, Linn, Story, Polk, Hardin, Hamilton, Dubuque and Clinton counties. It has been reported also from many places, as: Afton Junction, Ames, Armstrong, Iowa and Minnesota line near Ceylon (Minnesota), Elmore, Hampton, Harcourt, Keokuk, Des Moines, Mason City, Nora Springs, Ontario and Pilot Mound. It is especially common in the loess soil from Carroll to Lyon county and eastward and northward and is found extensively along railroads. It is found in probably every county of northern Iowa from Mississippi to Missouri rivers.

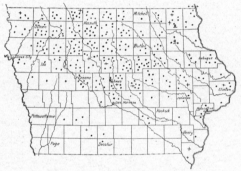

FIG. 27-A. Distribution of Quack Grass.

Extermination.—Experiments made at Ames indicate that quack grass can be exterminated. When it covers considerable areas it may be necessary to summer fallow. The land should be plowed in August when the small grain crop has been removed. The first plowing should be shallow, not more than two or three inches deep, followed by harrowing with a common drag. This will expose a large number of the "roots". If the grass appears again, run over the field with a disc and drag. This should be repeated during the remainder of the season. In the spring plow the soil six or seven inches; drag and expose the "roots". The field should be kept free from weeds of all descriptions during the entire growing season. It may be necessary to go over the field at least once a week to remove all of the quack grass. *Where land brings as much per acre as in Iowa, no farmer can afford to leave his land fallow. The field should be given the same treatment in both the fall and early spring as outlined above. Sow thickly with one of the following crops: sorghum, sudan, millet, buckwheat, or rye. These crops will not entirely kill the quack grass but will reduce its vitality to such an extent that what remains may be easily treated by plowing six or seven inches deep in the fall, following with a harrow. Very little quack grass will remain after this treatment.* Experience has shown that quack grass is shallow-rooted and that the roots will not grow readily through the soil beyond a depth of six inches.

FIG. 27-B.   Western Wheat Grass (*Agropyron Smithii*).   Common along railroads and in northwestern Iowa.   The distribution of *A. Smithii* is shown in fig. C and of slender Wheat Grass (*A. tenerum*) in fig. D. *a,* empty glumes; *b,* flowering g umes with flowers.

(*U. S. Dept. of Agr.*)

The following suggestions for exterminating the weed are made by Fletcher and Clark: ''Let the plant exhaust its substance in the production of a hay crop, which should be cut and removed as soon as the head is formed and before it is in bloom.   Plow shallow and cultivate until the root-stocks have been brought to the surface by implements that can be forced, after repeated applications, to

FIG. 27-C. Distribution of Western Wheat Grass.

the full depth of the furrow. A disc is not satisfactory because the cuttings from the root-stocks are difficult to gather and they perpetuate the growth, wherever transplanted. When brought to the surface the root-stocks should be gathered and burnt or removed. This should be done at once before the plant has had an opportunity to renew its growth. For Manitoba, S. A. Bedford recommends plowing up the couchgrass late in the spring and seeding at once to barley, three bushels to the acre.''

FIG. 27-D. Distribution of Slender Wheat Grass.

Chemical Composition.—Various chemical analyses have been made of quack grass. The following were reported by Weems from material grown in Iowa:

NATURAL CONDITION

Sample	Date	Height inches	Water	Fat	Protein	Albu-minoids	Crude fiber	Ash	Nitrogen free extract
1	4-18-1896	4- 8	73.96	1.15	5.13	(4.57)	6.13	3.14	10.49
2	5- 6-1896	16.24	79.06	.81	4.41	(2.47)	5.66	3.11	6.95
3	5-20-1896	20-30	79.56	1.51	4.64	(2.11)	4.96	2.09	7.24
4	6- 1-1896	26.28	75.84	1.47	4.23	(2.04)	6.68	2.66	9.64
5	6-15-1896	26-28	80.56	1.28	1.35	(1.32)	5.05	2.12	9.64

WATER FREE SUBSTANCE

1				4.41	19.70	(17.57)	23.55	12.08	40.26
2				3.86	21.06	(11.80)	27.12	14.84	33.12
3				7.37	22.71	(10.34)	24.28	10.24	35.40
4				6.08	17.52	(8.44)	27.56	11.00	37.84
5				6.59	6.96	(6.80)	25.97	10.93	49.55

It is not as valuable for pasturage as blue grass but it compares very favorably with timothy in regard to the amount of protein and nitrogen free extract it contains.

Squirrel-tail Grass (*Hordeum jubatum* L.).

Description.—An annual or winter annual from 6 inches to 2 feet high, producing fibrous roots which form solid, compact bunches, leaves not unlike those of blue grass, but paler in color, from 2 to 4 inches long, pale green or purplish in color; spike consisting of a number of 1-flowered spikelets, three occurring at each joint, one being perfect, the other spikelets awl-shaped, rudimentary, and borne on short stalks, one sterile spikelet occurring on each side of the perfect flower, which bears a long awn; at each joint will be found 6 empty long-awned glumes spreading at maturity, giving to the plant its bristly appearance; when mature, the spike breaks up into joints consisting of the rudimentary spikelets and a perfect flower, so that each joint has one "seed," the number of "seeds" in a spike varying from 35 to 60. A single cluster of plants may therefore produce from three hundred to two thousand mature "seeds". The plant has a wonderful capacity for "stooling". From a single plant as many as forty spikes may be produced, and the number no doubt often exceeds this.

Distribution.—Squirrel-tail grass originally was abundant in the vicinity of alkali lakes and along the borders of streams west of Missouri river; it also occurred sparingly on the North Atlantic coast. Now, however, it is common across the continent. In Iowa it is abundant in all parts of the state not only in pastures but in meadows, fields and gardens, and is frequent in Story, Marshall, Clinton, Scott, Polk, Carroll, Greene, Sac, Ida, Johnson, Winnebago, Kossuth, Cerro Gordo, Howard, Winneshiek, Jones, Clayton and Allamakee counties.

Extermination.—Squirrel-tail or wild barley is a very pernicious weed along roadsides and in pastures and meadows; it not only prevents the growth of the better grasses but injures live stock. As this weed is very common in pastures, the best way to treat it is to mow the infested pastures before the grass has matured its

seed. Since this weed is an annual or winter annual, this treatment will effectively dispose of the plant except as the seed is
blown in from neighboring fields and roadsides. Cultivation will

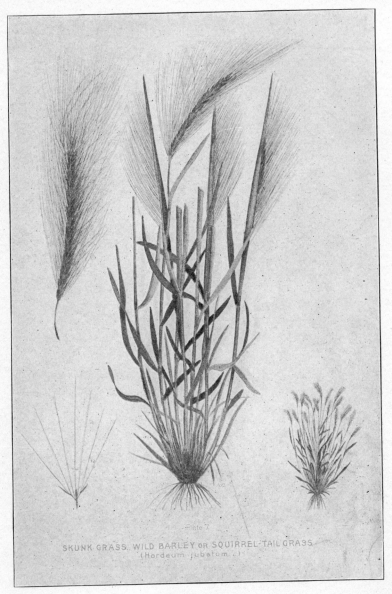

SKUNK GRASS, WILD BARLEY OR SQUIRREL-TAIL GRASS
(Hordeum jubatum L.)

FIG. 28.   Squirrel-tail Grass or Wild Barley (*Hordeum jubatum*).   Meadows, pastures
and roadsides.
(*After Clark and Fletcher.*)

FIG. 28-A. Distribution of Squirrel-tail Grass.

readily destroy the weed and where it is abundant in fields shallow cultivation followed by the disk and harrow should be effective.

Clark and Fletcher, in regard to exterminating this grass, which in Canada is known as Skunk-tail Grass, say: "There is no diffi-culty in eradicating this grass from any land which can be plowed, as the usual method of breaking in June will destroy it. It gives most trouble in waste places where it ripens its seed, which is spread abroad in every direction by wind and water. It grows freely about the edges of hay sloughs on the prairie and is generally ripe before the hay is cut. The remedy in this case would be cutting before the seed is formed."

FIG. 28-B. Squirrel-tail Grass or Wild Barley (*Hordeum jubatum*). Widely distrib-uted in Iowa pastures, roadsides, etc.
(*Photograph by Charlotte M. King.*)

Chemical Composition.—Analyses have been reported from Iowa and South Dakota. The following report is by Weems from Iowa:

NATURAL CONDITION

Sample	Date	Height inches	Water	Fat	Protein	Albu-minoids	Crude fiber	Ash	Nitrogen free extract
1	5-20-1896	10.15	80.51	.97	4.33	(3.00)	7.13	2.19	4.87
2	5-26-1896	23.24	72.60	1.59	3.38	(2.36)	10.10	2.35	9.98
3	6- 5-1896	23.24	67.97	.94	3.74	(2.75)	12.47	2.70	12.18
4	6-17-1896	24.25	54.39	1.68	5.80	(3.76)	17.85	4.00	16.28

WATER FREE SUBSTANCE

Sample	Date	Height inches	Water	Fat	Protein	Albu-minoids	Crude fiber	Ash	Nitrogen free extract
1				4.97	22 21	(15.43)	36.59	11.24	24.99
2				5.82	12.36	(8.62)	36.90	8.46	36.46
3				2.94	11.78	(8.57)	38.92	8.43	37.93
4				3.69	12.71	(8.24)	39.14	8.78	35.68

Little Barley (*Hordeum pusillum* Nutt.).

Description.—An annual, 4 to 10 inches high; culms more or less geniculate at the lower nodes; sheaths smooth, the uppermost often inflated and enclosing the base of the spike; leaf-blade 1 inch to

FIG. 29. Little Barley (*Hordeum pusillum*). Roadsides, fields. Common in southern Iowa.
(*Photographed by Colburn.*)

FIG. 29-A.   Distribution of Little Barley.

3 inches long, usually a little pubescent on the lower surface;
spikes narrow, 1 inch to 3 inches long; empty glumes rigid, the
4 internal ones of each group dilated above the base, those of the
central spikelet sublanceolate, all awn-pointed; outer glumes of
the imperfect lateral spikelets setaceous; flowering glume of the
central spikelet awned; awn equaling those of the empty glumes;
florets of the lateral spikelets awnless, or nearly so.

Distribution.—Little barley is common in Missouri and Illinois
and on the plains; it is becoming plentiful in southeastern Iowa
and in Pottawattamie, Story, Polk, Madison, Lee, Scott, Linn and
Marshall counties.

Extermination.—This annual weed is easily destroyed by cultivation. It comes up abundantly in streets and along roadsides.
The production of seed in such places makes it possible for nearby
farm land to be infested by the seed. The plants whenever found
should be cut to prevent seeding.

Chemical Composition.—According to the Wyoming Experiment
Station the composition is as follows:*

	Natural condition	Water free substance
Water	5.79	----------
Ash	9.25	9.82
Ether extract	1.77	1.88
Crude fiber	31.58	33.52
Crude protein	6.49	6.89
Nitrogen free extract	45.12	47.89

*Bull. Wyo. Agr. Exp. Sta. 87; compiled by Henry G. Knight, Frank E.
Hepner, Chemists; and Aven Nelson, Botanist.

CYPERACEAE, SEDGE FAMILY.

This family contains few economic plants. The chufa is used as food for hogs. The papyrus of the ancients, and the so-called rushes of our ponds belong to this family. Many of the plants grow in low grounds.

Northern Nut Grass (*Cyperus esculentus* L.).

Description.—A grasslike plant growing from 1 foot to 2½ feet high; with triangular stems, leafy at the base when young, later leaves terminating the stems; spikes of numerous spikelets with 12 to 30 light chestnut or straw-colored flowers; scales of the spikelets rough-margined; achene longer than broad.

This perennial weed spreads extensively by its underground nut-like tubers. It is closely related to the Southern Nut Grass (*Cyperus rotundus* L.).

Distribution.—Northern nut grass is quite generally distributed

FIG. 30. Northern Nut Grass (*Cyperus esculentus*). Corn fields, especially low grounds. Young plants have a yellowish color. Weed spreads by the "roots."
(*Photograph by Ia. Agr. Exp. Sta.*)

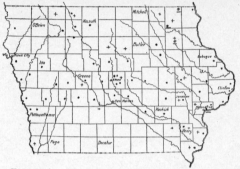

FIG. 30-A. Distribution of Northern Nut Grass.

in the state and occurs frequently in North America from New Brunswick to Texas; common especially in low spots, where it is easily recognized by its yellowish brown color. It is common in Story, Polk, Johnson, Marshall, Linn, Kossuth, Jones, Lee, Carroll, Boone, Greene and Ida counties.

Extermination.—This weed can be exterminated only by thorough cultivation. Running the harrow over the field when corn is young will not exterminate the weed, for the little offshoots sprout again, giving rise to many more plants. Running the cultivator through the field is more effective than to harrow it, but not sufficient to destroy all plants of the nut grass. In badly infested fields it will be necessary to use the hoe, to completely eradicate the weed.

JUNCACEAE, RUSH FAMILY.

These grasslike plants are related to the lilies. They generally grow in low grounds and are of little economic importance.

Slender Rush (*Juncus tenuis* Willd.).

Description.—A leafy perennial with wiry stem, 9 to 18 inches high; leaves flat or channeled; flowers in panicles, the panicles shorter than the involucral leaves; flowers green, sepals lanceolate-acute, spreading in fruit; capsule green; seeds small, ribbed.

Distribution.—A cosmopolitan weed widely distributed in North America; common along beaten paths and fields, especially in pastures, in every part of Iowa, and frequent in Story, Marshall, Linn, Cerro Gordo, Clayton, Winnebago, Howard, Jones, Clayton, Allamakee, Lee and Winneshiek counties.

Extermination.—This weed is not difficult to exterminate by cultivation. Where it occurs in pastures that cannot be cultivated,

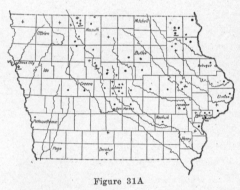

Figure 31   Figure 31A

FIG. 31. Wire Grass or Slender Rush (*Juncus tenuis*). Common in pastures along
roadsides.
(*Photographed by Colburn.*)
FIG. 31-A. Distribution of Slender Rush.

an effort should be made to start a leguminous plant like white
clover which will kill out the rush to some extent.

LILIACEAE, LILY FAMILY.

This family contains a number of economic plants like onion,
garlic, leek, chives, such cultivated ornamental plants as the lily,
lily of the valley, and hyacinth and some poisonous plants as the
colchicum and bunch flower.

Common Bunch-Flower (*Melanthium virginicum* L.).

Description.—Tall, leafy-stemmed plants 3 to 5 feet high; leaves
linear, the lower sheathing, the upper similar and sessile; flowers
in an ample panicle, fragrant; perianth of flat segments greenish
yellow; styles persistent, capsule 3-celled; 8 to 10 seeds in each
cavity.

Distribution.—The Bunch-flower is found in low meadows and prairies from New England to Iowa river basin, Minnesota, Texas and Florida. Common only from eastern central Iowa to the Missouri line.

FIG. 32. Bunch-Flower (*Melanthium virginicum*) In meadows, eastern and southern Iowa. Poisonous.
(*Photograph by Gardner.*)

FIG. 32-A. Distribution of Bunch-Flower

Extermination.—This weed is common only in native meadows. It is killed when these meadows are broken up and cultivated.

Wild Onion (*Allium canadense* L.).

Description.—A perennial herb, with small scapose bulb; bulb coat somewhat fibrous; flowers umbellate, umbels densely bulbiferous; perianth of six divisions which are narrowly lanceolate, as long as the six stamens or longer; capsule 3-celled, not crested; seeds black.

Distribution.—It is common in moist meadows in many parts of Iowa, including Boone, Story, Marshall, Allamakee, Clayton, Jones, Howard and Polk counties. Wild onion is distributed from New Brunswick to Wisconsin, Texas and Florida.

Extermination.—This weed is common in native meadows, but seldom persists like the wild garlic (*Allium vineale*) of Europe in

FIG. 33. Wild Onion (*Allium canadense*).
(*Photograph by Charlotte M. King.*)

cultivated fields. Thorough cultivation of the field with a plow and disk and cultivator will destroy the weed.

FIG. 33-A.   Distribution of Wild Onion.

DICOTYLEDONEAE, DICOTS.

Stem formed of pith, wood and bark; between the bark and wood, the cambium layer, an annual ring of wood, is formed each year; leaves netted veined; flowers generally on the plan of five; embryo with a pair of cotyledons. Rose, pigweed, potato, bean, clover, Russian thistle, horse nettle, Canadian thistle belong to this division.

URTICACEAE, NETTLE FAMILY.

This family embraces such economic plants as the fig, India rubber tree, hemp, hop, and such trees as the hackberry and elm.

Hemp (*Cannabis sativa* L.).

Description.—A rough, stout, dioecious annual, 3 to 10 feet tall; inner bark of tough fibers; leaves digitate, of 5 to 7 linear-lanceolate, coarsely toothed leaflets, the upper alternate; flowers green; staminate, in compound racemes; pistillate, in erect spikes, each consisting of a calyx of a single sepal folded around the ovary and 2 filiform stigmas; fruit an achene; endosperm fleshy; embryo curved.

Distribution.—Hemp is found growing in waste places from New Brunswick south to North Carolina and west to Minnesota, Kansas and Rocky mountains. Widely distributed through cultivation, it often becomes a troublesome weed. It is found in many parts of Iowa; reported from Story, Dubuque, Clinton, Polk, Boone, Allamakee, Winneshiek, Marshall, Howard, Clayton, Hardin, Grundy, Plymouth, Pottawattamie, Fremont and other counties.

Extermination.—Hemp is easily killed by cultivation. Rotation of crops will control it.

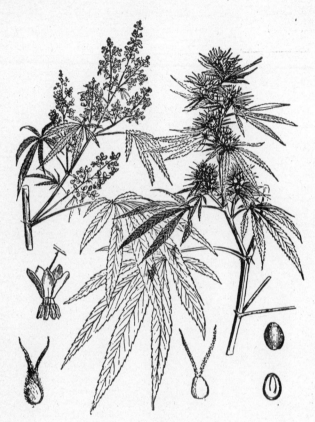

FIG. 34. Hemp. (*Cannabis sativa*).
(*After Faguet.*)

FIG. 34-A. Distribution of Hemp.

Nettle (*Urtica gracilis* Ait.).

Description.—A perennial, stinging herb from 2 to 6 feet high; sparingly bristly; leaves ovate-lanceolate, sharply serrate, with long petioles, 3 to 5-nerved, sparingly pubescent, petioles usually

FIG. 35. Stinging Nettle (*Urtica gracilis*).
(*Photographed by Photo Section, Ia. Agr. Exp. Sta.*)

bristly; flowers inconspicuous, paniculate, dioecious or of staminate and pistillate flowers; achene compressed, inclosed by the persistent calyx. Hairs multicellular at base, urticating.

Distribution.—This plant extends from eastern Canada to Wisconsin, Minnesota, central Canada and Louisiana; it is found along roadsides, borders of thickets and woods; occasionally in gardens and waste places especially in eastern and southern Iowa. It is especially common in northeastern Iowa, along roadsides and in gardens in Clayton, Allamakee, Winneshiek, Jones and Linn counties.

FIG. 35-A.   Stinging Nettle *(Urtica gracilis)* showing root system.
(Photographed by Photo Section, Ia. Agr. Exp. Sta.)

FIG. 35-B. Distribution of Nettle.

Extermination.—The perennial root stocks make this weed quite persistent and difficult to destroy, because the weed often occurs in inaccessible places along fence-rows; however, persistent cultivation will exterminate the weed.

*Chemical Composition.**

FRESH OR AIR DRY MATERIAL

Water	Ash	Protein	Fiber	Nitrogen free extract	Fat
82.44	2.30	5.50	1.96	7.13	0.67

WATER FREE SUBSTANCE

Water	Ash	Protein	Fiber	Nitrogen free extract	Fat
	13.1	31.4	11.2	40.5	----

Pellitory (*Parietaria pennsylvanica* Muhl.).

Description.—A low, annual, simple, or sparingly branched minutely downy plant; oblong-lanceolate, thin leaves with opaque dots; flowers monoeciously polygamous, shorter than involucre; glomerate except in the lower axils; stigma sessile.

Distribution.—Pellitory is found from Massachusetts to Minnesota and southward. It is common in Iowa in shady places lawns and woods.

Extermination.—This weed is usually exterminated by cultivation. It may be destroyed by the application of iron sulphate at the rate of 100 pounds to a barrel of water.

*Compiled by Jenkins and Winton: Bull. Off. Exp. Sta. 11.

FIG. 36.   Pellitory *(Parietaria pennsylvanica).*   Common in shady places near buildings.
(Photographed by Hart.)

FIG. 36-A.   Distribution of Pellitory.

Fig. 36-B. Pellitory (*Parietaria pennsylvania*).
(*Photograph by Photo Section, Ia. Agr. Exp. Sta.*)

POLYGONACEAE, BUCKWHEAT FAMILY.

This family contains the pie plant, canaigre, smartweed, prince's feather, and buckwheat.

Curled Dock, Yellow Dock (*Rumex crispus* L.).

Description.—A smooth perennial from 3 to 4 feet high; leaves with strongly wavy and curled margins, lanceolate and acute, lower leaves with bases somewhat truncate or inclined to be heart-shaped; flowers collected in dense whorls, extended or prolonged into racemes, entirely leafless above, but below with small leaves; six sepals, the three outer herbaceous, leaflike, the three inner larger and somewhat curled, and after flowering forming the valves of the fruit, which surround the 3-angled fruit, each valve bearing a grain.

Distribution.—It is native to Europe where it has long been known as a troublesome weed; it is common throughout eastern

North America, Pacific coast, and Rocky Mountains, and abundant in Iowa in clover meadows, along roadsides and in pastures. The curled dock is common everywhere in the state, including Story, Marshall, Tama, Carroll, Boone, Linn, Jackson, Clinton, Jones,

FIG. 37.   Curled Dock, Yellow Dock, Sour Dock (*Rumex crispus*).   Common in low grounds, clover meadows, fields, etc.
(Photographed by Colburn.)

FIG. 37-A.   Distribution of Curled Dock.

Dubuque, Clayton, Cerro Gordo, Winnebago, Plymouth, Woodbury, Fremont and Taylor counties.

Extermination.—One of the most efficient means of destroying this weed is to root it out by hand and this is done very readily in the spring when the soil is wet by taking hold of the plant just at the surface of the ground, giving the root a slight twist and at the same time an upward pull, when it will readily come from the soil. Where it is common, however, it is sometimes plowed or a spud is used. This method is not, however, so effective as the pulling method.

FIG. 37-B.   Curled Dock (*Rumex crispus*).   Roadsides, meadows, clover fields, etc.
(*Photograph by Charlotte M. King.*)

Clark and Fletcher suggest the following treatment: ''Sow clean seed. The prevalence of dock in meadows is due to sowing contaminated grass and clover seeds. Land worked under a short rotation of crops is never badly infested with docks. When the soil is soft after continued rain, they can be pulled from meadows and pastures. Pull or cut and destroy all seed-bearing plants before harvesting a clover seed crop. A handful of salt placed on the crown of docks, after cutting in dry hot weather, will extract the moisture and destroy the root; this is a remedy sometimes used in lawns and pastures when the soil is too hard and dry to permit pulling them.''

Mexican Dock (*Rumex mexicanus* Meisn.).

Description.—This is a tall upright plant similar to pale dock in appearance. It has narrow pale green leaves and a dense panicle.

Distribution.—This dock and pale dock are found in similar situations.

Extermination.—The same treatment for removal should be used as in case of pale dock.

Smooth Dock, Peach-leaved Dock (*Rumex altissimus* Wood.).

Description.—A tall smooth perennial; leaves pale, ovate, or oblong-lanceolate, thickish, not wavy margined; flowers in paniculate spikelike racemes, in crowded whorls, nodding pedicels, shorter than the fruiting calyx; valves broadly ovate or obscurely heart-shaped, one with a conspicuous pale grain; achene triangular, pale.

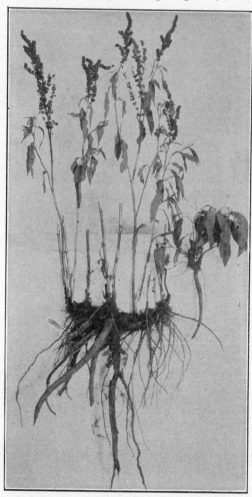

FIG. 38. Smooth Dock (*Rumex altissimus*).
(*Photographed by Photo Section, Ia. Agr. Exp. Sta.*)

Distribution.—It is common in the northern states and abundant in low grounds and highways, also in pastures throughout Iowa. It grows freely in Carroll, Boone, Story, Pottawattamie, Fremont, Monona, Woodbury, Cerro Gordo, Clayton, Clinton, Jones, Dubuque, Scott, Lee and Polk counties.

FIG. 38-A. Smooth or Peach-leaved Dock *(Rumex altissimus)*, Dandelion *(Taraxacum officinale)* and other weeds. The seed which spreads the weed comes from such places as this.

(Photograph by Charlotte M. King.)

FIG. 38-B. Distribution of Smooth Dock.

Extermination.—This weed has running roots and cannot be destroyed in the same way as sour dock. The roots are, however, shallow, and can be destroyed by giving cultivation which exposes the roots to the sun.

FIG. 38-C. Smooth or Peach-leaved Dock (*Rumex altissimus*). Low meadows, road-sides and pastures.
(*Photograph by Colburn.*)

Bitter Dock (*Rumex obtusifolius* L.).

Description.—A perennial herb, with roughish stem; leaves some-what wavy, the lowest ovate heart-shaped, obtuse, the upper ob-long-lanceolate, acute; flowers inconspicuous, greenish, on jointed pedicels; valves of the fruit conspicuous, toothed at the base.

Distribution.—Bitter dock is naturalized from Europe. Its range is from eastern Canada to Wisconsin, Minnesota and south to Texas and Florida. It is found in waste places, sparingly introduced into Iowa with clover seed. It has been observed in Story, Scott and Lee counties.

Extermination.—The yellow spindle-shaped root is easily pulled out by giving the plant a slight twist, especially when the ground is moist. Clover seed containing this weed should not be sown.

Fig. 39. Bitter Dock, Red-veined Dock (*Rumex obtusifolius*). Common in some clover meadows in southern Iowa.
(*Photographed by Colburn.*)

Fig. 39-A. Distribution of Bitter Dock.

Sheep Sorrel (*Rumex Acetosella* L.).

Description.—A low smooth annual or perennial, usually the latter, growing from 6 to 12 inches high, producing an erect stem, with horizontal, creeping woody root-stocks or rhizomes, petioled, narrowly-hastate, narrow lanceolate leaves, the upper linear; flowers on jointed pedicels, dioecious, small, in a terminal naked panicle;

FIG. 40.   Sheep Sorrel or Horse Sorrel (*Rumex Acetosella*).   Common in sandy and gravelly soil.
(*After Clark and Fletcher.*)

small green calyx; exserted stamens; the valves not enlarging in fruit.

Distribution.—Sheep sorrel has long been known as a trouble-some weed in Europe and in the northern states. It is perhaps indigenous to the United States, at least now common across the

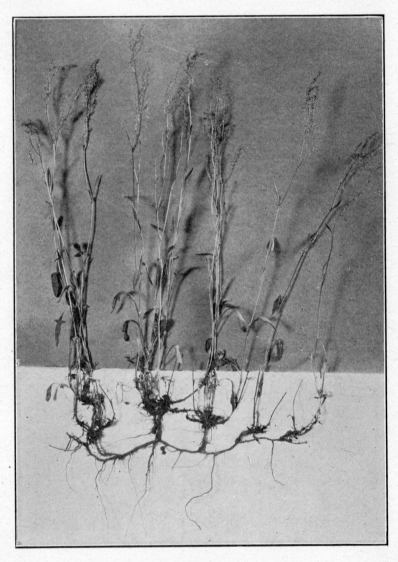

FIG. 40-A.   Sheep Sorrel (*Rumex Acetosella*).
(*Photographed by Photo Section, Ia. Agr. Exp. Sta.*)

continent in the north. It is common everywhere in Iowa, more particularly in sandy or gravelly soils. It is abundant in Clinton, Muscatine, Lee, Dubuque, Jones, Clayton, Allamakee, Cerro Gordo, Winnebago, Hancock, Marshall, Linn, Buchanan, Bremer, Hardin, Boone, Story, Hamilton, Emmet, and Palo Alto counties.

Extermination.—The plant succumbs quite readily to cultivation, and where the fields are thoroughly cultivated with hoed crops, it is seldom troublesome more than one season. In fact the vast majority of sorrel plants may be killed by cultivating the soil once or twice. The roots seem to be unable to stand drying. The soil on which it occurs should receive a heavy coat of manure to increase the growth of the crop plants. This method seems to be approved by Dr. Halsted, who says: ''This pest can be subdued by keeping the infested land under the plow for a short time.''

Clark and Fletcher say in regard to this weed: ''Sheep sorrel is said to be an index of soil characters. It seems to thrive best on sandy or gravelly soils deficient of lime. An application of lime to slightly acid soils produces a more vigorous growth of cultivated crops and curtails the opportunities of the sorrel to grow and spread. Old meadows and pastures that are overrun with it and that cannot well be brought under cultivation may be pastured with sheep for two, or three years to prevent it from seeding freely.

A three-year rotation of crops with good cultivation, including shallow plowing directly after hay crop and frequent cultivation until autumn to prepare for hoed crops, will keep sheep sorrel well under control even on lands that seem to be specially suited to its growth.''

Wallace's Farmer suggests the following: ''To control this weed in the meadows we would suggest applying manure and thickening up the grass stand. Putting the land into a cultivated crop destroys this weed.''

FIG. 40-B. Distribution of Sheep Sorrel.

Chemical Composition.—The ash of this weed is reported by Weinhold as follows:

Phosphoric acid	Potash	Sodium	Lime	Magnesia
9.7	19.7	1.3	14.0	9.4

Goosegrass, Dooryard Knotweed (*Polygonum aviculare* L.).

Description.—A scattered or somewhat ascending, bluish gray annual; leaves acute or acutish; flowers greenish with pinkish margins; achenes triangular, dull and minutely granular-striate.

FIG. 41.   Dooryard Knotweed (*Polygonum aviculare*).   Common in dooryards.
(*Photographed by Hart.*)

Distribution.—Native in the northern hemisphere, Asia and North America, common everywhere in Iowa in gardens and waste places. It is one of the most common weeds in dooryards in Clayton, Allamakee, Winneshiek, Winnebago, Hancock, Boone, Story, Polk,

Carroll, Dallas, Guthrie, Fremont and Woodbury counties. Usually affected by a white mildew.

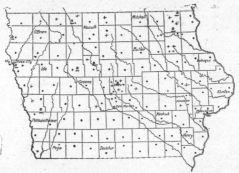

Fig. 41-A. Distribution of Dooryard Knotweed.

Extermination.—This annual weed can be destroyed only by giving the soil on which it occurs cultivation. It frequents dry and more or less beaten soils. Where it is abundant in lawns the soil should be stirred and sown to white clover.

Erect Knotweed (*Polygonum erectum* L.).

Description.—An annual, glabrous, stout, erect or ascending yellowish green herb, 1 foot to 2 feet high, with elliptical leaves; flowers yellowish and inconspicuous, 1 to 2, in an axil; stamens 5 to 6; achene dull, included.

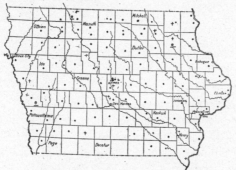

FIG. 42. Distribution of Erect Knotweed.

Distribution.—This weed is widely distributed from the northeastern part of North America to Manitoba, Wisconsin, Minnesota to Arkansas and eastward. It is common in Iowa, especially in the eastern part, and in Story, Boone, Marshall, Polk, Allamakee, Clinton, Clayton, Jones, Jackson and Dubuque counties.

FIG. 42-A.   Erect Knotweed (*Polygonum erectum*).   Common in many parts of the
state.
(*Photographed by Hart.*)

Extermination.—Erect knotweed is easily exterminated by cultivation.

Bushy Knotweed (*Polygonum ramosissimum* Michx.).

Description.—An erect or ascending, green or yellowish green smooth herb, 2 to 4 feet high; leaves linear or lanceolate, tapering into a petiole; flower inconspicuous, greenish; stamens 3-6; style short; achene 3-angled.

Distribution.—The range of this plant extends from Manitoba to Texas. It is found also in Pennsylvania. The weed is frequent in fields in many parts of Iowa, in Story, Boone, Worth, Marshall, Winnebago, Linn, Buchanan, Webster and Cerro Gordo counties.

Extermination.—Easily exterminated by cultivation.

FIG. 43.   Bushy or Erect Knotweed *(Polygonum ramosissimum)*.   Common in fields.
(Photographed by Hart.)

FIG. 43-A.   Distribution of Bushy Knotweed.

Pink Smartweed *(Polygonum lapathifolium* L.).

Description.—Pink smartweed is a native, glabrous, erect annual, with stem swollen at the nodes; lanceolate, acuminate leaves with short ciliate petioles; racemes panicled, nodding, with many flowers; calyx white or pink, small 5-parted; 6 stamens, style included; achene lenticular.

Distribution.—It occurs from New England to Nebraska and Louisiana. This weed is native to Europe. It is common in eastern North America, and grows everywhere in Iowa, preferring moist situations; in Monona, Woodbury, Fremont, Story, Marshall; Linn, Mahaska, Johnson, Lee, Van Buren, Jackson, Clinton and Dubuque counties.

FIG. 44.   Smartweed (*Polygonum lapathifolium*).
(*Photographed by Photo Section, Ia. Agr. Exp. Sta.*)

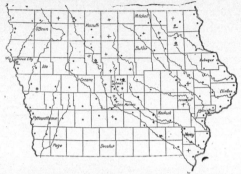

FIG. 44-A.   Distribution of Pink Smartweed.

Extermination.—Easily exterminated, after drainage of slough, by cultivation.

Marsh Smartweed, Tanweed (*Polygonum Muhlenbergii* (Meisn.) Wats.).

Description.—A somewhat pubescent or scabrous perennial with large black roots, decumbent or erect; leaves lanceolate to ovate, narrowly acuminate; flowers in rather long hispid spikes; sepals 5, bright rose color; stamens 5, styles 2-cleft, exserted. Frequently only sterile plants, or flowering rather late in the season; trichomes multicellular, at base with thick outer epidermal walls.

Distribution.—This weed is common from Canada to Florida and west, and is found in all parts of Iowa. It is an exceedingly variable plant; it may be found in very moist situations, and in stagnant water, or in somewhat higher but poorly drained situations. The plant is characterized by black thickish roots. This weed is common in Boone, Webster, Marshall, Linn, Hancock, Winnebago, Cerro Gordo, Johnson, Lee, Scott, Muscatine, Clinton, Dubuque and Clayton counties.

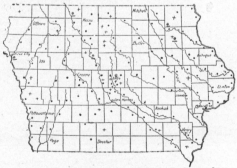

FIG. 45.   Distribution of Marsh Smartweed.

Extermination.—Marsh smartweed or tanweed is a persistent perennial, and since it grows in wet places it is particularly difficult to destroy. The best method of treating it is by thorough cultivation, exposing all the root-stocks to the sun, then removing the young plants as rapidly as they make their appearance.

Wallace's Farmer suggests the following treatment: "It grows less vigorously on well drained land, hence the first step in eradication is to drain the field thoroughly. The summer fallow is perhaps the best course of treatment. Plow the infested patch early and

FIG. 45-A. Marsh Smartweed, Tanweed *(Polygonum Muhlenbergii)* showing root system.
(Photographed by Photo Section, Ia. Agr. Exp. Sta.)

keep the disk and plow working on it regularly all summer long. All the roots that can be located should be pulled up and burned after they have been dried out. A heavy pitchfork and plenty of muscle will soon fill a wagon box with the long, tough, yellow roots. A heavy seeding of sorghum helps to weaken the stand, but we

FIG. 45-B. Marsh Smartweed, Tanweed *(Polygonum Muhlenbergii).*
(Photographed by Photo Section, Ia. Agr. Exp. Sta.)

have seen patches as vigorous as ever a year after two succeeding crops of sorghum had been grown in an effort to smother out the pest.''

FIG. 45-C. Marsh Smartweed, Tanweed (*Polygonum Muhlenbergii*). (*Photograph by W. Newell.*)

Heart'sease, Pennsylvania Smartweed (*Polygonum pennsylvanicum* L.).

Description.—An annual 1 foot to 2 feet high, with lanceolate leaves; branches below the flowers beset with numerous stalked glands; flowers whitish or rose-colored; stamens 6 to 8, style 2-cleft; fruit an achene, 1¾ lines long, flattened, brown, shining, part of the calyx remaining attached to the base.

Distribution.—Pennsylvania smartweed is common from New England southward and westward and in every part of Iowa;

coming up abundantly in corn fields, in some cases forming a
mass of rose-colored flowers; also growing up abundantly in grain
fields after harvest. It has been noticed as particularly common
in Story, Boone, Webster, Cerro Gordo, Winnebago, Kossuth,
Emmet, Lyon, Palo Alto, Marshall, Linn, Tama, Clinton, Dubuque,
Johnson, Iowa, Allamakee and Winneshiek counties.

Fig. 46. Pennsylvania Smartweed *(Polygonum pennsylvanicum)*.
(Photographed by Photo Section, Ia. Agr. Exp. Sta.)

FIG. 46-A. Distribution of Pennsylvania Smartweed.

Extermination.—This smartweed is easily exterminated by cultivation.

FIG. 46-B. Pennsylvania Smartweed (*Polygonum pennsylvanicum*). Common in corn fields. (*Photograph by W. Newell.*)

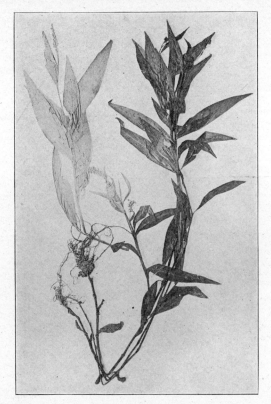

FIG. 47. Common Smartweed or Water Pepper *(Polygonum Hydropiper)*. *(Photographed by Colburn.)*

Water Pepper (*Polygonum Hydropiper* L.).

Description.—Much like *P. Persicaria* but more slender and often decumbent; flowers greenish on slender nodding spikes; achenes dull in color and the whole plant more or less acrid.

Distribution.—Water pepper is widely distributed in eastern North America. It is naturalized from Europe and may be indigenous in the northwest. The weed is widely distributed in Iowa, being especially abundant in Clayton, Allamakee, Clinton, Jones, Winneshiek, Cerro Gordo, Jackson, Linn, Winnebago, Buchanan, Story, Boone and Carroll counties.

Extermination.—This weed is usually found in moist places and is not very troublesome in cultivated fields except in low places. Fields that are badly infested with it should be plowed and drained and if possible some leguminous plants like alsike clover should be sown.

Lady's Thumb, Smartweed (*Polygonum Persicaria* L.)

Description.—A nodding, smooth, glabrous annual; sheaths bristly ciliate; leaves lanceolate, marked with a conspicuous dark or lunar spot; spikes short cylindrical; peduncles smooth; achene flattened, smooth and shining.

Distribution.—Lady's thumb is native to Europe and has become common in eastern North America, Rocky mountains and on the Pacific coast. Common everywhere in Iowa, particularly in waste places and gardens, and growing up abundantly after grain

FIG. 48.　Lady's Thumb *(Polygonum Persicaria.)*　Common in gardens, fields and along roadsides.
(Photographed by Photo Section, Ia. Agr. Exp. Sta.)

has been harvested. It is frequent in Boone, Story, Greene, Carroll, Pottawattamie, Fremont, Woodbury, Lyon, Ida, Sac, Kossuth, Cerro Gordo, Madison, Van Buren, Lee, Scott, Clinton, Dubuque, Clayton, Jones and Winneshiek counties.

FIG. 48-A. Distribution of Lady's Thumb.

Extermination.—This weed is easily destroyed by cultivation. The main point, however, is to prevent seed production, which may be accomplished by cutting off the plants after they have started to produce flowers.

Water Pepper or Smartweed (*P. hydropiperoides* Michx.).

Description.—A perennial; not acrid; leaves narrowly lanceolate or oblong; small flesh-colored flowers in erect slender spikes; achenes smooth, sharply triangular.

FIG. 49. Distribution of Water Pepper.

Distribution.—Water pepper is distributed in swamps from eastern Canada southwest to Mexico; it is also distributed across the northern states to California; common in low wet places in many

FIG. 49-A.   Water Pepper (*Polygonum hydropiperoides*).   Common in low places,
fields, etc.
(*Photographed by Photo Section, Ia. Agr. Exp. Sta.*)

parts of Iowa, especially in Dubuque, Clayton, Jones, Winneshiek
and Cerro Gordo counties.

Extermination.—Since this perennial weed is most abundant in
sloughs, drainage must be resorted to before an effective means of
exterminating it can be used.   After drainage it will give little
trouble in cultivation.

The water smartweed (*Polygonum acre* H. B. K.), which resembles *P. hydropiperoides* very closely, is a nearly smooth perennial with stems rooting at the decumbent base; stems erect, whitish or flesh-colored flowers in dense spikes. It is common in low grounds. The seeds of *P. acre* are shiny while those of *P. hydropiperoides* are dull.

FIG. 49-B.   Water Smartweed (*Polygonum acre*).
(*Photograph by Photo Section, Ia. Agr. Exp. Sta.*)

FIG. 49-C.   Distribution of Water Smartweed.

Prince's Feather (*Polygonum orientale* L.).

Description.—A tall annual, branching widely at the top. Leaves large, ovate, pointed. Sheaths ciliate. The dense pendulous spikes are of bright rose-color.

Distribution.—Sometimes occurs as an escape from cultivation.

Extermination.—Readily removed by cultivation.

Black Bindweed or Wild Buckwheat (*Polygonum Convolvulus* L.).

Description.—An annual, twining, with smooth joints; leaves halberd or heart-shaped; flowers in corymbose racemes; achene dull black, triangular and minutely roughened.

Distribution.—This weed is widely scattered with grain seed, especially with wheat and oats. It is often very troublesome in small grain fields. In Iowa, however, it occurs in gardens and along roadsides in Boone, Greene, Madison, Warren, Taylor, Van Buren, Lee, Scott, Muscatine, Polk, Marshall, Iowa, Ida, Sac, Lyon, Kossuth, Cerro Gordo, Hancock, Winnebago, Jones, Clayton, Fremont and Allamakee counties.

FIG. 50. Distribution of Black Bindweed.

Extermination.—It is not difficult to destroy the weed by giving clean cultivation, since it succumbs easily to such treatment. Only clean seed should be sown.

Clark and Fletcher recommend as follows: ''Sow clean seed grain. The seeds retain their vitality for a relatively short period, probably not longer than three years, except in the drier soils of the western plains. The suppression of this pest is therefore largely dependent on the prevention of a continued supply of fresh seeds to the soil. This weed gives little trouble on land under a short rotation of crops, including hay, for two years.

The seeds of wild buckwheat do not germinate in the spring until the soil is quite warm. Most of the early plants can be destroyed in the grain crops by an application of the harrow when the grain

FIG. 50-A.   Black Bindweed *(Polygonum Convolvulus)*.
(After Clark and Fletcher.)

is about three inches high. The young plants soon root firmly and the harrowing, to be effective, must be done just as they emerge from the ground.''

FIG. 50-B. Black Bindweed or Wild Buckwheat (*Polygonum Convolvulus*). Common in grain fields and waste places.
(*Photographed by Photo Section, Ia. Agr. Exp. Sta.*)

Climbing False Buckwheat. (*Polygonum scandens* L.).

Description.—A smooth perennial twining plant, with slightly halberd-shaped leaves and naked sheaths. The fruit is broadly winged. The achene is smooth and shining.

Distribution.—Common in moist thickets.

Extermination.—The plant is not likely to be troublesome. It may be destroyed by clean cultivation.

FIG. 51. Climbing False Buckwheat (*Polygonum scandens*).
(*Photographed by Photo Section, Ia. Agr. Exp. Sta.*)

CHENOPODIACEAE, GOOSEFOOT FAMILY.

This family contains the spinach, sugar beet, beet and salt bushes.

FIG. 51-A. Ragged Sailor (*Polygonum orientale*).
(*Photographed by Photo Section. Ia. Agr. Exp. Sta.*)

FIG. 52. Winged Pigweed or Western Tumbleweed (*Cycloloma atriplicifolium*)
Sandy soil, Muscatine Island, etc.
(*Photographed by Colburn.*)

Winged Pigweed (*Cycloloma atriplicifolium* (Spreng.) Coult.)

Description.—An annual with alternate sinuate-toothed petioled leaves; small inconspicuous flowers in open panicles; seeds winged; herb diffusely spreading or often spherical in form similar to the Russian thistle or Iowa tumbleweed.

FIG. 52-A. Winged Pigweed (*Cycloloma atriplicifolium*). Seed and cross section of ovary.
(After W. J. Beal, Mich. Agr. Exp. Sta.)

Distribution.—Winged pigweed is native from Manitoba and

Minnesota, to Illinois, Arkansas and the Rocky mountains. In Iowa it is found along Mississippi river in Dubuque, Muscatine, Lee and Clinton counties, in Linn county, and along Missouri river.

FIG. 52-B. Distribution of Winged Pigweed.

Extermination.—This weed is easily exterminated by cultivation. In Iowa it has probably been spread with western grass seed and in stock cars.

Mexican Fireweed (*Kochia Scoparia* (L.) Schrad.).

Description.—An annual, erect, puberulent or glabrate herb; leaves lanceolate to linear, ciliate acuminate; flowers sessile in the axils of the upper leaves, forming short dense-bracted spikes; segments of fruiting calyx each with a short triangular horizontal wing.

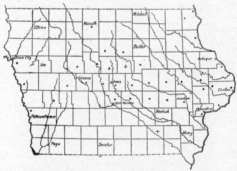

FIG. 53. Distribution of Mexican Fireweed.

Distribution.—Mexican fireweed is found in waste places; it is also commonly cultivated, and is now a frequent escape in Iowa. It is common in many of the northern states, Rocky mountains and the Pacific coast. The plant is a native of eastern Europe and western Asia.

Extermination.—This weed is easily exterminated by cultivation.

Fɪɢ. 53-A.   Mexican Fireweed.   (*Kochia Scoparia.*)   A frequent escape from cultivation.
(*Drawn by F. C. Collins.*)

Mexican Tea (*Chenopodium ambrosioides* L.).

Description.—A smoothish or slightly pubescent annual; strong scented; leaves oblong or lanceolate, entire or cut-pinnatifid, nearly sessile; spikes densely flowered, leafy; flowers in small, dense, axillary spikes; calyx 3-parted enclosing the fruit. The wormseed, a variety of the Mexican tea (*C. anthelminticum*), is an annual or sometimes a perennial; leaves more strongly toothed; the flowers usually in bractless panicled spikes.

Distribution.—Mexican tea is found southward, occurring, however, from Maine to California. The wormseed has nearly the same distribution, occurring northward to Minnesota and Wisconsin. Neither of these weeds is common in Iowa.

Extermination.—In Iowa both of these weeds are easily exterminated by cultivation. Do not permit any of their seeds to mature.

FIG. 54. Mexican Tea (*Chenopodium ambrosioides*). In southern Iowa; streets and fields.

(Photographed by Colburn.)

FIG. 54-A. Distribution of Mexican Tea.

FIG. 54-B.   Plant hair or trichome of *Chenopodium Botrys.*   *a,* from stem;
b, glandular trichome from calyx.
(Drawn by Charlotte M. King.)

Maple-leaved Goosefoot (*Chenopodium hybridum* L.).

Description.—A bright green annual from 2 to 4 feet high;
widely branching, with an unpleasant odor like that of stramonium;
leaves thin, triangular, heart-shaped, sinuate-toothed; flowers inconspicuous, in loose, racemose panicles; calyx covering the fruit;
seed firmly attached to the pericarp.

Distribution.—This goosefoot is frequently found in woods and
waste places; its range extends from Kansas to Manitoba, Wiscon-

FIG. 55. Distribution of Maple-leaved Goosefoot.

sin and Minnesota and southward; it is common in Story, Boone,
Marshall, Clinton, Polk, Woodbury, Pottawattamie, Dubuque, Allamakee and Cerro Gordo counties.

Extermination.—This annual weed can be killed by giving clean
cultivation. Sometimes it is distributed with clover seed, but less
frequently than the other species. Only clean clover seed should
be sown.

FIG. 55-A. Maple-leaved Goosefoot (*Chenopodium hybridum*). Frequent in woods and
waste places.
(*After Mich. Agr. Exp. Sta.*)

Lamb's Quarters, Pigweed.   (*Chenopodium album* L.).

Description.—An erect annual from 1 foot to 4 feet high; young plants generally mealy, older plants smooth; leaves rhombic-ovate to lanceolate or the upper sometimes linear, acute, lower commonly

Plate 13

LAMB'S QUARTERS or PIGWEED
(Chenopodium album *L.*)

FIG. 56.   Lamb's Quarters *(Chenopodium album)*. Common in gardens and fields. *(After Clark and Fletcher.)*

toothed; flowers produced in clustered, dense-spiked panicles; calyx 5-parted, nearly covering the seed; seeds surrounded by a loose pericarp forming an utricle.

Distribution.—This plant is a native of Europe; it is widely naturalized in eastern North America and the Rocky Mountains, and it occurs in Utah and on the Pacific coast. It is found everywhere in Iowa in cultivated fields and in gardens as well as along highways.

Extermination.—Plants of this species produce an enormous number of seeds. The young plants are easily destroyed by cutting off below the ground. Covering the young plants is not ef-

FIG. 56-A. Lamb's Quarters (*Chenopodium album*).
(*Photographed by Photo Section, Ia. Agr. Exp. Sta.*)

fective unless the entire plant is covered. Older plants may be destroyed by pulling them up. The weed by means of the shade it produces destroys other vegetation underneath it.

Chemical Composition.—According to a report of the Bussey Institution, the chemical composition is as follows:*

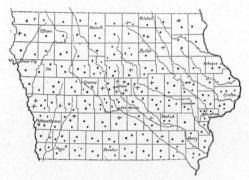

FIG. 56-B. Distribution of Lamb's Quarters.

FRESH OR AIR DRY MATERIAL

Water	Ash	Protein	Fiber	Nitrogen free extract	Fat
80.80	3.02	3.94	2.55	8.93	0.76

WATER FREE SUBSTANCE

	15.7	20.5	13.3	46.5	4.0

Orach (*Atriplex patula* L. var. *hastata* (L.) Gray).

Description.—A pale green or purplish, slightly scurfy annual, 2 to 3 feet high; leaves slender-petioled, narrowly lanceolate-hastate, entire or somewhat sinuate-dentate; flowers inconspicuous, interrupted, in slender-panicled spikes.

Distribution.—Orach is found from eastern Canada to Wisconsin and Iowa. In Iowa the weed has a widely scattered occurrence, and is becoming more abundant.

Extermination.—Orach is easily exterminated by cultivation. Sheep are fond of it and may be utilized to eradicate the weed.

*Bull. Bussey Inst., 1877: Jenkins and Winton; Office Exp. Sta., Bull. 11.

Fig. 57.   Orach (*Atriplex patula* var. *hastata*).   Streets, gardens, roadsides.
(*Photographed by Colburn.*)

Fig. 57-A.   Distribution of Orach.

Russian Thistle (*Salsola Kali* L. var. *tenuifolia* G. F. W. Mey.).
Description.—An herbaceous, smooth or slightly pubescent annual, diffusely branched from the base, from 1½ to 3 feet high, spherical in the mature form; leaves fleshy, alternate, succulent, linear, subterete, 1 inch to 2 inches long, pointed in the older speci-

mens, upper leaves in the mature plant persistent, each subtending two leaf-like bracts and a flower; stem and branches red; apetalous flowers solitary and sessile; calyx consisting of 5 persistent lobes, enclosing the dry fruit which is usually rose-colored, about 1 inch to 12 inches long; 5 stamens nearly as long as the calyx; pistils with 2 slender styles producing a single obconical depressed seed, dull gray or green, without albumen; embryo spirally coiled; on germination cotyledons are subterete. The plant flowers in July or August, the seeds maturing in August.

Distribution.—Russian thistle is native of Russia and western Asia. Since its introduction into the Dakotas it has been widely scattered in the northern states and is common from Minnesota to the Pacific northwest and in the Rocky mountains from Montana to New Mexico. It is widely scattered in Iowa but abundant only during dry years, along the right of way of railways, and in the vicinity of stockyards. Especially common in sandy and gravel soil. The immature plants in Colorado are used for silage. It is said to make excellent food.

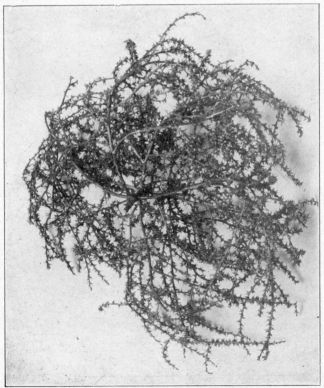

FIG. 58. Russian Thistle (*Salsola Kali* var. *tenuifolia*). Common in western Iowa. Fleshy herb becoming spiny.
(*Photographed by Gardner.*)

Extermination.—Since the Russian thistle is an annual, it would seem an easy matter to destroy it; and as a matter of fact, when taken in time, it is not a difficult weed to remove. Its noxiousness comes largely from the fact that the plant is very productive of seeds. A Russian thistle plant once cut off at the surface of the ground, will never grow again; hence in cultivated fields it is not likely to prove a great pest. The problem is, however, a very different one in pastures, meadows and roadsides; here the weeds cannot be removed by cultivation and many of them mature their seeds unobserved. The removal of these weeds along the roadsides is important, because it is largely from this source that our fields become infested. The removal of such weeds can be best accomplished by running over the patch with a mower.

Fletcher and Clark recommend as follows: "Hand-pull wherever practicable. Harrowing growing crops is an effective remedy; it is easily killed by this method when young. The harrow should be applied just before the grain emerges from the ground and again when the crop is three inches high."

Wallace's Farmer suggests the following treatment: "Russian thistle is easily controlled by cutting it off just below the surface of the ground before it seeds in August. It has not proved a dangerous weed east of Mississippi river."

CHEMICAL COMPOSITION.

	Original sample	Dry matter
Water	84.52	....
Dry matter	15.48	....
100 parts contain:		
Water	84.52	....
Crude ash	3.41	22.01
Ether extract (crude fat)	.34	2.20
Nitrogen free (soluble carbohydrates)	6.10	39.39
Crude fiber	2.78	17.94
Crude protein (total nitrogen x 6.25)	2.86	18.46
True albuminoids (albuminoid N x 6.25)	(2.22)	(14.35)
	100.00	100.00

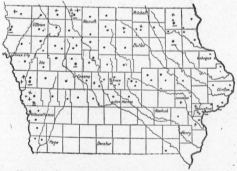

FIG. 58-A. Distribution of Russian Thistle.

AMARANTHACEAE, PIGWEED FAMILY

This family contains few economic plants. Some members of the Amaranthaceae, like the cock's-comb, are grown for ornamental purposes.

Rough Pigweed or Redroot (*Amaranthus retroflexus* (L.).

Description.—A roughish, more or less pubescent annual, 3 to 5 feet tall; leaves ovate or rhombic-ovate, undulate; long petioled, entire; flowers in thick spikes crowded in a stiff or bunchy, spiky panicle; bracts subulate, longer than the mucronate or obtusely-tipped sepals.

Distribution.—Redroot is a weed throughout North America, especially eastward; it is abundant in every county in the state.

Extermination.—This weed is frequently distributed in clover

Fig. 59. Rough Pigweed or Redroot (*Amaranthus retroflexus*). Common in gardens, roadsides and fields.
(*Photographed by Photo Section, Ia. Agr. Exp. Sta.*)

seed; sowing clean clover seed in a clean field is a preventive measure.

Fletcher and Clark recommend as follows: ''When embedded in

REDROOT PIGWEED or GREEN AMARANTH
(Amaranthus retroflexus z.)

FIG. 59-A.   Rough Pigweed *(Amaranthus retroflexus).*
(After Clark and Fletcher.)

the soil, the seeds retain their vitality for several years, though probably not more than five in a moist soil, and produce seedling plants only when brought by cultivation within about two inches of the surface."

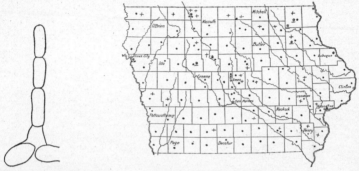

FIG. 59-B. Trichomes or plant hairs from stem of Pigweed. (*Drawing by Charlotte M. King.*)

FIG. 59-C. Distribution of Pigweed.

Chemical Composition.—According to the University of Minnesota the composition is as follows:*

Dry matter	Crude protein	Ether extract	Nitrogen free extract and fiber	Ash
97.00	26.54	1.56	62.86	9.24

Tumble-weed (*Amaranthus graecizans* L.).

Description.—A smooth, pale green, much-branched annual; at maturity a spherical mass, which separates easily from the root; leaves oblong-spatulate or ovate; small flowers greenish, inconspicuous, polygamous, several together in small axillary clusters, small and pointed.

Distribution.—This weed is common in waste grounds in North America, especially from Ohio westward. After maturity the detached leafless plants may be seen rolling over fields. This is one of the common Iowa tumble-weeds and frequently may be seen piled up against fences.

*Bull. Minn. Agr. Exp. Sta. 11, by Harry Snyder.

FIG. 60.   Iowa Tumble-weed or Tumbling Pigweed (*Amaranthus graecizans*). Common in
corn fields.   Plant grows in circular form, separates from the root in the autumn
and rolls over and over, scattering the seeds.

(Photographed by Hart.)

FIG. 60-A.   Distribution of Tumble-weed.

FIG. 60-B. Tumble-weeds (*Amaranthus graecizans*) lodged in a fence.
(*Photographed by H. I. Featherly.*)

Prostrate Pigweed (*Amaranthus blitoides* Wats.).

Description.—A diffusely branched, prostrate herb, spreading on the ground, often in mats 4 or 5 feet long; leaves obovate or spatulate; flowers inconspicous, greenish, in short axillary clusters.

Distribution.—Common in every county in the state of Iowa and east to northeast; indigenous to the Rocky Mountain regions.

Extermination.—Prostrate pigweed is easily exterminated by cultivation.

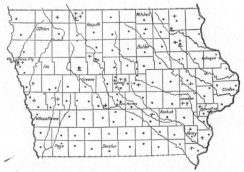

FIG. 61. Distribution of Prostrate Pigweed.

Fig. 61-A.   Prostrate Pigweed (*Amaranthus blitoides*).   Common along roadsides, streets, fields, and in waste places.
(*Photographed by Hart.*)

Water Hemp (*Acnida tuberculata* Moq.).

Description.—A tall, erect annual; leaves lanceolate to rhombic-ovate, acute, or acutish; flowers dioecious; pistillate flowers small, green, clustered in naked or leafy terminal and axillary spikes; staminate flowers pale; dehiscent pericarp thin.

The *Acnida tamariscina* (Nutt.) Wood, of similar habit, has circumcissile fruit, but otherwise is like the *A. tuberculata.*

Distribution.—Common along water courses, prairies and marshes from northeast to Minnesota and Dakota. Found in Iowa in Story, Boone, Polk, Pottawattamie, Woodbury, Emmet, Cerro Gordo, Clinton, Linn, Marshall and Allamakee counties. This weed is especially common in cultivated river bottoms on Des Moines, Cedar, Mississippi and Missouri rivers.

The *A. tamariscina* occurs near Commerce, Polk county, in bottoms. Probably is found in many other places.

FIG. 62. Water Hemp (*Acnida tuberculata*).
(*Photographed by Photo Section, Ia. Agr. Exp. Sta.*)

FIG. 62-A. Distribution of Water Hemp.

Extermination.—Water hemp is easily exterminated by cultivation, and is not long present in cultivated fields. The seed is not infrequent in clover seed.

NYCTAGINACEAE, FOUR-O'CLOCK FAMILY.

This family contains the well known cultivated four-o'clock.

Four-o'clock, Umbrella Plant (*Oxybaphus nyctagineus* (Michx.) Sweet).

Description.—A nearly smooth, deep-rooted perennial 2 to 4 feet high; forking leaves, broadly ovate, cordate, or lanceolate, opposite, rounded or truncate at base; petioled involucre; flowers persistent; fruit obovoid, pubescent; calyx bell-shaped, rose or purple; stamens generally 3.

FIG. 63.   Wild Four-o'clock (*Oxybaphus nyctagineus.*)   Common in fields, along roadsides and on railway embankments. The plants have long, stout roots. *(Photographed by Colburn.)*

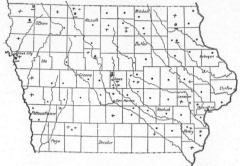

FIG. 63-A. Distribution of Wild Four-o'clock.

Distribution.—The range of this plant is from Manitoba to Louisiana, introduced eastward; it is common in cultivated fields, on railway embankments and in waste places.

Extermination.—This weed is multiplied by both its seeds and its root; however, it is not difficult to destroy it by cutting off the roots during dry weather.

Wallace's Farmer suggests the following treatment: ''The wild four-o'clock, although not yet very common in the corn belt, has possibilities of becoming a bad weed. It is a perennial, with a big, fleshy root and spreads freely from the seed. It spreads very little from the root. This weed may be exterminated in time by cutting it off close to the ground every year just before it seeds.''

CARYOPHYLLACEAE, PINK FAMILY.

This family contains the well known carnation, spurrey and garden pink.

Chickweed (*Stellaria media* (L.) Cyrill.).

Description.—An annual, or winter annual, the spreading stems of which are marked with one or more pubescent lines; leaves ovate or oblong, from one-half inch to 2½ inches long, lower leaves on hairy petioles, sepals 4 or 5, greenish; petals 4 or 5; shorter than the calyx and 2-parted; stamens 3 to 10; styles 3. Pod ovoid.

Distribution.—Chickweed is widely distributed in the northern states to the Pacific coast. It is common in many places in lawns and in shady places, although not especially troublesome except on the lawn, where it often runs out blue grass.

Extermination.—This weed is easily exterminated by cultivation. Since the lawn, however, cannot be cultivated the best and most effective means of exterminating the weed is to spray with iron sulphate which may be used at the rate of 100 pounds to a barrel of water. This spray should be used as soon as the plants make their appearance and repeated two to five times during the season.

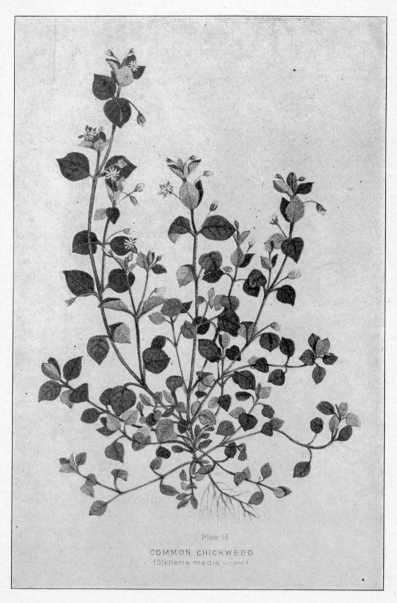

Plate 18

COMMON CHICKWEED
(Stellaria media)

FIG. 64. Chickweed (*Stellaria media*). Found in gardens, lawns, dooryards. *(After Clark and Fletcher.)*

FIG. 64-A. Distribution of Chickweed.

Common Mouse-ear Chickweed (*Cerastium vulgatum* L.).

Description.—A spreading perennial plant, with clammy-hairy stems; leaves oblong, upper bracts herbaceous; flowers clustered.

Distribution.—Naturalized from Europe; occurs in fields and dooryards. Especially common along Mississippi river in eastern Iowa, in Mississippi loess soil.

Extermination.—Clover can be used to crowd it out.

The Larger Mouse-ear Chickweed (*Cerastium viscosum* L.).

Description.—The larger mouse-ear chickweed is a perennial with obovate, clammy, hairy stem; leaves varying from oblong to lanceolate; flowers clustered at first; sepals rather obtuse, small.

Extermination.—The several species of the genus *Cerastium* are dealt with in the same way.

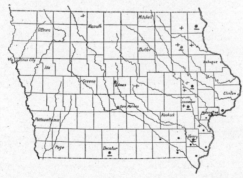

FIG. 65. Distribution of Larger Mouse-ear Chickweed (*Cerastium viscosum.*)

FIG. 65-A. Mouse-ear Chickweed (*Cerastium vulgatum*). Common in pastures.
(Photographed by E. H. Richardson.)

Nodding Chickweed (*Cerastium nutans* Raf.).

Description.—A clammy, pubescent, much-branched annual with slender, erect stems 6 to 20 inches high; leaves oblong, lanceolate, acute, the lowest spatulate; flowers numerous in open loose cymes; pods nodding on the stalks, curved upward, larger than the calyx.

Distribution.—From New England to Minnesota, especially southward in southern Iowa and Missouri.

FIG. 65 B. Nodding Chickweed *(Cerastium nutans)*. Common in fields, waste places and streets, southern Iowa.
(Photographed by Colburn.)

Extermination.—This annual is easily exterminated by cultivation. When it occurs in places that cannot be cultivated, like pastures and lawns, a spray of iron sulphate at the rate of 100 pounds to a barrel of water may be used effectively.

Corn Cockle (*Agrostemma Githago* L.).

Description.—A hairy annual weed, clothed with long, soft hairs;

leaves linear-lanceolate, acute or long-acuminate; flowers purple and long peduncled; calyx lobes long, linear, surpassing the purplish red petals; seeds large, roughened and black.

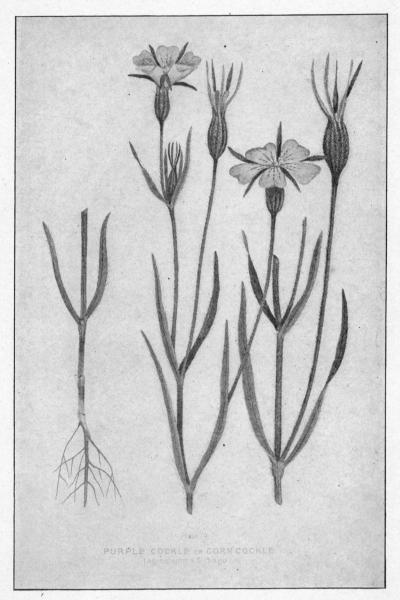

FIG. 66. Corn Cockle (*Agrostemma Githago.*) In grain fields.
(*After Clark and Fletcher.*)

Fig. 66-A. Distribution of Corn Cockle.

Distribution.—A weed long known as troublesome in European grain fields, and widely scattered throughout the grain growing section of North America. It is most abundant in Iowa in the wheat-growing section but occasionally is found in other places around grain elevators. It has persisted more or less in northeastern Iowa.

Extermination.—This weed is an annual and in order that it may be checked in its spread, only clean seed should be sown. The seed should be put into clean soil.

Fletcher and Clark recommend as follows: "In the prairie provinces, harrowing the grain crop just before it emerges from the ground and again when it is about three inches high keeps down this weed. Where the land is infested with purple cockle, a thorough summer fallow is the best method of getting rid of it."

Red Cockle (*Lychnis dioica* L.).

Description.—Biennial; leaves ovate, oblong; flowers reddish, day-blooming; calyx-teeth triangular lanceolate, acute. Capsule globose.

Distribution.—In waste grounds, especially in eastern United States.

Extermination.—Can be removed by cutting below the surface. Clover seed containing seed of red cockle should not be sown.

White Campion (*Lychnis alba* Mill.).

Description.—A freely branching biennial, with a slightly pleasant odor; leaves ovate-oblong or ovate-lanceolate; flowers loosely paniculate, white or pink, fragrant; capsule ovoid-conical, swelling with the ripening of the pod; petals 2-cleft, crowned.

FIG. 67. White Campion *(Lychnis alba)*. In clover meadows.
(Photographed by Photo Section, Ia. Agr. Exp. Sta.)

Distribution.—White campion has been introduced with clover seed from Europe, but is not, however, as common in the east as *Lychnis dioica.*

FIG. 67-A. Distribution of White Campion.

Extermination.—This weed can be exterminated by cutting off the plants when in bloom or by cutting them off a few inches below the surface of the ground. Since this weed is being spread with European clover seed, care should be used to sow only clean clover seed.

Catchfly (*Silene dichotoma* Ehrh.).

Description.—A tall, more or less hirsute annual, somewhat

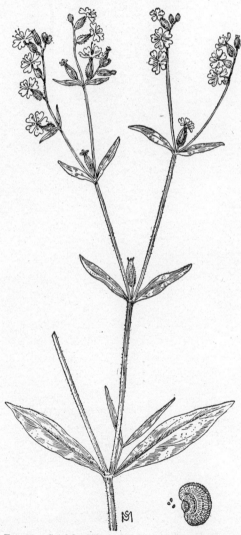

FIG. 68. Catchfly (*Silene dichotoma*). In waste places.
(*W. J. Beal, Mich. Agr. Exp. Sta.*)

viscid, pubescent; leaves lanceolate or oblanceolate; flowers in branched racemes, short-pediceled in the forks, or solitary at the nodes; calyx 5-ribbed, hirsute; petals white or pink, bifid.

Distribution.—Catchfly was introduced from Europe; it has spread occasionally in clover fields from the northeast to Iowa and Texas, also to the Pacific coast.

FIG. 68-A. Distribution of Catchfly.

Extermination.—A remedy in this case is to sow only clean clover or alfalfa seed in clean soil. Thorough cultivation should be given. No catchfly plants should be allowed to go to seed.

Night-flowering Catchfly (*Silene noctiflora* L.).

Description.—A viscid, pubescent annual from 2 to 3 feet high; lower leaves spatulate, upper lanceolate and pointed; flowers few, large, peduncled, white, fragrant; calyx prominent veined; pod enlarged in ripening of the fruit.

Distribution.—Night-flowering catchfly is found in waste places in Europe, Canada to Manitoba and southward. It is found in many counties in Iowa. This weed is becoming more common in this state. The Mississippi loess is an especially favorable habitat.

Extermination.—This weed is easily exterminated by cultivation. It has been widely spread in recent years with clover seed, particularly clover seed coming from the east and from Europe. Only clean clover seed on clean soil should be sown.

Fletcher and Clark made the following suggestions for exterminating the weed: "Farmers who sow clover and grass seed free from the seeds of catchfly will not long have trouble with it on lands worked under a short rotation of crops. A rotation of crops exclusive of alsike seed should be adopted for six or eight years. Grass or clover seed containing catchfly should be thoroughly

cleaned in mills equipped with screens specially designed to remove this impurity, and should not be used on land that may later
be required for the production of alsike seed.''

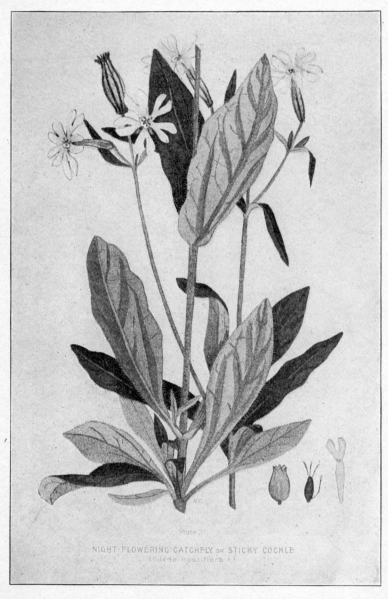

FIG. 69. Night-flowering Catchfly *(Silene noctiflora)*. In clover meadows, gardens, etc.

(After Clark and Fletcher.)

FIG. 69-A. Distribution of Night-flowering Catchfly.

Bouncing Bet (*Saponaria officinalis* L.).

Description.—Perennial herbs with large flowers in cymose clusters; calyx narrowly ovoid or oblong, 5-toothed; petals clawed or unappendaged, stamens 10, styles 2, pod 1-celled or incompletely 2 or 4-celled and 4-toothed at the apex.

FIG. 70. Bouncing Bet (*Saponaria officinalis*) near a building. Seeds mature and spread from such places.
(*Photograph by Charlotte M. King.*)

Distribution.—About forty species of the genus are found in Europe, Asia and northern Africa. *Saponaria officinalis* is frequently cultivated in old gardens. The mucilaginous juice forms a lather with water and is valuable for taking grease spots out of woolen cloth. Bouncing Bet commonly escaped from gardens to

FIG. 70-A. Bouncing Bet, Soapwort *(Saponaria officinalis)*.
(Photographed by Photo Section, Ia. Agr. Exp. Sta.)

roadsides and railway embankments in many parts of Iowa, but especially in northeastern and eastern Iowa. Bouncing Bet is one of the striking and common weeds along roadsides in Winneshiek, Clayton, Allamakee and Delaware counties, and especially on the Mississippi loess soil.

FIG. 70-B. Boouncing Bet (*Saponaria officinalis*).

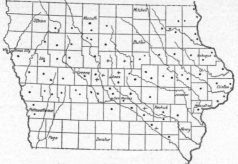

FIG. 70-C. Distribution of Bouncing Bet.

Extermination.—Though this weed is a perennial it is not difficult to destroy in cultivated fields and gardens. In lawns and
places where the soil is not cultivated it is best to dig up the
patches, remove the dirt from the roots and let the sun dry them;
covering the patch with tarred paper will kill the weed, if it is
kept covered long enough, say from six to eight weeks.

Cow-herb (*Saponaria Vaccaria* L.).

Description.—A glabrous annual, from 1 foot to 2 feet high with
opposite ovate-lanceolate leaves; flowers in corymbed cymes; calyx
5-angled, enlarged and angled in fruit; petals pale red.

Distribution.—This weed has long been known as troublesome
in grain fields in Europe, and is common in North America. It is
common in Iowa only where wheat is grown.

FIG. 71. Distribution of Cow-herb.

Extermination.—To use clean seed sown in clean soil is the best
method of prevention for the weed.

Clark and Fletcher suggest the following treatment: ''Sow clean
seed. Prevention is the best and least expensive method of fight-

ing it. It is a large showy plant and when not present in excessive
numbers can easily be hand-pulled. The seed will not retain its
vitality long; when land is seeded to timothy or western grass and
left for a few years, the supply of vital seeds in the soil will be
greatly reduced, if not entirely exhausted.''

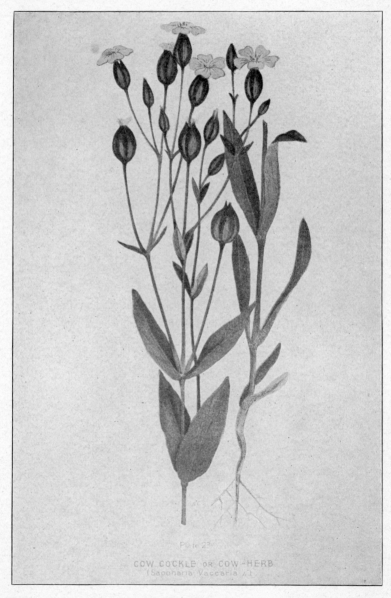

FIG. 71-A. Cow-herb (*Saponaria Vaccaria*). In grain fields.
(*Clark and Fletcher.*)

PORTULACACEAE, PURSLANE FAMILY.
This family contains the well known moss rose, spring beauty, etc.

Pusley, Purslane (*Portulaca oleracea* L.).

Description.—A fleshy, prostrate, smooth annual with scattered

Fig. 72.   Purslane or Pusley (*Portulaca oleracea*).   Gardens and corn-fields.
(*After Clark and Fletcher.*)

obovate or wedge-shaped leaves; small sessile flowers with a 2-cleft calyx; 5 small, yellow petals, inserted on the calyx; stamens 7 to 12, style deeply 5 to 6 parted; seeds small, finely rugose.

FIG. 72-A. Distribution of Purslane.

Distribution.—Purslane is native to Europe and is common from the Atlantic to the Pacific especially in cultivated soil. It is common everywhere in the state in gardens and in corn fields.

Extermination.—Purslane is not difficult to exterminate if the green weeds are placed in piles or removed from the garden. They may be fed to hogs. It should be said that the leaves and stems show considerable vitality, since the whole plant is fleshy. Fletcher and Clark say: ''A three-year rotation, including summer-fallow directly after the removal of a crop of early clover, followed by a hoed crop and again by cereal grain for the third year, will keep it in check. If given access to corn and potato fields, sheep will feed on late purslane plants, and if their pasture is short, will prevent many of them from seeding.''

Chemical Composition.—According to a report of the Bussey Institution* the chemical composition is as follows:

FRESH OR AIR DRY MATERIAL

Water	Ash	Protein	Fiber	Nitrogen free extract	Fat
92.61	1.56	2.24	1.03	2.16	0.40

WATER FREE SUBSTANCE

	Ash	Protein	Fiber	Nitrogen free extract	Fat
	21.1	30.2	19.9	29.4	5.4

RANUNCULACEAE, BUTTERCUP FAMILY.

The plants of this family are acrid. There are few economic

*Bull. 1877: Jenkins and Winton, Bull. Off. Exp. Sta. 11.

plants among them; some like the peony, columbine, buttercup, larkspur and aconite are cultivated for ornamental purposes.

Small-flowered Crowfoot (*Ranunculus abortivus* L.).

Description.—A small, slightly pubescent, succulent biennial; from 6 inches to 2 feet high, with multiple roots; root leaves roundish or kidney-shaped, crenate; stem leaves often 3 to 5-lobed or parted, mostly toothed; petals small, pale yellow; shorter than the reflexed calyx; carpels minute.

Fig. 73. Crowfoot (*Ranunculus abortivus*).   Common in woodland pastures.
(*Photographed by Hart*)

Distribution.—Common everywhere in Iowa in waste places along roadsides and occasionally in fields. This crowfoot is especially common in woodland pastures. It occurs eastward to Newfoundland, south to Florida and north to Manitoba, also in the Rocky mountains.

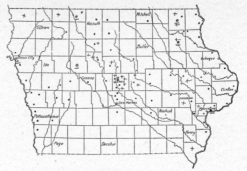

FIG. 73-A.   Distribution of Crowfoot.

Extermination.—This weed is easily exterminated by cultivation.

Swamp Buttercup, Creeping Buttercup (*Ranunculus septentrionalis* Poir.).

FIG. 74.   Creeping Buttercup, Swamp Buttercup (*Ranunculus septentrionalis*).   Common in low grounds.   Flowers yellow.
(*Photographed by Hart*)

Description.—A branching, prostrate, smooth or sometimes pubescent perennial with multiple fibrous roots, frequently rooting at the nodes and often forming long runners; leaves large, petioled, 3-divided, divisions mostly cuneate, petals obovate, larger than the spreading calyx; achenes flat, strongly margined, pointed by a stout straight beak.

Distribution.—This plant is common in fields and woodland pastures, especially in low grounds from eastern Canada to Manitoba; south to Kansas and Kentucky. It is common in Iowa in low places in Story, Boone, Marshall, Polk, Linn, Clinton, Buchanan, Emmet, Worth, Woodbury, Pottawattamie, Plymouth, Kossuth, Dallas, Guthrie, Fremont and Allamakee counties.

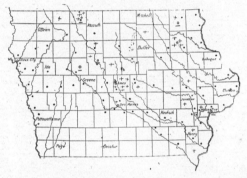

FIG. 74-A. Distribution of Creeping or Swamp Buttercup.

Extermination.—Drainage of the soil and thorough cultivation will soon exterminate this weed.

Prairie Larkspur (*Delphinium Penardi* Huth.).

Description.—A perennial pubescent or hairy herb, more or less glandular above, with simple, erect stem, 3 to 5 feet high; leaves 3- to 5-parted, divisions 2 to 3 cleft; the numerous flowers white, or bluish white, in elongated raceme, spur ascending or erect; follicle many-seeded.

Distribution.—This larkspur occurs from Illinois and Wisconsin westward and northward. It is common on gravelly knolls along railroads throughout the state of Iowa.

Extermination.—This perennial is easily exterminated by cultivation. The roots of the plant readily succumb when exposed to the sun.

FIG. 75. Prairie Larkspur (*Delphinium Penardi*). Common on gravelly knolls.
(*Drawing by Ada Hayden.*)

CRUCIFERAE, MUSTARD FAMILY.

This family contains the well known sweet alyssum, cabbage, cauliflower, rape, radish, turnip, white and black mustard, water cress, etc. They are all pungent herbs.

Hoary Alyssum (*Berteroa incana* (L.) DC.).

Description.—A tall, green, erect annual or biennial with entire, pubescent, pale green, lanceolate leaves; flowers white, 2-parted; pods canescent.

Distribution.—Hoary alyssum is said to be common in northeastern United States and becoming frequent in other Atlantic states; it is found in Mississippi and adjacent states. It occurs not infrequently in Iowa. It was reported from Ida county in 1912, where it was thought to have been introduced with clover seed.

Extermination.—Only clean clover and alfalfa seed should be sown. The plant succumbs readily to cultivation.

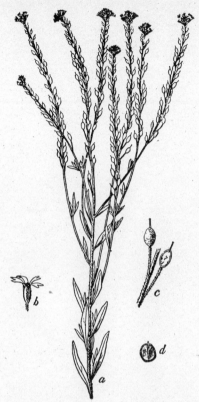

FIG. 76. Hoary Alyssum *(Berteroa incana)*; *a*, flowering stem; *b*, flower; *c*, pods; *d*, section of ovary. A weed of clover fields.

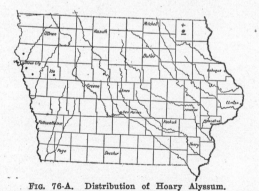

FIG. 76-A. Distribution of Hoary Alyssum.

Pennycress *(Thlaspi arvense* L.).

Description.—An annual or winter annual with simple, smooth, erect or branching stem; leaves of stem clasping, with arrow-shaped base; root leaves petioled; flowers white; petals nearly equal; seeds purplish brown, longer than broad; cotyledons accumbent.

Distribution.—Pennycress is common in waste places, particu-

STINKWEED or FIELD PENNYCRESS
(Thlaspi arvense.)

FIG. 77. Stinkweed or Field Pennycress (*Thlaspi arvense*). Grain and clover fields. (*After Clark and Fletcher.*)

FIG. 77-A.   Distribution of Pennycress.

larly in clover fields. It occurs in Story, Woodbury, Winneshiek, Allamakee and some other counties in the state. More frequent in the northern than the southern part of the state. It is common in Manitoba, Minnesota, Dakota and eastern Canada, particularly in the prairie provinces. The weed is abundantly distributed by spring floods and also to some extent by clover seed.

Large Peppergrass (*Lepidium virginicum* L.).

Description.—An erect annual or winter annual, at first quite simple, later much branched, 8 inches to 2 feet high; leaves divided, entire or with irregular, pointed teeth; flowers small, white; pod circular or oval with a little notch at the upper end; seeds light brown, elongated, with a prominent ridge on one side, on addition of water becoming mucilaginous; cotyledons accumbent.

Distribution.—Large peppergrass is native to the Mississippi valley, east to New England; it is quite common in Missouri, Illinois and Ohio. It is widely scattered in Iowa, being particularly common in timothy meadows in some years.

Extermination.—This peppergrass sometimes comes up abun-

FIG. 78.   Distribution of Large Peppergrass.

dantly in the fall. The fields should, therefore, be plowed in the fall and when sowing small grain given a thorough dragging. In corn fields the ordinary methods of cultivation will destroy the weed. The plants should not be permitted to seed. The seed of this peppergrass is frequent in timothy seed. Only clean timothy seed should be sown.

FIG. 78-A. Large or Virginia Peppergrass (*Lepidium virginicum*). Common in fields, gardens, etc.; along roadsides.
(*Photographed by Colburn.*)

Small Peppergrass (*Lepidium apetalum* Willd.).

Description.—Much like the foregoing, an annual or winter annual, 8 inches to 2 feet high, but with smaller leaves and pods; flowers small, greenish; seeds light brown, elongated, with prominent ridge on one side, becoming mucilaginous when moistened with water; cotyledons incumbent.

Distribution.—Small peppergrass is common in the northern states from New England across the continent; apparently native in the west; in the east introduced from Europe. It is abundant

Plate 28

WILD PEPPERGRASS
(Lepidium apetalum Willd.)

FIG. 79. Small Peppergrass *(Lepidium apetalum)*. Common in timothy meadows, fields, etc.
(After Clark and Fletcher.)

in fields and waste places. In some years it is particularly common in timothy and clover meadows.

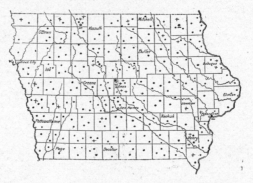

FIG. 79-A. Distribution of Small Peppergrass.

Extermination.—The peppergrasses are not difficult to exterminate in cultivated fields, since they are annuals or winter annuals. In growing timothy seed it is important above all to have
a field as clean from weeds as possible. Timothy should therefore
be sown in a field that has been under thorough and clean cultivation for several years and clean seed only should be used. In this
way the peppergrass can largely be prevented from spreading.

Fletcher and Clark make the following suggestions: ''Only
autumn plants which live through the winter give trouble in grain.
Thorough surface cultivation in the spring, with the plow, disc or
broad-shared cultivator, is efficacious. Immature seeds may ripen
in the pods when plowed down.''

European Peppergrass (*Lepidium campestre* (L.) R. Br.)

Description.—An annual, soft downy, low growing plant; leaves
somewhat arrowshaped; flowers white, inconspicuous; pods ovate,
winged, with a narrow notch.

Distribution.—This peppergrass is of European origin, and is
becoming common in fields and along roadsides in some sections.
Occasionally found in different parts of Iowa.

Extermination.—As with other peppergrasses this plant seeds
early in the spring. Mowing will do little good. Cultivation or
digging will remove the weed.

FIG. 79-B. European or Field Peppergrass (*Lepidium campestre*).
(*Photograph by E. H. Richardson.*)

Shepherd's Purse (*Capsella Bursa-pastoris* (L.) Medic.)
Description.—An annual or winter annual 1 foot to 1½ feet

high; root leaves clustered, nearly divided or merely toothed; stem leaves sessile; flowers small, white, in fruit spreading; pods much wider above than below, many-seeded; seeds light brown, elongated,

Plate 29

SHEPHERD'S PURSE
(Capsella Bursa-pastoris (L.) Medic.)

FIG. 80. Shepherd's Purse *(Capsella Bursa-pastoris)*. Common in gardens, fields and waste places.
(After Clark and Fletcher.)

with a prominent ridge, mucilaginous when moistened with water; cotyledons incumbent; trichomes stellate, roughened.

Distribution.—Shepherd's purse is native to Europe and is one of the most common early spring flowers from the Atlantic to the Pacific. It is common everywhere in gardens and fields in the state.

Extermination.—Clark and Fletcher state: "It has an enormous power of propagation; a single plant will ripen 50,000 seeds. Waste places should be cleared as far as practicable and seeded to grass.

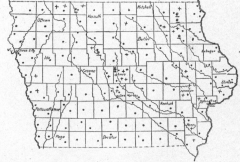

FIG. 80-A. Plant hair or trichome of Shepherd's Purse.
(*Drawing by Charlotte M. King.*)

FIG. 80-B. Distribution of Shepherd's Purse.

FIG. 80-C. Shepherd's Purse (*Capsella Bursa-pastoris*). Weed in city streets.
(*Photograph by Charlotte M. King.*)

It does not give serious trouble on lands worked under a short rotation, with clean cultivation of hoed crops. Sow clean grass and clover seeds.''

False Flax (*Camelina sativa* (L.) Crantz.).

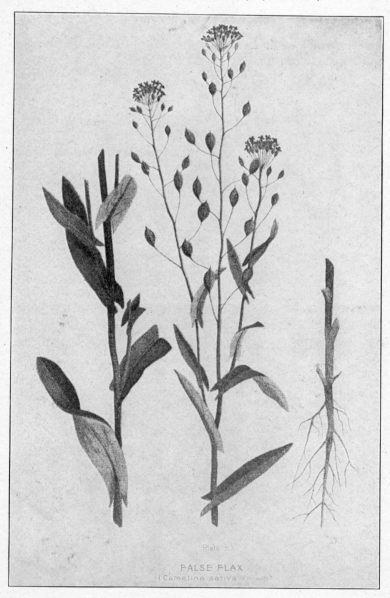

FALSE FLAX
(*Camelina sativa*)

FIG. 81.   False Flax (*Camelina sativa*). In grain and flax fields, waste places,
(*After Clark and Fletcher.*)

FIG. 81-A. Distribution of False Flax.

Description.—An erect annual with single or sparingly branched stem, 1½ feet high, smooth or slightly pubescent stellate hairs; leaves erect, lanceolate or arrow-shaped, entire or nearly so; flowers small, yellow, pedicels in fruit spreading; pod obovoid, one-fourth inch long, smooth, reticulate, margined from beak down along placental side with smaller ribs between them; seeds light brown, 1 line long, minutely pitted, caulicle prominent, running lengthwise with a prominent groove between it and the cotyledons, which are incumbent; on the addition of water the seeds become mucilaginous.

Distribution.—This weed is particularly common in the grain growing sections of the north, including Dakota, Manitoba and Saskatchewan. In recent years it has become quite common in Iowa, particularly in the northern counties.

Extermination.—Clark and Fletcher recommend the following treatment: "When a crop of winter wheat is infested with false flax, harrowing in the spring kills the young plants without injuring the wheat. A thorough summer-fallow, with cultivation the previous fall and continuous cultivation throughout the summer, is recommended for fields badly infested with this weed."

Ball Mustard (*Neslia paniculata* (L.) Desv.).

Description.—An erect, slender annual or biennial, 1 foot to 3 feet high, with stem simple up to the inflorescence; stem and leaves, both covered with stellate pubescence; sessile leaves oblong, very narrow, sagittate at base; racemes elongate; flowers small, yellow, about one-eighth inch in diameter; seed-pods nearly spherical, 2-celled with one small yellow seed in each cell, sometimes but one developing.

Distribution. — Ball mustard is found in grain fields in Canada, the Dakotas and occasionally in northwestern Iowa.

E x t e r m i n a t i o n—The growth of this weed can be prevented by use of clean seed; it is easily destroyed by cultivation.

Jointed Charlock (*Raphanus Raphanistrum* L.).

Description. — Biennial or annual, having a slender root, rough leaves, lyrate, pinnatifid, with a large terminal lobe; flowers yellowish, fading to white, or purplish veined; pods linear or oblong, jointed, 2 to 8-seeded.

FIG. 82. Ball Mustard (*Neslia paniculata*); *a*, flowering stem; *b*. pod; *c*, seed. (*Schuyler Mathews in Mich. Agr. Exp. Sta. Bull.*)

Distribution.—The jointed charlock has become common; it is spreading eastward in fields and waste places, and has been reported in grain fields in Worth and a few other counties in the northern part of Iowa. It is said to have been largely distributed with oats seed.

Extermination.—This weed may be exterminated by cultivation. Only clean seed oats in clean fields should be sown.

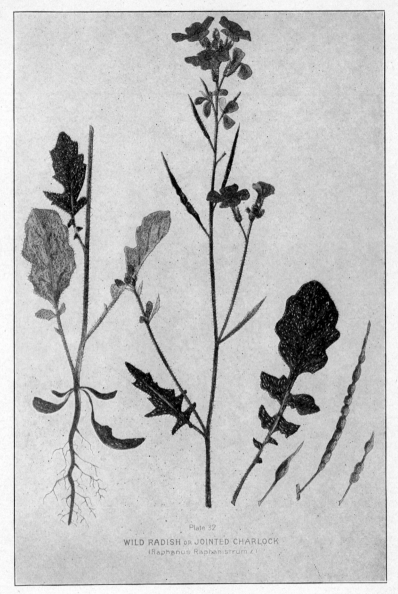

FIG. 83. Wild Radish or Jointed Charlock (*Raphanus Raphanistrum*). In oat fields
in northern Iowa.
(After Clark and Fletcher.)

Mustard or English Charlock (*Brassica arvensis* (L.) Ktze.).

Description.—Lower leaves divided nearly to the middle, with

FIG. 83-A. Distribution of Jointed Charlock.

divisions unequal, terminal lobe larger, upper leaves not stalked
as a rule, much smaller than the lower; flowers yellow, large and
very fragrant; pods 1 inch to 2 inches long, irregular in outline,
appearing somewhat nodose, 3 to 7-seeded or occasionally more,
upper part of pod forming a beak; seeds round, brownish black,
darker than in *B. nigra* and minutely pitted, when moistened becoming mucilaginous.

Distribution.—Mustard or charlock has been known as a pest of
the grain fields from the earliest historical record, throughout the
grain growing section of the world; it is common everywhere in
Iowa, but most abundant in the small spring grain growing section
of northern and northwestern Iowa where it was introduced with
flax.

Extermination.—The first and most important consideration in
connection with the extermination of mustard is that the oats or
wheat should be freed from mustard seed. Then this grain should
be sown on clean fields, preferably fields that have been in pasture
or meadow. Nothing has done so much to remove the weeds from
the fields of northwestern Iowa as keeping the land in pasture and
meadow. If the grain is to be sown in a corn field there should
have been no mustard the previous season. Although the small
grain has been sown on a clean field there is always a chance that
some mustard seeds from previous years will retain their vitality
in the soil. If much of this mustard should come up it may become necessary to use a spray of iron sulphate. Where the mustard is abundant the use of sulphate at the rate of 100 pounds to a
barrel of water is a very effective means of destroying the weeds.

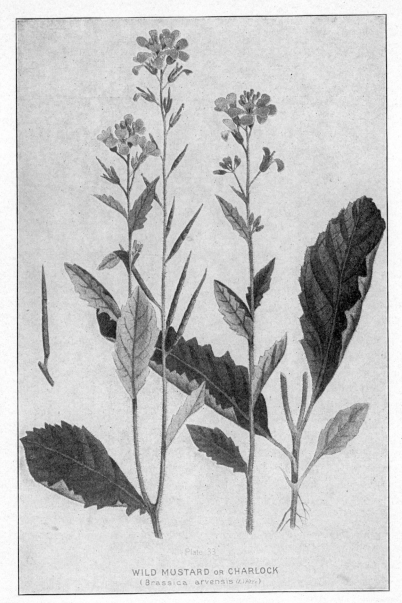

WILD MUSTARD or CHARLOCK
(Brassica arvensis *L.Ktr.*)

FIG. 84. Wild Mustard or Charlock *(Brassica arvensis)*. Common in roadsides and grain fields.

(After Clark and Fletcher.)

Chemical Composition.—According to the University of Minnesota the chemical composition is as follows:*

Dry matter	Crude protein	Ether extract	Nitrogen free extract and fiber	Ash
91.79	15.75	1.55	75.59	7.11

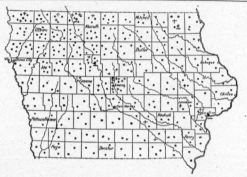

FIG. 84-A. Distribution of Wild Mustard.

Indian Mustard (*Brassica juncea* L. Cosson).

Description.—This is a tall growing, glabrous plant. The upper leaves are slender oblong, narrow at the base. The lower leaves are lyrate. The pedicels are slender, spreading.

Distribution.—Becoming very common in fields.

Extermination.—Infested lands may be cleared of the weed by hoeing. The seeds of this plant are freely carried in oats.

Black Mustard (*Brassica nigra* (L.) Koch.).

Description.—A tall, coarse, much-branched annual, 2 to 5 feet high; leaves variously divided or only deeply cut, the terminal lobe the largest, sharply toothed, upper leaves small, simple, as a rule linear; leaves as a rule not smooth, but somewhat bristly, at least on the veins; flowers yellow, smaller than in charlock; pods smooth, about one-half inch long, 4-cornered, tipped with a slender beak; seeds black or reddish brown, smaller than in charlock; cotyledons incumbent; trichomes not stellate, simple, rough.

Distribution.—This weed is common in the northern states and extends across the continent. It is abundant in some places in Iowa, in waste places and vacant lots; apparently, however, it is less common than common charlock.

Extermination.—This weed can be exterminated by the same method that is used with common charlock.

*Snyder; Bull. Minn. Agr. Exp. Sta., 101.

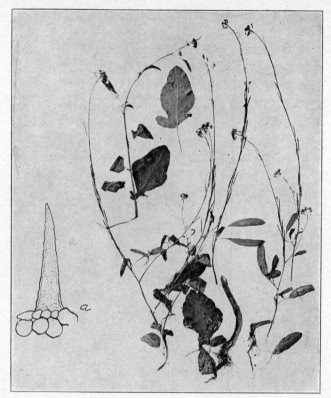

FIG. 85.   Black Mustard *(Brassica nigra)*.   Fields, gardens and roadsides.
(Photographed by Colburn.)

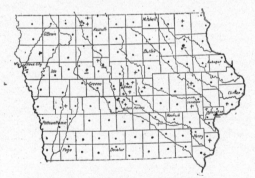

FIG. 85-A. -Distribution of Black Mustard.

Rocket *(Eruca sativa* L.).

Description.—An annual or biennial herb with stout, 4-sided
stem; lower leaves lyrate, incised or pinnatifid, upper leaves

FIG. 86-A. Distribution of Rocket.

FIG. 86. Rocket *(Eruca sativa)*. Introduced with alfalfa seed.
(*Drawn by F. O. Collins.*)

smaller, lobed, or entire; flowers white or yellowish white with dark veins; fruit an oval, elongated silique containing many more or less compressed seeds in 2 rows.

Distribution.—Rocket is a native of western Asia and the Mediterranean region, but is cultivated as a salad plant and often is an escape. It has been introduced into Iowa with alfalfa seed in Woodbury, Plymouth, O'Brien, Clay, Mitchell, Pottawattamie, Mills, Ida, and Sac counties.

Extermination.—The weed can be exterminated by cutting the plants off a few inches below the surface of the ground or by giving the field where it grows thorough cultivation.

Hare's-ear Mustard (*Conringia orientalis* (L.) Dumort.).
Description.—A slightly succulent annual; leaves light green, sessile, obtuse, racemes becoming elongated in fruit; petals much

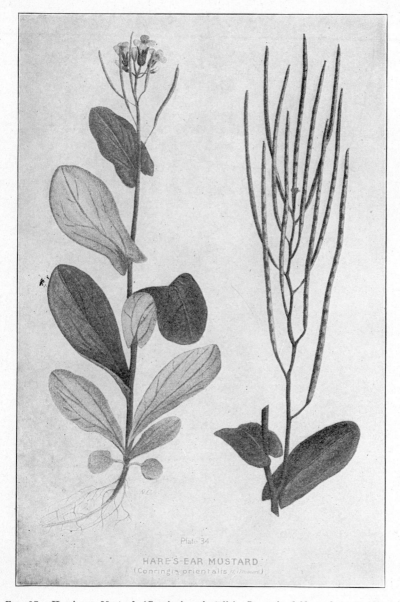

FIG. 87. Hare's-ear Mustard (*Conringia orientalis*). In grain fields and waste places in northwestern Iowa.
(*After Clark and Fletcher.*)

longer than the sepals; pods long, linear 4-angled, spreading; cotyledons incumbent.

Distribution.—Hare's-ear mustard is common eastward, and is appearing in the Mississippi valley. It occurs in Woodbury, Webster and Page counties and probably in many other places in Iowa.

Extermination.—This mustard is easily exterminated by cultivation.

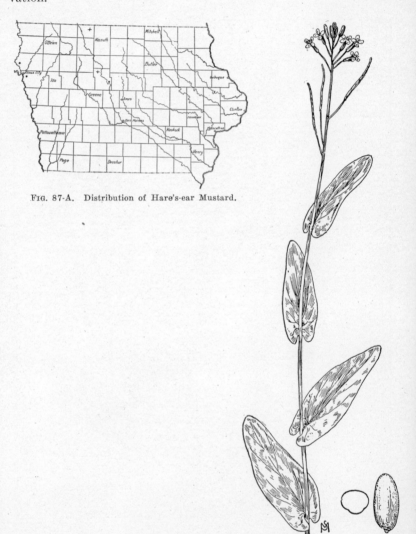

Fig. 87-A. Distribution of Hare's-ear Mustard.

Fig. 87-B.   Hare's-ear Mustard *(Conringia orientalis)*.   Flowering stem, seed and cross section of seed.   Appearing in several counties in Iowa.

Hedge Mustard (*Sisymbrium officinale* (L.) Scop.).

Description.—A slender, erect annual or winter annual, 1½ to 2½ feet high; lower leaves divided, upper entire or hastate at base; flowers small, yellow, borne in spikelike racemes; seeds small, brown; cotyledons incumbent.

Distribution.—Found everywhere in the state, notably in Story, Boone, Polk, Clinton, Linn, Marshall, Hardin, Black Hawk, Wood-

FIG. 88.   Hedge Mustard (*Sisymbrium officinale*).
(*Photographed by Photo Section, Ia. Agr. Exp. Sta.*)

bury, Pottawattamie, Carroll, Jasper, Monroe, Scott, Lee, and Allamakee counties.

Extermination.—Hedge mustard is easily exterminated by cultivation; also by using a mixture of 100 pounds of iron sulphate
to one barrel of water as a spray.

FIG. 88-A.   Distribution of Hedge Mustard.

Chemical Composition.—According to the University of Minnesota the chemical composition is as follows:*

Dry matter	Crude protein	Ether extract	Nitrogen free extract and fiber	Ash
94.5	16.52	1.43	74.18	7.87

Tumbling Mustard (*Sisymbrium altissimum* L.).

Description.—A leafy, branched annual from 1 foot to 4 feet
high, lower leaves runcinate, pinnatifid, irregularly toothed, or
wavy margined, upper leaves smaller, threadlike. The flowers are
pale in color and much larger than those of common hedge mustard. The long rigid slender pods are divergent.

Distribution.—This weed is native to east Europe. It has become widely scattered in the northern states, particularly in the
west from Minnesota to Washington, and in Canada. It has wide
occurrence in Iowa in the vicinity of railroad watering tanks,
elevators and stockyards. It it less common in the southern half
of the state than elsewhere in the state. This weed is spreading
rapidly and in many places is as common as common hedge
mustard.

*Snyder: Bull. Minn. Agr. Sta., 101.

Extermination.—The young mustard plants are easily killed by cultivation. They are likely to occur in some commercial seed like timothy, therefore, only seed free from seed of tumbling mustard should be used.

FIG. 89.   Tumbling Mustard *(Sisymbrium altissimum).* In grain fields, railways, etc. *(After Clark and Fletcher.)*

FIG. 89-A. Distribution of Tumbling Mustard.

Marsh Cress (*Radicula palustris* (L.) Moench.).

Description.—An annual or biennial, erect, smooth, or slightly pubescent herb; from 1 foot to 1½ feet high; leaves pinnately cleft or parted, pinnatifid; the lobes toothed; upper leaves sessile; flowers yellowish in racemes; pods ellipsoid or ovoid.

FIG. 90. Marsh Cress *(Radicula palustris)*. Common in low grounds.
(Photographed by Colburn.)

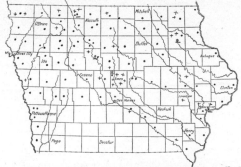

FIG. 90-A. Distribution of Marsh Cress.

Distribution.—Marsh cress grows in wet places or in low grounds; it is of frequent occurrence in oat fields and meadows; abundant in Iowa, especially in northern Iowa. It is common throughout the northern United States. Marsh cress is not infrequently distributed with clover seed that is grown in Iowa. During moist seasons this weed is more common and conspicuous in fields than in dry seasons.

Extermination.—This weed may be exterminated by drainage of the soil followed by clean cultivation.

Horseradish (*Radicula Armoracia* (L.) Robinson).

Description.—A stout perennial with long, deep roots; leaves large, oblong, crenate or pinnatifid, the latter produced in the spring; stem leaves lanceolate, or oblong cordate; flowers with 4 green sepals and 4 white petals, not common; pods short, globular, but fruit seldom found. At least no fruit has been reported in Iowa.

Distribution.—Horseradish is native to eastern Europe and in-

FIG. 91. Distribution of Horseradish.

troduced in west Europe and the United States, and is largely an escape from cultivation. It is common from the Atlantic to the Pacific and is found in every part of Iowa. Roadsides, Story and Hardin counties.

Extermination.—The horseradish is one of the most persistent of our weeds; no other weed will stand such rough treatment. It may be hoed and cultivated and still it persists in coming up. Some years ago we tried the following plan: The land was plowed, then harrowed and the roots were picked up. The process was repeated after the lapse of a week, after which young plants again made their appearance. These young plans were cut off with a hoe below

FIG. 91-A. Horseradish *(Radicula Armoracia).* Escaped from cultivation; a rather persistent weed.
(Photographed by Photo Section, Ia. Agr. Exp. Sta.)

the ground as soon as they appeared. This treatment was kept up for two years, and in this way most of the horseradish was removed. Quack grass near the horseradish received the same treatment and was killed in a single season, the season being dry. Very little progress in destroying the plant would have been made in a wet season.

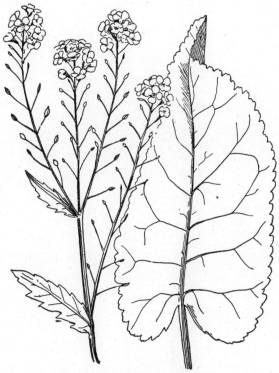

FIG. 91-B. Horse Radish (*Radicula Armoracia*). (*Drawing by Charlotte M. King.*)

Winter Cress (*Barbarea vulgaris* R. Br.)

Description.—A biennial, with yellow flowers, plant 1 ft. to 2 ft. high; stem furrowed, simple or branched; lower leaves simple or pinnately parted, terminal lobe the largest, round or ovate; upper leaves obovate, cut, toothed or pinnatifid at the base; flowers bright yellow; pods erect or slightly spreading; cotyledons accumbent.

Distribution.—Winter cress is found throughout eastern North America from Labrador to Maryland, Iowa, Manitoba, Rocky mountains, Pacific slope. It is common in northern Iowa, and increasing in the state. It is a cosmopolitan weed widely found in Europe, Asia, Africa and Australia. Some seasons very abundant, 1926.

Extermination.—This perennial weed is not difficult to kill if the field is given an early plowing followed by a subsequent disking and harrowing, being thus put in a good state of tilth for the crop.

FIG. 92.   Winter Cress *(Barbarea vulgaris.)*
(Photographed by Colburn.)

FIG. 92-A.   Distribution of Winter Cress.

CAPPARIDACEAE, CAPER FAMILY.

This family contains the caper which is used for pickling, the Rocky mountain bee plant, etc.

Stinkweed, Clammy Weed (*Polanisia graveolens* Raf.).

Description.—A fetid annual with glandular hairs; leaves with 3 oblong leaflets; flowers in leafy racemes; 6 petals, white, with claws, notched at the apex; stamens about 11, scarcely exceeding the petals; not elongated, bearing a gland behind the base of the ovary; pod short, stalked; seeds rough. The *P. trachysperma* T. & G. has larger flowers with long exserted stamens and sessile pods.

FIG. 93. Stinkweed, Clammy Weed *(Polanisia graveolens)*. In sandy places, gravelly soils, etc.
(Photographed by Hart)

Distribution.—Stinkweed extends from Iowa to Kansas and eastward to New England; it is common in sandy soil along railroad embankments, as on Muscatine Island, Lower Skunk river and near Camanche.

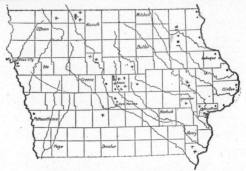

FIG. 93-A.   Distribution of Stinkweed.

FIG. 93-B.   Stinkweed *(Polanisia trachysperma)*.   Common in sandy soils, railway embankments and gravelly soils.
(Photographed by Colburn.)

Extermination.—The weed is easily exterminated by cultivation.

The land should be cultivated as soon as a fresh growth of the weed develops. Great care must be taken not to plow down any full-sized pods, even though they may be green, as it has been proven that in the dry climate of the west such seeds can ripen beneath the soil. The most important measure to be used in order to clear the land of stinkweed is the harrowing of the growing crop to kill the seedlings. The harrowing should commence before the crop emerges from the ground and be repeated when the grain is about three inches high.

Rocky Mountain Bee-plant or Stinking Clover (*Cleome serrulata* Pursh.).

Description.—A smooth annual; leaves of 3 lanceolate, oblong leaflets, somewhat fleshy; flowers in bracteate racemes; petals usually rose-colored, short-clawed; stipe of pod as long as the pedicel.

FIG. 94. Rocky Mountain Bee-plant (*Cleome serrulata*). Fields, roadsides in western Iowa. (*Photographed by Colburn.*)

FIG. 94-A. Distribution of Rocky Mountain Bee-plant.

Distribution.—This plant occurs in western ·Iowa, Minnesota and northward; in Utah, Colorado, Montana and westward. It is common in Iowa in Fremont, Mills, Pottawattamie and Woodbury counties, occasionally in Polk county. This is an excellent bee plant.

Extermination.—This weed is easily exterminated by cultivation.

ROSACEAE, ROSE FAMILY.

This family contains the well known rose, apple, pear, quince, plum, peach, almond, strawberry, blackberry, raspberry, spiraea, etc.

FIG. 94-B. Rocky Mountain Bee-plant
(*Cleome serrulata*).
(*Drawing by Ada Hayden.*)

Cinquefoil, False Strawberry, Five-finger (*Potentilla monspeliensis* L.).

Description.—A hairy annual or winter annual from 1 foot to 2½ feet high; leaves 3-foliate, leaflets obovate to oblanceolate, the uppermost toothed nearly the whole length; flowers in close cymes, calyx large, 5-cleft with 5 bractlets; petals 5, yellow, small; stamens 15 to 20; style terminal; trichomes simple, long pointed, thick-walled.

Distribution.—Five-finger is naturalized from Europe. It is common in eastern Canada, New England, to Kansas; in Iowa, in Story, Boone, Polk, Clinton, Lyon, Carroll, Woodbury, Kossuth, Webster, Marshall, Cerro Gordo, Worth, Winnebago, Allamakee and other counties.

Extermination.—As this weed is frequently introduced with

FIG. 95. Cinquefoil, False Strawberry, Five-finger (*Potentilla monspeliensis.*) Common in gardens, timothy meadows, etc. *a*, plant hair; *b*, showing cell-wall. (*a and b, drawings by Charlotte M. King.*)
(*Photograph by Hart.*)

clover seed, only clean clover seed in a clean field should be sown. The weed should be cut off below the surface of the ground and the soil thoroughly cultivated.

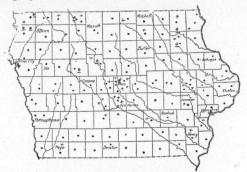

FIG. 95-A. Distribution of Cinquefoil.

Silverweed (*Potentilla Anserina* L.).

Description.—Herbaceous perennial, spreading by slender run-

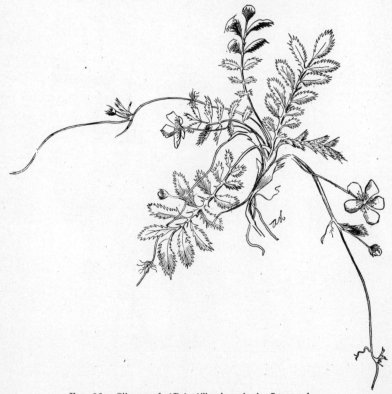

FIG. 96.   Silverweed *(Potentilla Anserina)*. In marshes.
(Drawing by Ada Hayden.)

ners; numerous white-tomentose and silky-villous leaves, all radical; pinnate leaflets, 7 to 21 with smaller ones between, oblong,
sharply serrate, silky-tomentose beneath; flowers with 5 bright
yellow petals; peduncles elongated; styles filiform.

Distribution.—Silverweed is common eastward in brackish
marshes; also in the Dakotas and the Rocky mountains; common
in Wright county, and may be looked for in other places in Iowa.

FIG. 96-A.   Distribution of Silverweed.

Extermination.—This weed may be destroyed by giving shallow
cultivation, exposing the roots to the sun.   Care must be used to kill
the weed on its first appearance as it is quite persistent.

Stickweed (*Geum canadense* Jacq.).

Description.—A perennial herb from 1½ to 2 feet high; leaves
pinnate, the lower of 3 to 5 leaflets or undivided; stem leaves 3-
divided or 3-lobed, sharply toothed; stipules ovate-oblong; flowers
white; calyx bell-shaped; deeply 5-cleft; petals 5; stamens many;
pistils numerous; styles jointed and bent near the middle, the
upper part falling away and the lower part hooked.

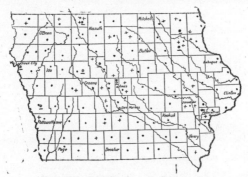

FIG. 97.   Distribution of Stickweed.

Distribution.—Stickweed is widely distributed in northern United States and frequently found in woods or adjacent fields; especially common in northeastern Iowa.

Extermination.—This weed is easily scattered by animals by means of the hooked achenes; thorough cultivation will destroy the plants.

Fig. 97-A. Stickweed, White Avens (*Geum canadense*). White flowers with burlike fruit scattered by animals. In pastures and fields.
(Photograph by Hart.)

Wild Rose (*Rosa pratincola* Greene).

Description.—Low shrub with very prickly stem; compound leaves of 7 to 11 leaflets, broadly elliptical to oblong-oblanceolate, subcuneate at base, short stalked or sessile, serrate; stipule narrow, glandular toothed; flowers corymbose, calyx tube urn-shaped, 5 sepals, smooth or occasionally hispid, petals 5, rose-colored; fruit oblong, ovaries hairy.

FIG. 98. Wild Rose *(Rosa pratincola)*. Grain fields, roadsides.
(Photograph by Ada Hayden.)

Distribution.—This wild rose is common in prairies and fields from Texas to Minnesota, west to Colorado. It is common everywhere in Iowa, including Story, Polk, Emmet, Dickinson, Palo Alto, Clay, Kossuth, Winnebago, Allamakee, Clinton, Muscatine, Scott, Decatur and Pottawattamie counties.

Extermination.—This weed often persists in grain fields of northern Iowa. Thorough cultivation for a few seasons will, however, usually destroy the weed.

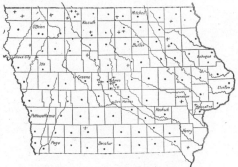

FIG. 98-A. Distribution of Wild Rose.

Smooth Rose (*Rosa blanda* Ait.).

Description.—Stems 1 foot to 4 feet high, wholly smooth, or occasionally with prickles. Stipules of the leaves dentate; leaflets 5 to 7. Cuneate at the base; flowers large, rose-colored, solitary.

Distribution.—This rose has a general range from Newfoundland westward to the Great Lakes and Missouri. It is found in hilly localities in Iowa.

Extermination.—This rose may be eradicated by the same means as are used for *Rosa pratincola.*

FIG. 99.   Partridge Pea *(Cassia Chamaecrista).*
(Photograph by Photo Section, Ia. Agr. Exp. Sta.)

LEGUMINOSAE, PULSE FAMILY.

This family contains the clover, pea, beans, cowpea, soybean, honey locust, lupines, vetches, coffee bean, senna, and ornamental plants as red bud, sweet pea, caragana, etc.

Partridge Pea (*Cassia Chamaecrista* L.)

Description.—Annual plants with simple branches. Leaflets 10 to 12 pairs, linear-oblong. The large yellow flowers on slender pedicels, 2 or 3 of the showy yellow petals bearing a purple spot at the base.

Distribution.—Grows on clay banks and sandy fields.

Extermination.—Readily destroyed by cutting.

Rattle-box (*Crotalaria sagittalis* L.).

Description.—Hairy annual from 3 inches to 1 foot high, with a small tap-root; stem branched, villous, terete or wing-margined; leaves oval or oblong-lanceolate, from one-half to one-third inch

FIG. 100.   Rattle-box (*Crotalaria sagittalis*).   Common in sandy soil, Missouri river bottoms.
(Photograph by Colburn.)

wide, edge of the leaf entire or somewhat wavy and hairy; stipules
united and decurrent on the stem, becoming inversely arrow-
shaped; peduncles produce a few yellow flowers about one-fourth
inch in diameter; calyx 5-cleft, standard of the flower large, heart-
shaped; keel scythe-shaped; stamens monadelphous, anthers of two
sizes, 5 smaller and roundish; pod large, inflated, bears a close
resemblance to that of the garden pea, greenish at first, becoming
blackish, varying in size from three-fourths to one inch in length
and about 1 inch in diameter; seeds from one-half to one-tenth
inch in diameter, flattish, kidney-shaped, when mature breaking
away from the point of attachment and rattling in the pod, hence
the name ''rattle-box''.

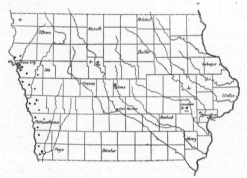

Fig. 100-A.   Distribution of Rattle-box.

Distribution.—Common from New England to Minnesota, southwest to north Texas. In Iowa abundant only along Missouri river,
the Des Moines near Fort Dodge, and in sandy fields and streams
of southern Iowa.

Extermination.—This weed occurs mostly in the Missouri bottoms, generally on more or less sandy soil. It succumbs readily to
cultivation. The raw sandy prairies on which it occurs should be
broken up and sown to some leguminous crop, like alfalfa, which
will crowd the weed out.

Rabbit-foot or Stone Clover (*Trifolium arvense* L.).

Description.—A silky branching annual plant, a foot or less in
height. Heads grayish, silky.

Distribution.—This clover has become naturalized from Europe.
It is found in dry sandy soils, and along roadsides. It is common
only in a few counties in Iowa, including Hancock and Winneshiek.

The Yellow Clover (*Trifolium agrarium* L.).

Description.—A smoothish annual, usually upright, with obovate-oblong leaflets, all three from the same point (palmate) and nearly sessile; stipules narrow; corolla yellow, persistent.

Distribution.—This clover is common in sandy fields and roadsides from eastern Canada west to Wisconsin and Minnesota and to Iowa; common along roadsides in northeastern Iowa.

Extermination.—The same treatment should be used as for low hop-clover. It is readily destroyed with the hoe.

FIG. 101.   Yellow or Hop Clover (*Trifolium agrarium*).   Along roadsides.   Yellow flowers.
(Photograph by Colburn.)

Low Hop-clover (*Trifolium procumbens* L.).

Description.—A pubescent annual with spreading or ascending stems; leaves of 3 leaflets pinnate, the lateral at a small distance from the other, obovate, notched at the end; stipules ovate, short; flowers yellow, persistent, becoming dry in age.

Distribution.—This plant is naturalized from Europe; common in the eastern states. It is not uncommon in Story, Jackson, Dubuque, Clayton, Winneshiek and Delaware counties.

FIG. 102.   Low Hop-clover, Yellow Clover *(Trifolium procumbens).*   Clover fields, meadows, waste places.
(Drawing by Charlotte M. King.)
(Photograph by Hart.)

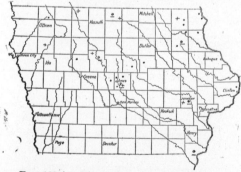

FIG. 102-A.   Distribution of Low Hop-clover.

Extermination.—Low hop-clover succumbs readily to cultivation. The seeds, however, may retain their vitality for some time in the soil. Clean seed should be used and sown in clean soil.

Yellow Sweet Clover (*Melilotus officinalis* (L.) Lam.).

Description.—An upright, usually tall, fragrant annual or biennial; leaves compound, leaflets obovate-oblong, obtuse, closely serrate; flowers yellow, pod smooth, prominently cross-ribbed. The *M. indica,* also with yellow flowers, has a gibbous and alveolate pod. This has been recently introduced.

Distribution.—Yellow sweet clover is native to Europe. It is widely scattered throughout the United States; abundant upon the Pacific coast, in the Great Basin country and the Rocky mountains; becoming abundant in the northern Mississippi valley. It is more or less frequent in many parts of Iowa, including Sac,

FIG. 103.   Yellow Sweet Clover (*Melilotus officinalis*).   Roadsides, streets and some fields.
(Photograph by Colburn.)

Story, Pottawattamie, Monona, Polk, Woodbury, Marshall, Greene, Jones, Linn, Dubuque and Webster counties; and less frequent in Clayton and Allamakee counties.

FIG. 103-A.   Distribution of Yellow Sweet Clover.

Extermination.—The weed is easily destroyed by cultivation. The seeds, however, preserve their vitality in the soil for some time.

Sweet Clover (*Melilotus alba* Desr.).

Description.—An erect annual or biennial 2 to 4 feet high; rather distant, compound leaves, leaflets obovate, oblong, obtuse, serrate, narrowed at the base, truncate, emarginate or rounded at the apex; flowers with white petals, small, fragrant; pod ovoid, reticulated and smooth.

FIG. 104.   Distribution of White Sweet Clover.

Distribution.—Sweet clover is native to Europe and abundant in all parts of the United States. It has been widely scattered by bee-keepers who have sowed it as a honey-bee plant. Sweet clover is abundant now in every part of Iowa, along highways, rights of way of railways, also in some fields. This plant has become extremely common throughout northern Iowa. The rights of way of railroads from Sac City to Iowa Falls, for example, and from Carroll to Council Bluffs and Carroll to Clinton are lined with it.

Extermination.—The only way to exterminate this plant is to prevent seed formation. This may be done by cutting the plants underneath the ground. In fact the young plants are easily exterminated in this way. The plants occur in meadows and pastures, coming largely from the weeds left growing along the roadsides. Road overseers should see that these chance plants are removed. According to a recent investigation of Prof. Ewart of Australia some of the seeds retain their vitality for a long time, some of them more than half a century. It is imperative, therefore, to prevent the formation of seeds so as not to sow for a future generation to eradicate. Sweet clover is used as a forage plant and considered quite valuable. Mr. Coverdale of Maquoketa considers it a most valuable plant. Mr. Westgate has recently brought together many valuable points in its favor.

FIG. 104-A. White Sweet Clover (*Melilotus alba*). Common along roadsides.
(Photograph by Colburn.)

The Farmer's Review says regarding the plant: "In Minnesota, Wisconsin, and Ohio there are laws against the plant known as sweet clover. We fail to see why this plant should be singled out and denominated as a weed. It certainly is not objectionable as a cover for waste places, and is easily controlled where its presence is not desired."

Chemical Composition.—The chemical composition according to the University of Wyoming is as follows:*

	Green	Air dry	Water free
Water	79.35	6.02	-----
Ash	2.10	9.57	10.18
Ether extract	0.53	2.42	2.52
Crude fiber	4.78	21.77	23.16
Crude protein	3.96	18.00	19.15
Nitrogen free extract	9.28	42.22	44.99

FIG. 104-B. White Sweet Clover (*Melilotus alba*). Along roadsides.
(Photograph by Charlotte M. King.)

*Bull. No. 70 compiled by Henry G. Knight, Frank E. Hepner, chemists, and Aven Nelson, botanist; Wyoming Experiment Station.

Black Medic (*Medicago lupulina* L.).

Description.—A procumbent, pubescent annual; compound leaves trifoliate; leaflets wedge-shaped, obovate, toothed at the apex; flowers yellow, in short spikes; pods kidney-form, 1-seeded.

FIG. 105.   Black Medic *(Medicago lupulina)*.   Clover and alfalfa meadows.
(Photograph by Hart.)

FIG. 105-A.   Distribution of Black Medic.

Distribution.—The black medic is naturalized from Europe and is common in alfalfa fields in the Rocky mountains and on the Pacific coast; common in waste places in eastern North America; reported from a number of counties in Iowa, as Wright, Kossuth and Story.

Extermination.—This annual is readily exterminated by giving thorough cultivation; care should be used in planting clover and alfalfa seed, because this weed seed is a common impurity, especially of the latter. The seed also retains its vitality for some time.

*Chemical Composition.**

FRESH OR AIR DRY MATERIAL.

Water	Ash	Protein	Fiber	Nitrogen free extract	Fat
78.52	1.37	3.40	6.31	9.20	1.11
		WATER FREE SUBSTANCE			
	6.4	15.8	29.3	43.4	5.1

Pink Parosela (*Dalea alopecuroides* Willd.).

Description.—An erect annual from 2 to 3 feet high, with pinnately-compound leaflets; smooth flowers, whitish or light rose-color, in cylindrical spikes; calyx villous; seeds kidney-shaped.

Distribution.—This plant is found from Minnesota to Alabama and the Rocky Mountains, common in western Iowa and introduced eastward in Wright, Boone and Story counties. It is especially common from Hamburg to Sioux City and Hawarden. The Missouri loess and bottoms are well adapted to it. Now used as a soil renovator.

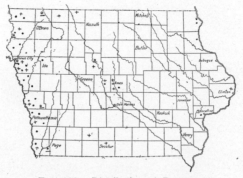

FIG. 106. Distribution of Parosela.

*Compiled by Jenkins and Winton, Bull. Off. Exp. Sta., 11.

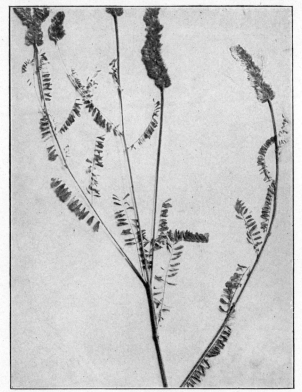

Fig. 106-A. Parosela (*Dalea alopecuroides*). Common in western Iowa and
along railroads.
(Photographed by Quade.)

Extermination.—Seeds of this dalea are sometimes found in alfalfa seed from the west, also in clover seed grown in western Iowa;
therefore care should be used in the selection of seed from these
regions lest it contain seed of dalea.   Dalea succumbs readily to
cultivation.

Rattle-box or Milk Vetch (*Astragalus canadensis* L.).

Description.—A tall, erect, smooth or pubescent perennial, 1 foot
to 4 feet high; leaves compound, leaflets 21 to 27, oblong; flowers
greenish cream-colored in spikes of variable length; pods crowded,
smooth, terete, occasionally somewhat sulcate; the seeds separate
from the pod, rattling, hence the common name.

Distribution.—Milk vetch is common in the northern Mississippi
valley, east to New York and south to Georgia, on borders of thickets, woods and native meadows.   It is common also in prairie
meadows.

Extermination.—This weed is easily exterminated by cultivation.

Fig. 107.   Rattle-box or Milk Vetch *(Astragalus canadensis).* Woodland pastures.
(Photograph by Charlotte M. King.)

Purple or Stemless Loco Weed (*Oxytropis Lamberti* Pursh.).

Description.—Nearly acaulescent, perennial herbs or shrubby plants, with tufts of very numerous short stems coming from a hard and thick root-stock containing many scaly stipules; stems and leaves covered with silky and finely appressed hairs, or smoothish; leaves pinnate; leaflets linear; flowers racemose or spicate, rather large and elongated, purple, violet, or sometimes white; stamens diadelphous; keel tipped with a sharp projecting point. This is one of the loco weeds, poisonous to cattle.

Distribution.—Purple loco weed grows in western Minnesota, western Iowa, and Missouri to Texas and New Mexico; north to British Columbia and Northwest Territory. In general this weed extends from Spirit Lake west to South Dakota and southward along the Missouri river.

Extermination.—It seldom gives much trouble in cultivated fields.

FIG. 108. Purple Loco Weed *(Oxytropis Lamberti)*. A weed poisonous to cattle. *(Drawing by F. C. Collins.)*

FIG. 108-A. Distribution of Purple Loco Weed.

Wild Liquorice *(Glycyrrhiza lepidota* (Nutt.) Pursh.).

Description.—A branching perennial 2 to 3 feet high, leaves compound of 15 to 19 oblong-lanceolate leaflets with mucronate points; young leaflets sprinkled with a resinous material; flowers in spikes, short peduncled, whitish; pods oblong, covered with hooked prickles, resembling a cocklebur.

FIG. 109.   Wild Liquorice *(Glycyrrhiza lepidota)*.   Occurs in western and central
parts of the state.
(Drawn by Ada Hayden.)

Distribution.—Wild Liquorice is common in the west, western
Iowa to Rocky mountains, Utah, New Mexico and Montana to Canada, also reported from the Great Lakes; commonly reported from
Story, Greene, Pottawattamie, Harrison, Monona, Fremont, Decatur, Sac, Webster, Carroll and Mills counties.

Extermination.—This plant is easily exterminated by cultivation. The seeds should not be allowed to mature. If the plants
occur in the pasture or meadow they should be cut off at the surface of the ground to prevent flowering. Where the land can be
cultivated give the ordinary plowing, followed by harrowing to

bring the roots to the surface so they are exposed to the sun; a few days' exposure to the sun will kill them.

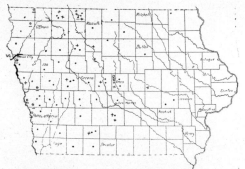

FIG. 109-A. Distribution of Wild Liquorice.

FIG. 110. Common Vetch (*Vicia sativa*). Common in grain fields, especially wheat fields, frequently found in screenings from flour mills.
(Photograph by Colburn.)

Common Vetch (*Vicia sativa* L.).

Description.—A smooth or slightly pubescent annual from 1

foot to 2½ feet high with simple stem; leaflets 5 to 7 pairs, obovate-oblong to linear, notched or mucronate at the tip; 1 or 2 nearly sessile flowers borne in the axils of the leaves, corolla violet-purple; pod linear, several-seeded, seeds black.

Distribution.—This weed has long been known as troublesome in the grain fields of Europe, and in the northern United States. It has been particularly abundant in northeastern and northwestern Iowa and in some of the grain growing sections of the southern part of the state. The weed has disappeared from Iowa since the abandonment of wheat culture; however, in Clayton, Allamakee and Winneshiek counties it has persisted on the highways.

FIG. 110-A. Distribution of Common Vetch.

Extermination.—To sow clean seed in clean soil is the only method of displacing the weed.

Chemical Composition.—The chemical composition of vetch (*Vicia sativa*) according to U. S. Department of Agriculture, *1880*; page 152, is as follows:

FRESH OR AIR DRY MATERIAL.

	Water	Ash	Protein	Fiber	Nitrogen free extract	Fat
Cut May 4, in full bloom	86.20	1.60	4.14	2.11	5.34	0.61
WATER FREE SUBSTANCE.						
		11.6	3.00	15.3	38.7	4.4

Wild Bean (*Strophostyles helvola* (L.) Britton).

Description.—An annual, with prostrate stem; compound leaves ovate to oblong-obovate, with a prominent rounded lobe at the base;

corolla greenish white and purplish; pod 4 to 8-seeded, large, usually pubescent.

FIG. 111.   Wild Bean *(Strophostyles helvola)*.   Common in sandy or gravelly soil, sandy river bottoms.
(Photograph by Colburn.)

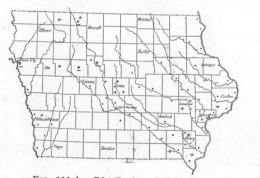

FIG. 111-A.   Distribution of Wild Bean.

Distribution.—The wild bean is common in sandy places in northern United States from Wisconsin, Minnesota and Texas east to Massachusetts. It is common in gravel pits on Muscatine Island, along Des Moines, Cedar, Iowa and Mississippi rivers.

Extermination.—This plant is easily exterminated by cultivation.

OXALIDACEAE, WOOD SORREL FAMILY.

This family contains the cultivated yellow and purple-flowered oxalis. Few of the plants are economic.

Yellow Field Sorrel (*Oxalis stricta* L.).

Description.—A pale green pubescent annual or perennial; leaves compound, with evident stipules; flowers pale yellow, cymose, 1 to 4, at length deflexed; in fruit columnar, short-pointed.

FIG. 112. Yellow Field Sorrel *(Oxalis stricta)*. Common in fields. *a*, Trichome or plant hair.
(a, drawing by Charlotte M. King; photograph by Hart.)

Distribution.—Field sorrel is common in fields and waste places from New England to Dakota; common in Iowa probably over the entire state, especially in fields, meadows and pastures, frequent in shady places.

Extermination.—Persistent cultivation and crop rotation will usually exterminate the weed.

FIG. 112-A. Distribution of Yellow Field Sorrel.

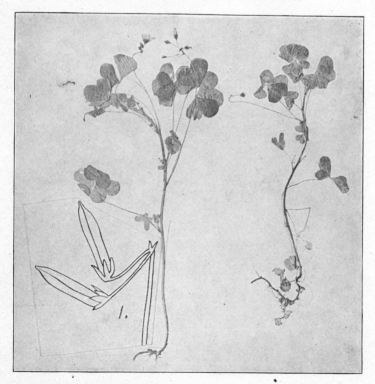

FIG. 113. Field Sorrel (*Oxalis corniculata*). Fields, gardens, etc.
(*Photograph by Colburn, ,1, fruits of O. stricta, drawing by Charlotte M. King.*)

Field Sorrel (*Oxalis corniculata* L.).

Description.—This is an erect or decumbent perennial herb, spreading by numerous slender, pale runners; leaflets 3; flowers in cymose clusters, yellow; peduncle ascending and sparingly pubescent.

Distribution.—Field sorrel is a very common weed in dry or moist soil throughout eastern North America.

Extermination.—Apply the same method as to the preceding species.

FIG. 113-A.   Distribution of Field Sorrel.

ZYGOPHYLLACEAE, CALTROP FAMILY.

A small family, with but one representative in our weed flora.

Caltrop, Puncture vine (*Tribulus terrestris* L.).

Description.—Caltrop is a hairy, procumbent annual, branching from the base, producing a stem which is a foot or more long, branches bear numerous small, compound leaves with short peduncles and small stipules at the base; each compound leaf has 4 to 8 pairs of short-stalked leaves; small, yellow, axillary flowers about one-half inch across with peduncle much shorter than leaves; fruit very spiny and divided into two nearly equal parts, each part consisting of 2 long spines, 2 shorter and a row of very short ones, forming a crest on the back; 5-angled, spiny fruit splits into 3 to 5 divisions.   The fruit punctures auto tires.

Distribution.—*Tribulus terrestris* was introduced from the Old World and occurs from the Atlantic states to Nebraska and Kansas and California; in Iowa it has been found only on Muscatine Island.

Extermination.—Caltrop is disseminated by wool, and hence the waste of woolen mills should not be thrown into the fields.   The weed is easily destroyed by cultivation.

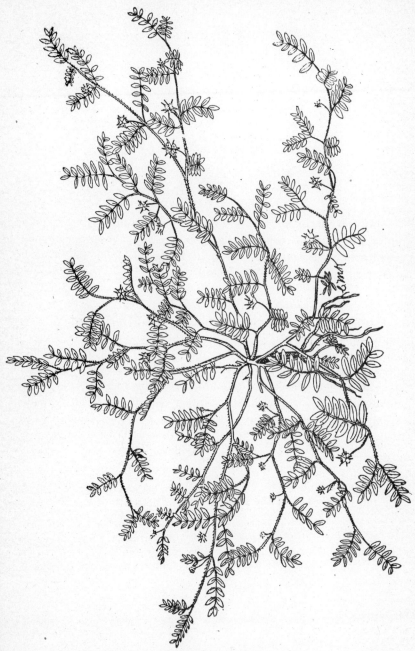

FIG. 115-A. Three-seeded Mercury (*Acalypha virginica*). Common in many parts
Muscatine Island.
(*Drawing by Ada Hayden.*)

FIG. 114-A.   Distribution of Caltrop.

EUPHORBIACEAE, SPURGE FAMILY.

Many of the plants of this family contain an irritating milky juice. Few are of economic importance. The poinsettia commonly cultivated in greenhouses, snow-on-the-mountain in gardens, and castor-oil bean belong to this family.

Three-seeded Mercury· (*Acalypha virginica* L.).

Description.—A smoothish or hairy annual from 1 foot to 2 feet high, turning purple, especially in the autumn; leaves ovate or oblong-ovate, sparingly serrate, long-petioled; sterile spike, few-flowered, pistillate flowers 1 to 3 at the base of staminate peduncle surrounded by a large leaf-like bract; capsule 3-lobed, subglobular, 2-valved carpels. The small, reddish, striate seeds are expelled from the plant to some little distance in a manner similar to the dispersal of the castor-oil bean.

Distribution.—This weed is distributed from Nova Scotia to Texas and northward to Minnesota. Common everywhere in Iowa along roadsides and in fields, where it is especially noticeable in the fall on account of the purple bracts.

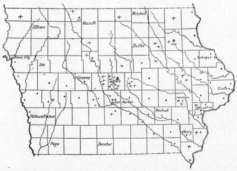

FIG. 115.   Distribution of Three-seeded Mercury.

Extermination.—Three-seeded mercury is not a difficult weed to exterminate. Thorough cultivation by preventing the formation of seed will eradicate the weed.

Fig. 115-A. Three-seeded Mercury (*Acalypha virginica*). Common in many parts of the state.
(*Drawing by Ada Hayden.*)

Spotted Spurge (*Euphorbia Preslii* Guss.).

Description.—An annual from 1 foot to 1½ feet high; erect or ascending; leaves oblique at the base, ovate, oblong, or sometimes

FIG. 116.　Spotted Spurge *(Euphorbia Preslii)*.　Common everywhere in the state.
(Drawing by Charlotte M. King.)

FIG. 116-A.　Distribution of Spotted Spurge.

oblong-linear, frequently falcate, serrate, generally with a conspicuous red spot or margin; flowers pedunculate in terminal cymes; appendages entire; pod glabrous; seeds ovate, sometimes wrinkled.

Distribution.—This spurge is found in loose soils in fields from New England and Canada to Wisconsin, Minnesota and Nebraska, also southward. It is common at Ames, McGregor, Dubuque, Muscatine, Des Moines, Boone, Carroll, Sioux City and Mason City.

Extermination.—This annual weed is easily exterminated by cultivation; therefore the practice of rotation of crops with thorough cultivation will control it. Seeds of several species of this genus retain their vitality for some length of time.

Creeping Spurge or Milk Purslane (*Euphorbia maculata* L.).

Description.—Slightly pubescent or hairy annual, with prostrate stems; leaves oblong-linear, oblique at the base; pubescent or sometimes nearly smooth, usually with a brown-red spot in the center; serrulate above, stipules lanceolate; flowers pedunculate in lateral

FIG. 117. Creeping Spurge (*Euphorbia maculata*). Sandy fields.
(Photograph by Quade, a, trichome or plant hair; drawing by Charlotte M. King.)

clusters; glands of the involucre minute; appendages usually red; pods acute-angled; seed sharply 4-angled with 4 shallow grooves across the sides; trichomes several-celled, gradually tapering to apex.

Distribution.—Creeping spurge is found in sandy fields, or generally in fields from New England and Canada westward. It is common in every part of Iowa, and has been noted particularly at Sioux City, Council Bluffs, Hamburg, Carroll, Mason City, McGregor and Dubuque.

Extermination.—The weed may be exterminated in the same way as given for the preceding species.

Fig. 117-A.   Distribution of Creeping Spurge.

Snow-on-the-Mountain (*Euphorbia marginata* Pursh.).

Description.—Stems stout, high, erect, hairy or smoothish; annual, from 2 to 3 feet high; leaves sessile ovate-oblong, acute; uppermost leaves white, petal-like margins.

Distribution.—Snow-on-the-Mountain occurs from Minnesota to Missouri and Colorado; also reported eastward to Ohio and South Carolina. A frequent escape from gardens in Iowa; common only in the western part from Sioux City to Turin, Council Bluffs, Glenwood and Hamburg.

Extermination.—This annual weed is easily exterminated by cultivation. The plant when young should be cut off below the surface of the ground.

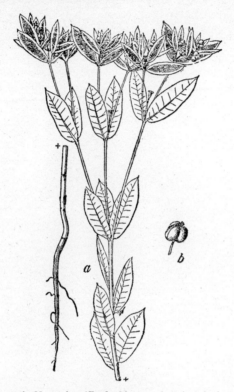

FIG. 118. Snow-on-the-Mountain *(Euphorbia marginata)*. A frequent escape from
gardens. *a*, Whole plant, one-third natural size; *b*, seed capsule, natural size.

FIG. 118-A. Distribution of Snow-on-the-Mountain.

Flowering Spurge (*Euphorbia corollata* L.).

Description.—A glabrous perennial plant 1 foot to 3 feet high; stem simple for half its length; leaves ovate to linear; umbel 3 to 7-forked, the forks again divided; involucres long-petioled, showy with petal-like white appendages; lobes minute. Seeds ash-colored.

Distribution.—This spurge is common in gravelly soils, in many parts of the state. It is often weedy.

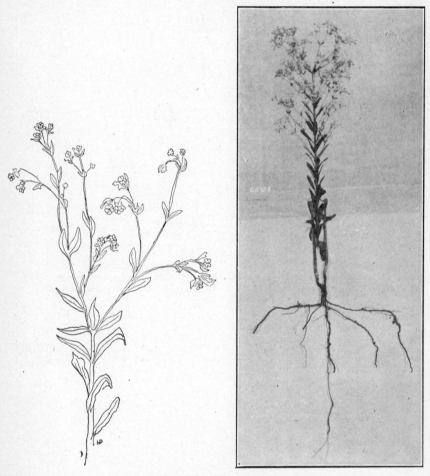

Fig. 119. Flowering Spurge (*Euphorbia corollata*). Common in sandy fields, gravel knolls and roadsides.
(*Drawing by Lois Pammel.*)

Fig. 119-A. Flowering Spurge (*Euphorbia corollata*) showing root system.
(*Photograph by Photo Section, Ia. Agr. Exp. Sta.*)

FIG. 119-B.   Flowering Spurge *(Euphorbia corollata).*
(Photograph by Photo Section, Ia. Agr. Exp. Sta.)

Cypress Spurge *(Euphorbia Cyparissias* L.).

Description.—Plant with perennial running root-stocks and densely clustered stems from 6 inches to 1 foot high; linear, crowded leaves; many-rayed umbel with glands crescent-shaped and granular pods.   Another spurge *(E. esula)* is becoming common.

Distribution.—This spurge is common westward from New England to Nebraska, and occurs usually in the vicinity of gardens and cemeteries.   It is common in some places in towns and cities, in-

FIG. 120. Cypress Spurge (*Euphorbia Cyparissias*).
(*Photograph by Photo Section, Ia. Agr. Exp. Sta.*)

FIG. 120-A. Distribution of Cypress Spurge.

cluding Ames, Clinton, Dubuque, McGregor, Cedar Rapids, Muscatine, Keokuk and Davenport.

Extermination.—This perennial weed by reason of its running root-stocks is often difficult to exterminate. In addition to its propagation by the running root-stocks it also propagates by its seeds. To eradicate this plant the ground should be given a shallow plowing and the root-stocks exposed to the sun. It may be necessary to repeat this process two or three times during the summer.

FIG. 120-B. Cypress Spurge *(Euphorbia Cyparissias)*. Yellow "flowered" plant with milky juice and narrow leaves. Escaped from gardens to roadsides.
(Photograph by Colburn.)

Caper Spurge (*Euphorbia Lathyrus* L.).

Description.—A glabrous annual or biennial, one to two feet high; thick narrow oblong leaves, those about the flower heart shaped. The umbel 4-rayed.

Distribution.—This spurge is found occasionally escaped from gardens. Also occurs in fields and along rights-of-way of railways; Ames and Hawarden.

ANACARDIACEAE, SUMACH FAMILY.

Many of the plants of this family are poisonous. The sumach and several others contain tannin. Some plants of the family, as the smoke tree, are cultivated for ornamental purposes.

Poison Ivy (*Rhus Toxicodendron* L.).

Description.—A climbing or trailing or sometimes erect shrub, clinging to trees or other objects by aerial rootlets; 3 leaflets; inconspicuous flowers; waxy fruit frequently remaining on plant until late winter or early spring. This plant is often mistaken for Virginia creeper (*Psedera quinquefolia* (L.) Greene), which, however, has 5 leaflets. Many persons are sensitive to poisoning from poison ivy, every part of which contains the poisonous principle.

Distribution.—Poison ivy is abundant throughout eastern North America and the Rocky mountains. It is common everywhere in Iowa, in hedge rows, thickets or woods.

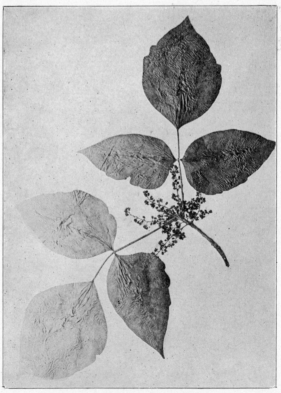

Fig. 121. Poison Ivy (*Rhus Toxicodendron*). Common in woods and along fences.
(*Photograph by Colburn.*)

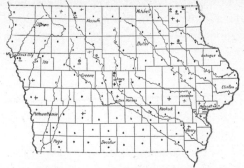

FIG. 121-A.   Distribution of Poison Ivy.

Extermination.—Poison ivy is not easily destroyed because in most cases it is troublesome in wood lots along fences and in yards. It spreads by long underground roots a yard or more in length.

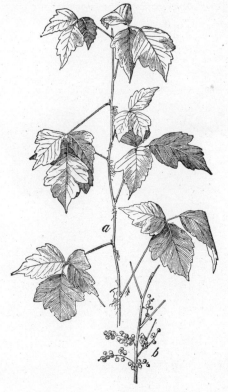

FIG. 121-B.   Poison Ivy (*Rhus Toxicodendron*).   *a*, spray showing rootlets; *b*, fruit. (*After Chesnut, U. S. Dept. Agr.*)

It is difficult to destroy except by giving thorough cultivation. If persistently cut off below the surface of the ground it can be destroyed. Sodium arsenite at the rate of one and one-half to two pounds to 52 gallons of water will help to destroy the weed. It is not, however, safe to use this since it is a strong poison. The usual remedy for ivy poisoning is to wash affected part of the skin with a solution of sugar of lead.

Soap and water used immediately is effective to prevent poisoning of the skin.

MALVACEAE, MALLOW FAMILY.

Cotton, hollyhock and okra are well known plants of this family.

Indian Mallow, Velvet-leaf, or Butter-print (*Abutilon Theophrasti* Medic.).

Description.—A tall annual from 2 to 4 feet high; plant with strong characteristic odor; leaves velvety, roundish heart-shaped,

FIG. 122.   Indian Mallow, Velvet-leaf, or Butter-print (*Abutilon Theophrasti*).   Common in corn fields, waste places, barnyards.
(Photographed by Colburn.)

taper-pointed; peduncles shorter than the petioles; corolla yellowish; carpels 12 to 15, hairy-beaked seeds rough, rather large and
blackish.

FIG. 122-A.   Pigweed, Foxtail and Indian Mallow in a potato patch.   There are too
many such garden patches in Iowa.
(Photograph by Pammel.)

FIG. 122-B.   Distribution of Indian Mallow.

Distribution.—Indian mallow is common in waste places, corn fields, vacant lots, barnyards, etc., throughout eastern North America. The plant is naturalized from tropical regions, probably India. This weed is becoming abundant in many places in Iowa, including McGregor, Marshalltown, Eldora, Boone, Ames, Cedar Rapids, Dubuque, Postville, Davenport, Des Moines, Clinton, Sioux City, Osceola, Hamburg and Keosauqua.

Extermination.—This plant propagates only by its seed, which retains its vitality for some length of time, having been known to germinate after a period of sixty years. The young plants are easily exterminated. The plant should be pulled up before it begins to flower. Wallaces' Farmer suggests the following treatment: "It has been seriously thought of by some persons as a substitute for manilla or sisal in the manufacture of binder twine. It is an annual, and if not allowed to go to seed, the farm can in time be cleared of it, but this will require a long time. The seeds have a most astonishing vitality. We have known cases where Indian mallow has been pulled up for fifteen years, not a plant being allowed to go to seed, and yet it makes its appearance every spring. Fortunately, it grows only on rich land, and is restricted largely to hog yards and feed lots and other places where the land is exceedingly rich. In fact, in sections of the country where it is being introduced, it may be found in almost every farmyard. Why farmers allow it to mature seed passes our comprehension. It goes variously by the names of velvet-weed, butter-print and in the locality of one of our farms, Davis weed, from the fact that it was introduced many years ago by a man named Davis, who regarded it as a rather good ornamental plant."

Prickly Sida (*Sida spinosa* L.).

Description.—An annual from 10 to 20 inches high; frequently much-branched; leaves ovate-lanceolate; serrate with a long petiole, peduncles in axils of leaves, 1-flowered; flowers small, yellow; 5 carpels, each 2-beaked.

Distribution.—The prickly sida is common in the southern states and as far north as Massachusetts, Kansas and southern Iowa. It is common at Keokuk, Ottumwa, Eddyville, Centerville and Oskaloosa.

Extermination.—This weed propagates entirely by its seeds, which retain their vitality for a considerable length of time on account of the hard seed coat. The growing plant is, however, easily destroyed by pulling the weed or by cultivation.

FIG. 123.   Prickly Sida *(Sida spinosa)*. Common in fields in southern Iowa.
(Photograph by Hart.)

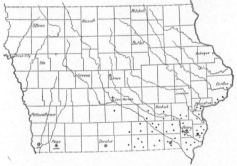

FIG. 123-A.   Distribution of Sida.

Cheeses or Common Mallow *(Malva rotundifolia* L.).

Description.—A procumbent biennial; leaves round, heart-shaped on long petioles, crenate; flowers white, petals longer than the calyx; a 3-leaved involucre at the base of the calyx; carpels pubescent.

Distribution.—This plant is native to Europe; a widely distributed weed in eastern North America, common in eastern and central Iowa in dooryards, barn lots, etc., in Story, Marshall, Polk, Marion, Linn, Clinton, Winneshiek and Allamakee counties. This is common not only in yards but in fields and waste places, where it has been noticed at Ames, McGregor, Clinton, Cedar Rapids, Sioux City, Carroll, Des Moines, Keokuk and Hamburg.

FIG. 124.　Common Mallow or Cheeses *(Malva rotundifolia).*　Common in dooryards, barn lots, etc.
(Mich. Agr. Exp. Sta.)

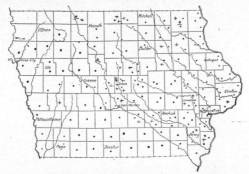

FIG. 124-A. Distribution of Common Mallow.

Extermination.—This weed is easily exterminated by cultivation. None of the seeds should be allowed to mature. The seeds retain their vitality for a considerable length of time.

Shoo-fly, Bladder Ketmia (*Hibiscus Trionum* L.).

Description.—A low, rather hairy annual from 1 foot to 2 feet high; upper leaves 3-parted with 3 lanceolate divisions, the middle longest; calyx inflated in fruit, membranous, 5-winged, with numerous dark nerves; flowers sulphur-yellow with a blackish eye, ephemeral.

Distribution.—Shoo-fly has become naturalized from Europe; common in fields and waste grounds in the southern states and eastward; especially in gardens. Widely distributed, becoming common in Iowa. It has been observed at Giard, Ames, Webster City, Keosauqua, Osceola, Indianola, Iowa City, Chariton, Sidney and Des Moines.

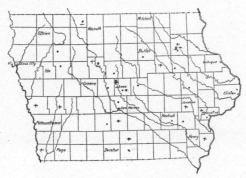

FIG. 125. Distribution of Shoo-fly.

Extermination.—A growing plant is not difficult to exterminate. Thorough cultivation and exposing the roots to the sun will destroy the plant. The seeds, however, retain their vitality for a considerable length of time. A correspondent of southeastern Iowa stated that this weed kept coming up in spite of constant and thorough cultivation. This was owing to the prolonged vitality of the seed.

FIG. 125-A.   Shoo-fly (*Hibiscus Trionum*).
(Photograph by Photo Section, Ia. Agr. Exp. Sta.)

FIG. 125-B.   Shoo-fly (*Hibiscus Trionum*) showing root system.
(Photograph by Photo Section, Ia. Agr. Exp. Sta.)

HYPERICACEAE, ST. JOHN'S-WORT FAMILY.

This small family contains a few ornamental plants with yellow flowers, commonly found in northern states.

St. John's-wort (*Hypericum perforatum* L.).

Description.—A branched perennial, 1½ to 2 feet high with runners; leaves elliptical, or linear-oblong, with pellucid dots; flowers numerous in cymes, petals deep yellow, black-dotted, twice the length of the lanceolate sepals.

Distribution.—St. John's-wort is common in eastern North America in clay soils. Abundant in Iowa only in eastern counties, especially northeastward, as at McGregor, Decorah, Waukon, Dubuque and New Albin.

FIG. 126.   St. John's-wort *(Hypericum perforatum).*   Old fields and woodland pastures,   eastern   and   northeastern   Iowa.
(Photograph by Quade.)

FIG. 126-A.   Distribution of St. John's-wort.

Extermination.—This weed spreads both by seeds and by runners. It is difficult to exterminate. Clark and Fletcher give the
following methods: "Close cutting several times during the summer will reduce it in pastures. An application of salt—a small
handful to each plant after close cutting in hot dry weather—will
kill it and may be practicable where the pest is not abundant and
the land cannot be brought under cultivation. The plant should
be prevented from going to seed. St. John's-wort is easily suppressed on land that can be cultivated under a systematic rotation
of crops. Where it is established, it would be well not to seed to
grass until it is suppressed."

ONAGRACEAE, EVENING PRIMROSE FAMILY.

A small family, some plants with showy flowers, a few cultivated
for ornamental purposes.

Evening Primrose or Cradle Weed (*Oenothera biennis* L.).

Description.—A stout, erect, pubescent or hirsute perennial, 3
to 5 feet high, sparingly branched; leaves lanceolate, or rarely
ovate-lanceolate, denticulate, acute, bracts shorter than or as long
as the capsule; flowers yellow, opening at evening, petals obovate,
stigma lobes linear, capsule subcylindrical; seeds small, brownish.

Distribution.—Evening primrose is common everywhere in eastern North America, Rocky mountains and Utah. It is abundant
along roadsides, borders of woods and fields, in every county in
Iowa.

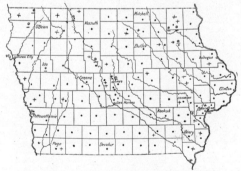

FIG. 127.   Distribution of Evening Primrose.

Extermination.—This plant spreads by seed, and is readily exterminated by cutting off the young plants a few inches below the
surface of the ground.

FIG. 127-A.   Evening Primrose (*Oenothera biennis*).
(Photograph by Photo Section, Ia. Agr. Exp. Sta.)

UMBELLIFERAE, CARROT FAMILY.

Carrot, celery, parsnips and caraway are members of this family.
It includes also many poisonous plants.

Cowbane (*Cicuta maculata* L.).

Description.—A smooth, marsh perennial, 2 to 5 feet high, with pinnately compound leaves, 2 or 3 times pinnate; leaves with long

FIG. 128. Cowbane (*Cicuta maculata*). In low moist meadows and roadsides.
(*Photograph by Colburn.*)

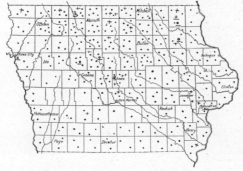

FIG. 128-A. Distribution of Cowbane.

petioles; coarsely serrate leaflets lanceolate to oblong-lanceolate, 1 inch to 5 inches long; stalks of umbellets numerous and unequal; flowers white; fruit broadly ovate to oval, small, 1½ inches long. The plant grows in marshes and in low grounds, the stems springing from thick fleshy underground roots tapering at the lower end, usually numbering from 3 to 8 although single specimens are also met with. On cutting the roots there is given off a sharp pungent odor, which becomes intensified on boiling.

Distribution.—Common throughout the northern states, southwest to Louisiana, Rocky mountains and Utah. Very common in woodlands, low grounds and swales in northern and northeastern Iowa. These low fields in July and August are sometimes white with it. The plant is less common in southern Iowa.

Extermination.—The land where cowbane occurs is low land which needs drainage. By plowing the field and breaking up the sod

FIG. 128-B. Cowbane *(Cicuta maculata)*. In low woods.
(Photograph by Caughey.)

the fascicled roots will be exposed to the sun and the weed will soon be destroyed.

FIG. 128-C.   Cowbane roots *(Cicuta maculata)*.   In low places.
(Photograph by Gardner.)

Caraway *(Carum Carvi* L.).

Description.—A smooth, erect, slender herb 1 foot to 2½ feet high, with fusiform roots; leaves pinnate with filiform divisions; flowers in umbels, white; calyx teeth small; fruit ovate, or oblong with filiform ribs.

Distribution.—The caraway plant is common in eastern North America, the Rocky mountains, Utah and scattered in places in Iowa, as Hardin, Story, Boone, Black Hawk, Dubuque and Clayton counties.

Extermination.—This weed is easily exterminated by cutting off the plants below the surface of the ground.

FIG. 129.   Caraway *(Carum Carvi)*.   Commonly escaped from gardens.   Flowers
white.
(Photograph by Quade.)

FIG. 129-A.   Distribution of Caraway.

Wild Parsnip *(Pastinaca sativa* L.).

Description.—A tall, stout, glabrous biennial with grooved stem;

leaves pinnately compound, cut-toothed; flowers yellow, small; calyx teeth obsolete; fruit oval, flattened dorsally, the lateral ribs with broad wings.

Distribution.—Wild parsnip is common in eastern North America, Rocky mountains and the Pacific coast. Common on roadsides in every part of Iowa. It is abundant at Ames, Marshalltown, Dubuque, Anamosa, McGregor, Decorah, Boone, Clinton, Keokuk, Hamburg, Sioux City and Carroll.

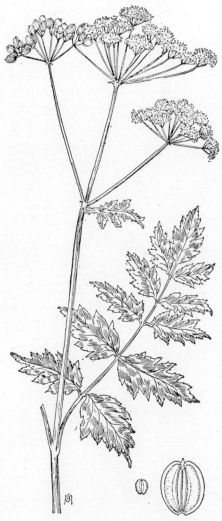

FIG. 130. Wild Parsnip *(Pastinaca sativa).* Common along roads.
(Mich. Agr. Exp. Sta.)

Extermination.—This plant is propagated by seeds. It is easily exterminated by cutting off the young plants a few inches below the surface of the ground. Cultivation of the soil destroys the weed.

FIG. 130-A. Distribution of Wild Parsnip.

Cow Parsnip (*Heracleum lanatum* Michx.).

FIG. 131. Cow Parsnip (*Heracleum lanatum*). Common in woodland pastures.
(*Photograph by Charlotte M. King.*)

Description.—A stout, hairy, pubescent perennial 4 to 8 feet high; leaflets broad and large, irregularly cut-toothed; flowers white, in broad umbels.

Distribution.—Cow parsnip is distributed from the Atlantic coast, Newfoundland, through the northern states and Allegheny mountains to California. It is common in the Rocky mountains. The cow parsnip is of especially frequent occurrence in woods of northeastern Iowa.

Extermination.—Cultivation and grubbing readily control this plant.

Queen Anne's Lace, Wild Carrot (*Daucus Carota* L.).

Description.—A bristly, hirsute biennial from 2 to 2½ feet high; leaves pinnately decompound; involucral bracts foliaceous; flow-

FIG. 132. Wild Carrot *(Daucus Carota).*
(Photograph by Colburn.)

ers in compound umbels, white, or occasionally pink; fruit oblong, flattened dorsally, carpel with 5 slender bristly primary ribs and 4 winged secondary ones, each of which bears a single row of barbed prickles.

Distribution.—Wild carrot is common in eastern North America,

FIG. 132-A. Wild Carrot (*Daucus Carota*). Common to clover meadows. Flowers in white umbels.
(*Photograph by Photo Section, Ia. Agr. Exp. Sta.*)

especially in dry fields. It is becoming common in Iowa clover fields in Scott, Story, Polk, Franklin, Linn, Clinton, Cerro Gordo, Boone, Webster, Sac and Clay counties. It has been rated as common at McGregor, Dubuque, Decorah, Waukon, Anamosa, Cedar Rapids, Marshalltown, Ames, Clinton, Mason City, Hamburg, Sioux City, Carroll and Boone.

Extermination.—This plant is easily killed by cutting off the plant a few inches below the surface of the ground. To prevent its introduction plant clean seed in land free from this weed.

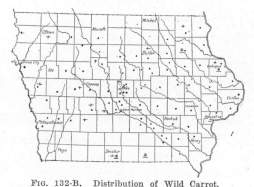

FIG. 132-B. Distribution of Wild Carrot.

APOCYNACEAE, DOGBANE FAMILY.

In the tropics several species of this family are important rubber producing plants. They are commonly called milk-weeds in Iowa, on account of their milky juice.

Spreading Dogbane (*Apocynum androsaemifolium* L.).

Description.—Root-stock horizontal, stem smooth, or rarely soft-tomentose, branched above, spreading, leaves ovate, petioled, cymes loose, spreading, both terminal and axillary; the latter pale rose color, open, bell-shaped; calyx segments shorter than the tubes of the corolla.

Distribution.—This plant is common along borders of thickets from eastern Canada to British Columbia to Arizona and Georgia. Abundant in northeastern Iowa in grain fields near thickets. It is essentially a plant of the forest.

Extermination.—Spreading dogbane produces long, creeping roots, which are quite tenacious of life. In order to destroy the weed, the field should be given a shallow plowing after the grain is harvested, followed by a disking in a week or ten days, depending on the character of the weather. This should be followed by a harrow. If the fall is dry dragging will probably get the larger number of these weeds.

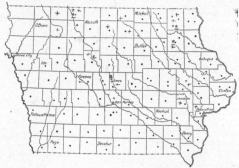

Fig. 133. Distribution of Spreading Dogbane (*Apocynum androsaemifolium*).

Indian Hemp (*Apocynum cannabinum* L.).

Description.—The root-stocks as in preceding species; the stem glabrous or more or less softly pubescent, 2 to 3 feet high, smooth, terminated by an erect, close, many-flowered cyme; corolla lobes nearly erect, the tube not longer than the lanceolate segments of the calyx, greenish white; the plant blooms in July and August.

Distribution.—Common species eastward and troublesome as a weed in northern Mississippi valley. Common in small grain fields and pastures in many parts of Iowa.

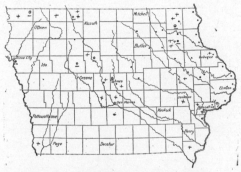

Fig. 134. Distribution of Indian Hemp.

Extermination.—This weed should be treated like spreading dogbane.

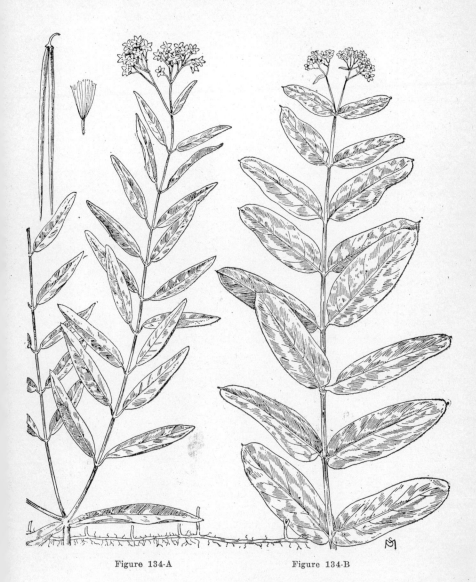

Figure 134-A   Figure 134-B

FIG. 134-A. Indian, Hemp (*Apoocynum cannabinum*).

FIG. 134-B. *Apoocynum cannabinum* var. *hypericifolium*. A low growing variety of the above, but with leaves broader at base and more abruptly pointed at apex.

(Schuyler Mathews in Mich. Agr. Exp. Sta. Bull.)

FIG. 134-C.   Indian Hemp (*Apocynum cannabinum*).
(Photograph by Photo Section, Ia. Agr. Exp. Sta.)

ASCLEPIADACEAE, MILKWEED FAMILY.

A few plants, only, are of economic importance. Some are cultivated for ornamental purposes. In Iowa they are commonly called milkweed. The milkweed pods are now used extensively for decorative purposes.

Showy Milkweed (*Asclepias speciosa* Torr.).

Description.—A perennial, with long, running roots. Plant 1 foot to 4 feet high, white-tomentose or canescent; leaves thick, broadly ovate or oval, petioled; pedicel glabrate above; flowers

FIG. 135. Showy Milkweed *(Asclepias speciosa)*. In grain fields, meadows and road-sides, northwestern Iowa.
(Photograph by Colburn.)

FIG. 135-A. Distribution of Showy Milkweed.

borne in dense umbels or rarely solitary, the pedicels stout; corolla purplish green, large, follicle erect or spreading on the recurved pedicels.

Distribution.—Showy milkweed is common from Minnesota to southern Iowa, Kansas, the Rocky mountains and Utah. In Iowa it is abundant in Emmet, Palo Alto and Dickinson counties.

Extermination.—This weed should be treated like common milkweed.

Milkweed (*Asclepias syriaca* L.).

Description.—This milkweed is a perennial herb with pale colored, long, running roots; a stout stalk 2 to 5 feet high, finely, softly pubescent or tomentose; leaves oblong, oval or ovate, obtuse or roundish at the base, the young leaf somewhat pubescent above, soon becoming glabrate; petioles stout, flowers from a few to many, borne in umbels; peduncles pubescent or tomentose; corolla dull purple or greenish purple, occasionally pale in color; fruit a fol-

Fig. 136.   Common Milkweed *(Asclepias syriaca).*
(Photograph by H. I. Featherly.)

licle and borne on erect pedicels; trichomes multicellular from a
single cell, somewhat floccose.

Distribution.—This milkweed is common from New England to
North Carolina and Kansas. In Iowa it is abundant in oat fields,
on highways and in gardens throughout the state.

Extermination.—Both milkweeds have the same habit of growth.
The weed is perhaps best known by its long roots, which are frequently 10 to 15 feet in length; another important characteristic

Fig. 136-A. Common Milkweed (*Asclepias syriaca*).
(*Photograph by Ada Hayden.*)

is that at frequent intervals the root produces adventitious buds from which new shoots arise.

Wallaces' Farmer says concerning this weed: ''We would advise our correspondent to plow this field as soon as possible and prepare his seed bed for winter wheat. By plowing it again next August he will undoubtedly weaken the stand. He will fail, however, unless in working his corn he uses surface cultivation. These weeds have no doubt been distributed through the field during the three years it was in corn by using a shovel cultivator, which takes

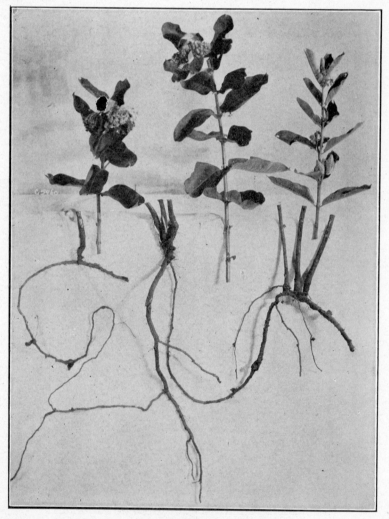

FIG. 136-B.   Common Milkweed (*Asclepias syriaca*) showing root system.
(Photographed by Photo Section, Ia. Agr. Exp. Sta.)

up the roots and carries them over the field in the same way that
many northern farmers are now seeding their fields with quack
grass and damaging them to the extent of from five to twenty dollars per acre. By giving these two thorough August plowings and
taking care of the roots that may be thrown up, then preparing
the seed bed very thoroughly for corn and giving it as far as practical surface cultivation, he will probably get rid of these noxious
weeds.''

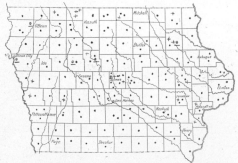

FIG. 136-C. Distribution of Common Milkweed.

FIG. 137. Whorled Milkweed (*Asclepias verticillata*).
(*Photograph by H. I. Featherly.*)

Whorled Milkweed (*Asclepias verticillata* L.).

Description.—A slender perennial plant, with linear leaves 3 to 6 in a whorl; grows to height of 2½ feet. Flowers greenish white, in loose umbels. This plant is poisonous to stock.

FIG. 137-A. Whorled Milkweed (*Asclepias verticillata.*)
(*Photograph by Photo Section, Ia. Agr. Exp. Sta.*)

Distribution.—Prairies, hillsides, open woods, somewhat sandy soil.

Extermination.—The milkweeds have deep roots and require frequent cutting.

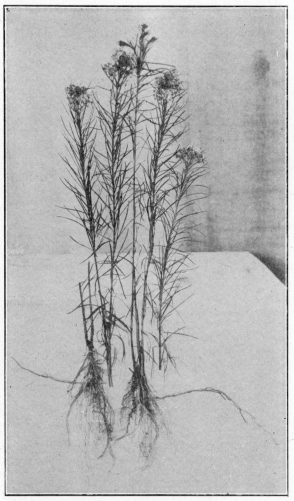

FIG. 137-B.   Whorled Milkweed (*Asclepias verticillata*) showing root system.
(Photograph by Photo Section, Ia. Agr. Exp. Sta.)

Climbing Milkweed (*Gonolobus laevis* Michx.).

Description.—A climbing perennial; leaves oblong, cordate with a deep, narrow sinus; flowers borne in axillary umbel-like cymes, 5 to 10 flowered, large greenish flowers; calyx 5-parted; corolla 5-

parted, wheel-shaped, the lobes narrowly linear-lanceolate, obtuse, larger than the calyx; anthers horizontal under the flattened stigmas; pollen masses 5 pairs, follicles thick.

FIG. 138. Climbing Milkweed (Gonolobus laevis). Troublesome in fields in southern Iowa.
(Drawing by Ada Hayden.)

A similar climbing weedy plant known as angle pod (*Vince-toxicum carolinense*) with warty pods occurs near Sidney.

FIG. 138-A.   Distribution of Climbing Milkweed.

Distribution.—Climbing milkweed is troublesome in woods and fields in the southern states. It is reported as troublesome from a few counties in southern Iowa. It is common in Appanoose, Clinton, Johnson, Iowa, Van Buren, Scott, Fremont, Mills and Woodbury counties. It is an excellent honey plant.

Extermination.—This perennial weed is as difficult to destroy as common milkweed. It should be given thorough cultivation. If this does not suffice the field should be made into a meadow.

CONVOLVULACEAE, MORNING-GLORY FAMILY.

The family contains few economic plants. Sweet potato and cultivated morning glory are representatives.

Blue Field Morning-glory (*Ipomoea hederacea* Jacq.).

Description.—Stems retrorsely hairy; leaves heart-shaped, 3-lobed, the lobes usually acute; peduncle variable in length; 1 to 3 flowers; calyx densely hairy below; corolla funnel-form, white and purple or pale blue; lobes of stigma and cells 3.

Distribution.—The blue field morning-glory is common in fields, especially in corn fields in southern Iowa, as at Ottumwa, Centerville, Keokuk and reaching as far north as Boone county along the Des Moines.

Extermination.—It is easily exterminated by cultivation. The seeds, however, keep their vitality for some time.

FIG. 139.   Blue Field Morning-glory *(Ipomoea hederacea)*.   Fields, common in southern Iowa and Missouri.
(Photograph by Colburn)

FIG. 139-A.   Distribution of Blue Field Morning-glory.

Annual Morning-glory *(Ipomoea purpurea* (L.) Roth.).

The annual morning-glory has heart-shaped leaves with retrorsely

hairy stem; peduncles long, umbellately 3 to 5 flowered, purple to
white.

FIG. 140.   Annual Morning-glory *(Ipomoea purpurea)*. A frequent escape from gardens into fields.

(Photograph by Colburn.)

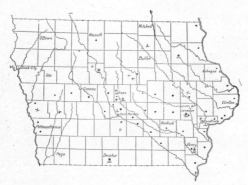

FIG. 140-A.   Distribution of Annual Morning-glory

Distribution.—This morning-glory, a native from tropical America, is common as a weed in waste and cultivated grounds from New England southwestward; abundant from Missouri southward, but rare in Iowa. It is commonly cultivated and is a frequent escape from cultivation in Hardin, Story, Marshall, Wapello and Marion counties.

Extermination.—It is an annual and is easily destroyed; however, the seeds retain their vitality for some time, frequently springing up for several seasons after the most thorough cultivation.

Hedge Bindweed or Morning-glory (*Convolvulus sepium* L.).

Description.—Smooth, occasionally, however, pubescent, twining around supports or trailing; leaves triangular, halberd or arrow shaped, the tip acute or pointed, the basal lobes obliquely truncate or sinuate lobed; flowering peduncles 4-angled with 2 leaf-like bracts which are commonly acute; corolla white or tinged with rose purple.

Distribution.—Hedge bindweed or morning-glory is common in the northern states and in the southwest from Texas to Canada, also in the Great Basin country. A form of it is found also in

FIG. 141.   Hedge Bindweed, or Wild Morning-glory *(Convolvulus sepium)*.
(Photograph by Photo Section, Ia. Agr. Exp. Sta.)

Europe and Asia. It is common in every section of Iowa not only in corn fields, but along highways and in small-grain fields, where it does much damage by pulling down crops.

FIG. 141-A.   Distribution of Hedge Bindweed or Morning-glory.

Extermination.—The morning-glory must be treated like horse nettle since it is a perennial. In addition to the usual methods of cultivation sheep have been recommended to destroy the weed, a method which is certainly applicable where the weed occurs in pastures.

In Wallaces' Farmer, Mr. L. C. Greene's experience in killing morning-glory is given as follows: "A farmer had 145 acres of corn. One piece of twenty acres, fall plowed, on a south slope, was planted to corn the first of May, and by the time the plowing and planting were all done it was near the last of May. The early planted field was thick with morning-glories and had received no cultivation since they commenced to grow. By the time the corn was four inches high the morning-glories were eight or more inches tall, growing in mats on the ground hunting for something to climb upon. The proprietor viewed the field, and instead of sending out the cultivator sent out three stirring plows and the planter soon followed. In two days the field was plowed and planted again and a fine crop of corn was raised with very little bother from the vines, and even the following year the vines bothered but little.

"Some years ago I fall plowed a small field that was badly infested with morning-glory vines and smartweed. The 24th of the next May I was ready for that field, but from a little distance it looked as if a mowing machine and a rake would be the proper tools to use. I plowed rather deep to do a good job, the planter immediately followed, and in four days after the planter some corn could be seen, and it was eight inches high when the cultivator got to it. It was just a matter of stirring the soil all season, for there were no large weeds to kill."

The Prairie Farmer makes these suggestions concerning the

eradication of morning-glory: "Another way to fight the morning-glory is to grow two or three pasture crops a year on the land for sheep. One of them ought to be a cultivated crop. The morning-glory would not be able to hold out long against such treatment. The strong point in favor of this method is the profitable character of the work."

Wallaces' Farmer says concerning its destruction: "They do not spread rapidly except under cultivation, as they grow mostly from the roots, and these are distributed over the fields by cultivators. If when the farmer first discovers a patch out of cultivation for a year or two he plows it shallow and frequently and harrows he can get rid of them. If he cultivates the plants with the rest of his field it is only a short time until he will find these weeds scattered all over his field. A great many ways have been suggested to get rid of this troublesome weed. Special attachments have been invented for the use on corn cultivators known as the morning-glory blades. These are designed to shave off the plants just below the surface of the ground."

"We certainly would fence up this pasture, or part of it, and would sow a mixture of grains that would furnish hog feed, and while we were at it would sow clover and timothy, and when the grains were three or four inches high turn in the hogs. The only trouble is that there are not enough hogs to go around the whole tract. We had a field in that condition twenty years ago. We made a hog pasture of it, and while the morning-glories are yet to be seen in the road alongside, there are none of them in the pasture, and have not been since the first year."

European Bindweed or Morning-glory (*Convolvulus arvensis* L.).

Description.—A deep-rooting perennial; stem procumbent, twining or creeping. Like the horse nettle, this species propagates freely by underground root-stocks; leaves 1 inch to 2 inches long, ovate, oblong, arrow-shaped, lobes at the base running to a point; flowers borne in 1-flowered peduncles with very small leaf-like bracts some distance from the flowers; flowers an inch or less long, short, broadly funnel-shaped, white or commonly of a rose tinge.

Distribution.—European bindweed is a troublesome weed in Europe and in eastern North America. It occurs also in the southern states and on the Pacific coast. It is scattered throughout many parts of Iowa in small patches. This weed has become very abundant in some localities as in Marshall, Story, Carroll and Polk counties, especially in pastures.

Extermination.—A short rotation of crops should be practiced, including late sown roots or other cultivated crops; rape is useful for this purpose. Frequent use of a broad-shared cultivator will destroy new growths and exhaust the vitality of the plants. No crop seeds containing those of field bindweed should be sown. Salt or lime, sometimes recommended to kill this weed, are useless unless applied in large quantities.

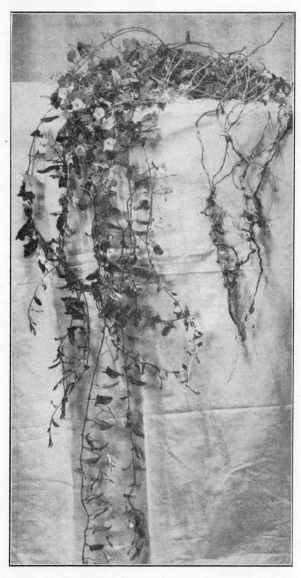

FIG. 142. European Morning-glory (*Convolvulus arvensis*).
(Photograph by Photo Section, Ia. Agr. Exp. Sta.)

FIG. 142-A. European Morning-glory (*Convolvulus arvensis*).
(*Photograph by Ada Hayden.*)

Prof. Hitchcock in Farmer's Review, says: "The black bind-weed or perennial morning-glory (*Convolvulus arvensis*), which I suppose is the kind meant, is a great pest and difficult to eradicate. If a patch is not too large, heavy mulching is the best way to destroy it. Then watch the patch closely and cut off immediately any stray shoot that may appear above its surface. Nothing but persistent watching and the careful cutting off of all parts above the ground will eradicate this weed."

Prof. Ten Eyck, quoted in Wallaces' Farmer, states that the only method of culture applicable to large areas which promises any great degree of control or destruction of the pest is very late fall or winter plowing. The plots which were plowed in November (no plowing was done later than November 20) showed a very scattering and feeble growth of bindweed on April 26, the date of inspection.

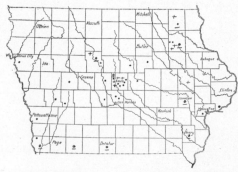

FIG. 142-B. Distribution of European Morning-glory.

FIG. 142-C. European Morning-glory or Bindweed (*Convolvulus arvensis*). Common in gardens and becoming frequent in Iowa.

(*Photograph by Colburn.*)

The weeds were thinner and more feeble also on the unplowed land which produced a crop of sowed cane or sowed kaffir last season, than they were on any of the lots cultivated in intertilled crops.

Clover Dodder (*Cuscuta Epithymum* Murr.).

Description.—A spreading, climbing plant; yellowish or reddish with a few minute scales in place of leaves; flowers whitish or pinkish in heads, small, globular, urn-shaped; cylindrical tube longer than the nearly erect, acute sepals; scales large-toothed; stigma elongated; style longer than the ovary; stamens exserted, fruit in capsules.

Distribution.—This weed has long been known as troublesome in Europe and has been more or less common in the Rocky mountains on clover and alfalfa. For some years it has been frequent in the east; becoming more abundant on clover and alfalfa.

Extermination.—Where the plant occurs the clover should be
cut at once and burned. The patch or field should be sown to
another crop, preferably to small grain or with corn.

Clark and Fletcher recommend the following treatment: "As
soon as the pest is noticed, the infected patches should be at once
mown with a scythe and the refuse removed and destroyed. Fields

FIG. 143. Distribution of Clover Dodder (*Cuscuta Epithymum*).

badly contaminated should be plowed before the seed has formed,
or the crop cut early for hay and the land then plowed. Clover
seed should never be taken from fields infested with this pest."

The Wisconsin Farmer states: "The problem of dodder control is strongly influenced by the character of the crop infested.
Red clover remains but two, or at most but three years without
reseeding. If the dodder is prevented from seeding it should be
eradicated within this time, or at least not interfere with the
course of crop rotation. Alfalfa should remain indefinitely, and
if dodder reseeds itself its control becomes much more difficult or
impossible. This is the prevailing condition in the west. The fact
that the small-seeded alfalfa dodder of the west has not become
established in the east is of special interest in this connection.
Clover dodder appears likely to prove the most troublesome in
alfalfa culture in the east.

"If the dodder occurs only in patches in the field it usually can
be controlled by hand methods. If it covers the greater part or all
of the field, plowing under the stand will probably be found
necessary. It then becomes important to know how far the crop
can be utilized without reseeding the land to dodder."

Field Dodder (*Cuscuta arvensis* Beyrich.).

Description.—Stems pale and slender, filiform; flowers rather
small, in sessile clusters; calyx with 5 obtuse broad lobes; corolla
with a short, wide tube, inflexed points, 5-lobed, acute or acumi-

nate, about one-half as long as the tube, tips reflexed; scales large and deeply fringed; stigmas capitate; capsules globose, indehiscent.

Distribution.—This parasitic plant occurs on shrubs, clover and other herbs from Massachusetts to Wisconsin and westward. Introduced with clover and alfalfa seed into Iowa.

The dodders are spread largely through such commercial seeds

Figure 144   Figure 144-A   Figure 144-B

FIG. 144.   Field Dodder (*Cuscuta arvensis*).
FIG. 144-A.   Flax Dodder (*Cuscuta Epilinum*).
FIG. 144-B.   Lesser Clover Dodder, Thyme Dodder (*Cuscuta Epithymum*).
(*Michigan Weeds—Mich. Agr. Exp. Sta. Bull. 267.*)

as flax, clover and alfalfa. Alfalfa dodder is a somewhat troublesome weed in sections of the United States and Europe where
alfalfa is grown; by importation it has made its way into the
Mississippi valley in recent years. There has been much complaint
about the appearance of clover and field dodder in the Mississippi
valley, largely spread, of course, through commercial seeds. The
dodder may be exterminated in the following way:

FIG. 144-C.   Distribution of Field Dodder.

Extermination.—The herbicidal treatment may be used to destroy
dodder. For this purpose a liberal application of a 10 per cent
solution of copper sulphate will be found efficacious.

As additional methods, the European investigators recommend a
strong solution of salt, of sulphide of lime, of carbolic acid, or of
sulphate of iron. These solutions destroy the dodder when found
in the vegetative condition, but should seed have formed, it will
be necessary to take the additional precaution of cutting and
burning the dodder, after the application of the herbicide. It
should be remembered that these solutions will not be effective
unless they come in direct contact with the plant. They will
injure the clover plant as well.

*If the patch is a small one, it is advisable to mow it, to rake the
material into a pile, and after allowing it to dry to burn it. The
field should be watched carefully for reappearance of the weed,
for if seed is formed, young dodder plants will make their appearance upon the new growth of clover. It is best therefore to follow
the mowing by hoeing if the spot is a small one and to continue
this for several weeks until all danger of infection is passed. Dewey
recommends keeping the soil stirred for about two inches to prevent any young plants from coming in contact with the clover.*

Wallaces' Farmer suggests the following treatment: "Where our readers find this yellow vine twining around their clover or alfalfa they must act promptly and effectively. If when they discover dodder they will cut it off close to the ground before it seeds no damage will follow, as dodder is an annual. It will not do, however, to trust to the scythe or mower, for the least particle of dodder which remains attached to the stubble will grow much more certainly than any corn or wheat will grow. Where a whole field is infested perhaps the safest way is to mow it before the dodder goes to seeding, use it for hay, and then plow it up for a crop the next year. Or, if we would rather lose a crop of hay than lose the stand, mow it, let it dry, and burn it, so as to destroy the dodder in the stubble."

HYDROPHYLLACEAE, WATERLEAF FAMILY.

The common waterleaf belongs to this family. Representatives of the family are more numerous in the west and south than in the east and north.

Common Ellisia (*Ellisia Nyctelea* L.).

Description.—Minutely or sparingly roughish hairy; stems

FIG. 145. Ellisia *(Ellisia Nyctelea)*. Common in early spring fields.
(Photograph by Colburn.)

forked, 6 to 14 inches high; leaves pinnately parted into 7 to 13 sparingly cut-toothed divisions; peduncles 1-flowered, opposite the leaves; flowers with calyx lobes lanceolate; pointed corolla white; seed large.

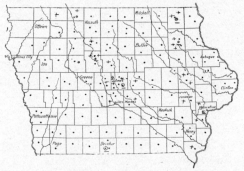

FIG. 145-A.   Distribution of Ellisia.

Distribution.—The ellisia is a spring weed found in waste, shady places; common everywhere in Iowa and a weed in cultivated fields. It is distributed from New Jersey to Kansas, and in the northwest territory.

Extermination.—Infested areas may be sown thickly with some leguminous crop, like clover, or blue grass may be started in these places. The weed is easily destroyed by cultivation.

BORAGINACEAE, BORAGE FAMILY.

Comfrey, bugloss, alkanet, blueweed and borage belong to this family. Many of the plants are scattered by animals by means of the burs.

Hound's Tongue (*Cynoglossum officinale* L.).

Description.—A coarse biennial herb, clothed with short, soft hairs; lower leaves oblong or oblong-lanceolate, the upper closely sessile with a slightly heart-shaped base; racemes nearly bractless, elongated in fruit; divisions of the calyx ovate, lanceolate, acute; corolla reddish purple, rarely white; nutlets flat on the broad upper face, splitting away at maturity.

Distribution.—Hound's tongue grows in fields and waste places, especially westward from New England to Quebec, Ontario, Minnesota, Manitoba and Kansas. This weed is common in some pastures in Boone, Story, Dubuque, Clayton and Allamakee counties. Widely scattered by animals. The burs attach themselves to their fleece.

FIG. 146. Hound's Tongue *(Cynoglossum officinale)*. In pastures. The burs are scattered by sheep.
(Photograph by Colburn.)

FIG. 146-A. Distribution of Hound's Tongue.

Extermination.—This weed is easily killed, if cut a few inches below the surface of the ground. The "seeds" are, however, widely scattered by animals; stray plants should be looked for.

Wild Comfrey (*Cynoglossum virginianum* L.).

Description.—Perennial hirsute herb with simple stem 2 to 3 feet high; root leaves large, rough; stem leaves lanceolate-oblong,

Fig. 147. Wild Comfrey (*Cynoglossum virginianum*). Woodland pastures.
(*Photograph by Colburn.*)

Fig. 147-A. Distribution of Wild Comfrey.

clasping by a heart-shaped base; flowers on long peduncles, pale blue, small; fruit broad, nutlets echinate, convex on the upper surface.

Distribution.—Wild comfrey is common in woods of the central Mississippi valley, New Brunswick to Ontario, Florida, Louisiana to Texas. Common in eastern to central Iowa in woods. The burs are scattered by becoming attached to the fur of domestic animals.

Extermination.—Sometimes persistent in newly made fields in the northern states. Cultivation for a few seasons will remove the weed.

Beggar's Lice (*Lappula virginiana* L.).

Description.—A coarse, pubescent biennial 2 to 4 feet high; lower leaves ovate, orbicular, cordate, long-petioled; stem leaves ovate-oblong or oval; flowers nearly white; globose nutlets which are flattened and barbed on the back.

FIG. 148. Beggar's Lice (*Lappula virginiana*). Common in woodland pastures.
(Photograph by Colburn.)

Distribution.—Common especially in woods northward, from New Brunswick to Wisconsin and Minnesota, also from Kansas to Louisiana. Common on borders of woods and in wooded pastures in Iowa.

Extermination.—The first season the plant should be cut a few inches below the surface of the ground. When the plants shoot up the second season give the same treatment. The plants are disseminated by animals. Stray plants which are likely to occur along fences should be looked for and destroyed.

Stickseed (*Lappula echinata* Gilibert).

Description.—An erect annual 1 foot to two feet high; pale, leafy, hispid with erect branches; leaves linear or linear-oblong; racemes 1-sided; bracteolate; calyx segments lanceolate; corolla blue; nutlets rough-granulate or tuberculate on the back, the margins with a double row of slender prickles.

Distribution.—Stickseed is a weedy plant in Europe, where it is native. It is abundant in waste places along roadsides from eastern Canada and New England to Minnesota, Kansas and British Columbia. Common along roadsides and gravelly places and rocky hillsides in eastern Iowa, notably in Dubuque, Clayton, Allamakee and Winneshiek counties, found rarely in Story county.

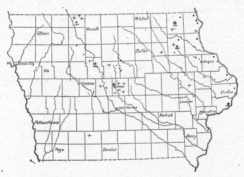

FIG. 149.   Distribution of Stickseed.

Extermination.—The plant should be destroyed before the seeds form, by cutting it off below the surface of the ground.

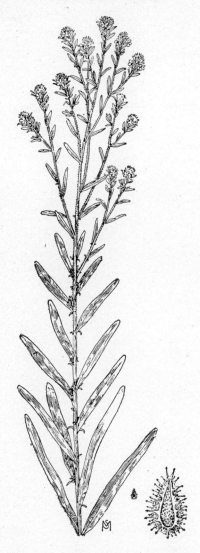

FIG. 149-A.   Stickseed, Bur Seed (*Lappula echinata*).   Along roadsides.
(*From Mich. Agr. Coll. Exp. Sta. Bull.*)

Corn Gromwell (*Lithospermum arvense* L.).

Description.—A pubescent annual with stems 6 to 12 inches high, and bright green, lanceolate, linear or oblong, sessile leaves; flowers sessile or nearly so, white; calyx segments longer than the corolla tube; corolla funnel-form; nutlets smooth.

FIG. 150. Corn Gromwell ōr Puccoon (*Lithospermum arvense*). A common roadside and field weed of Europe. Southern Iowa and Missouri. Small white flowers. (*Photograph by Colburn.*)

Distribution.—This is a common weed in fields in the east, and may be looked for in southeastern Iowa. It is one of the most common weeds in grain fields in Europe.

Extermination.—The plants are easily destroyed. As the seed coat is hard, the seeds probably retain their vitality for some time.

VERBENACEAE, VERBENA FAMILY.

The common cultivated verbena and lemon verbena belong to this family.

White Vervain (*Verbena urticaefolia* L.).

Description.—A tall slightly pubescent perennial; leaves oblong, acute, coarsely toothed, petioled; spikes long, slender, flowers small, white.

Distribution.—This weed is a native of tropical America. It is a weed of thickets and waste, rather low grounds.

Fig. 151. White Vervain *(Verbena urticaefolia).*
(Photograph by Photo Section, Ia. Agr. Exp. Sta.)

Extermination.—White vervain is readily destroyed by cutting.

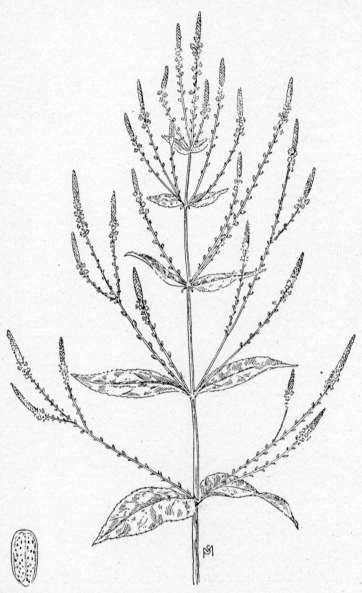

FIG. 151-A. White Vervain, Nettle-leaved Vervain *(Verbena urticaefolia)*.
(Mich. Agr. Exp. Sta.)

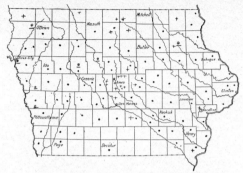

FIG. 151-B. Distribution of White Vervain.

Blue Vervain (*Verbena hastata* L.).

Description.—A tall perennial 4 to 6 feet high; leaves lanceolate, coming to a point, cut-serrate, lower leaves often lobed; flowers in erect, linear, corymbed spikes, violet-blue or rarely pink; trichomes simple, long, acuminate.

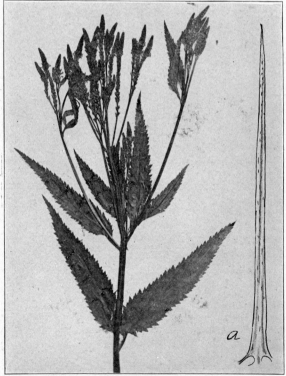

FIG. 152. Blue Vervain *(Verbena hastata)*. Common in low pastures and meadows.
a Trichome.
(Photograph by Quade, a, drawing by Charlotte M. King.)

Distribution.—This vervain is found in damp situations in every county in the state of Iowa; also to the Atlantic coast and westward and southward. Especially in low meadows, hybrids between this and the nettle leaved vervain are not uncommon.

FIG. 152-A. Blue Vervain (*Verbena hastata*).
(*Photograph by Photo Section, Ia. Agr. Exp. Sta.*)

FIG. 152-B. Distribution of Blue Vervain.

Extermination.—This weed, though abundant in low grounds, seldom gives trouble in fields which have been drained and thoroughly cultivated. It spreads chiefly by the seed.

Hoary Vervain (*Verbena stricta* Vent.).

Description.—A soft, pubescent perennial 1 foot to 3 feet high; leaves downy, ovate or oblong, serrate and sessile; large blue

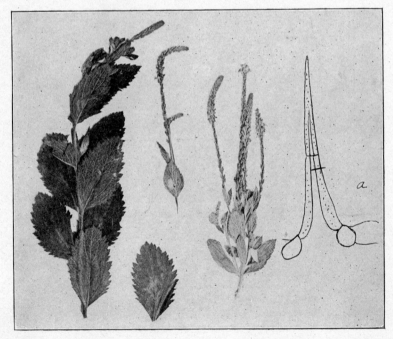

FIG. 153. Hoary Vervain (*Verbena stricta*). Common in pastures. Plant with blue flowers. Plant hair, trichome, to the rightt
(*General aspect photographed by Colburn. a, drawn by Charlotte M. King.*)

flowers borne in a dense sessile spike, 6 inches to 1 foot long; trichomes several-celled, thick-walled, pitted.

Fig. 153-A. Hoary Vervain (*Verbena stricta*).
(*Photograph by Photo Section, Ia. Agr. Exp. Sta.*)

Distribution.—Hoary vervain grows in dry soils of Ohio to the prairies of Wyoming, New Mexico and Texas. It is commonly naturalized eastward and is a common weed in every part of Iowa.

This weed is especially common in gravelly or sandy soils eastward; westward frequent in pastures with heavier soils.

FIG. 153-B. Distribution of Hoary Vervain.

Extermination.—This weed is easily destroyed by cultivation.

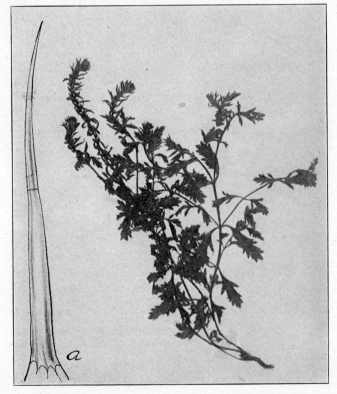

FIG. 154.   Prostrate Vervain *(Verbena bracteosa).* a, Plant hair or trichome. Common along roadsides, streets and gravelly places; small blue flowers.
(Photograph by Quade, a, drawing by Charlotte M. King.)

Common or Prostrate Vervain (*Verbena bracteosa* Michx.).

Description.—A widely spreading, hairy annual; leaves wedge-lanceolate, cut-pinnatifid or sometimes 3-cleft; flowers in spikes, with large bracts, small, purple; trichomes few-celled from a broad several-celled base.

Distribution.—Prostrate vervain is common in waste places, road-sides, walks, gravelly and sandy fields from Virginia to Wisconsin and Minnesota and southward.

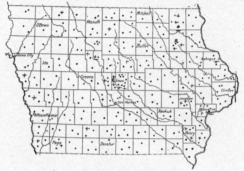

FIG. 154-A.   Distribution of Prostrate Vervain.

Extermination.—It is easily exterminated by cultivation.

LABIATAE, MINT FAMILY.

The common peppermint, scarlet sage, catnip, pennyroyal, thyme and basil belong to this family. All are aromatic plants.

American Germander (*Teucrium canadense* L.).

Description.—A perennial, downy, erect herb 1 foot to 3 feet high with running root-stocks; leaves pubescent, short-petioled, downy beneath, ovate, lanceolate, serrate with a rounded base; floral leaves small; flowers in ample wandlike spikes; calyx 5-toothed, the upper lobes obtuse; corolla purple, rose or whitish.

Distribution.—From New England to Mexico and northwest to Manitoba. Common in Iowa alluvial grounds in pastures, mead-ows, grain fields, etc. It spreads rapidly by its underground rhizomes.

Extermination.—A very troublesome weed in the north. It is, however, an excellent bee-plant. Should have the same treatment as quack grass. The root-stocks should be exposed and allowed to dry.   After plowing the field follow with a disc and harrow once a week after the small grain crop is removed.

L. H. Pammel in the Weekly Register says: ''Germander is a troublesome weed found in many parts of northern Iowa.   It produces root-stocks, very much as in the case of mint and quack grass.   Each severed portion produces a new plant, and for this

Fig. 155.   Germander *(Teucrium canadense)*.
(Photograph by Photo Section, Ia. Agr. Exp. Sta.)

reason it is somewhat difficult to destroy. The only way to exterminate this weed is by thorough cultivation. Plowing in the fall during the dry season, then plowing again in the spring and giving thorough cultivation during the growing season should destroy the weed without difficulty.''

FIG. 155-A. Germander *(Teucrium canadense)*.
(Photograph by Photo Section, Ia. Agr. Exp. Sta.)

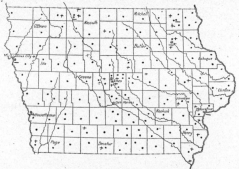

FIG. 155-B.   Distribution of Germander.

Catnip (*Nepeta Cataria* L.).

Description.—A perennial, erect herb, 1 foot to 3 feet high; leaves ovate, cordate, coarsely serrate, petiolate, whitish, downy underneath; flowers in cymose clusters; corolla whitish, dotted with purple; trichomes several-celled, rough, thick-walled. The plant has a sharp pungent odor.

Distribution.—Catnip spreads rapidly by its underground root-stocks and seeds. It has become one of the most common weeds of roadsides in Story, Marshall, Linn, Webster, Allamakee, Clayton and Winneshiek counties.

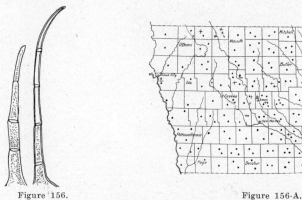

Figure 156.   Figure 156-A.
FIG. 156.   Plant hair or trichome from leaf of Catnip.
(*Drawing by Charlotte M. King.*)
FIG. 156-A.   Distribution of Catnip.

Extermination.—Give the same treatment as for motherwort.

Chemical Composition.—According to the University of Minnesota* the chemical composition is as follows:

---

*Snyder: Bull. Univ. Minn. Agr. Exp. 101.

Dry matter	Crude protein	Ether extract	Nitrogen free extract and fiber	Ash
94.30	22.25	2.66	63.07	12.77

FIG. 156-B. Catnip (*Nepeta Cataria*).
(*Photograph by Photo Section, Ia. Agr. Exp. Sta.*)

FIG. 156-C. Catnip *(Nepeta Cataria)* showing root system.
(Photograph by Photo Section, Ia. Agr. Exp. Sta.)

Ground Ivy or Creeping Charley (*Nepeta hederacea* (L.) Trevisan).
Description.—A creeping, trailing perennial, with leaves all

alike, petioled, round, kidney-shaped, crenate, smooth, green on both sides; flowers light blue in axillary whorls of about 6, appearing in early spring and summer.

Distribution.—Ground ivy is native to Europe, widely naturalized in the northern states, especially in shady places. Common

FIG. 157.   Ground Ivy or Creeping Charley *(Nepeta hederacea)*. Common in
some gardens.
(Photograph by E. H. Richardson.)

everywhere in Iowa, especially in Story, Boone, Marshall and Clayton counties.

FIG. 157-A. Distribution of Ground Ivy.

Extermination.—This weedy plant is somewhat difficult to exterminate in lawns, but can be destroyed by thorough cultivation.

Self-heal, Heal-all, Carpenter Weed (*Prunella vulgaris* L.).

Description.—Self-heal is a low, perennial weed with ovate-oblong, entire or toothed leaves, hairy or smoth; flowers collected in heads of 3-flowered clusters, corolla violet or flesh-color, or rarely pale in color, longer than the purplish calyx which is tubular bell-shaped.

Distribution.—This plant is widely distributed in northern United States, westward across the continent in clay soils and woods, also from Newfoundland to Florida. This weed is especially common not only in woods but in fields in eastern Iowa, on the Mississippi loess.

FIG. 158. Distribution of Self-heal.

Extermination.—This weed is not difficult to exterminate by

giving cultivation with a cultivator and hoe.   The weed is mainly
spread by seed, which is not uncommon in clover seed.

FIG. 158-A.   Self-heal, Heal-all (*Prunella vulgaris*).
(*Photograph by Photo Section, Ia. Agr. Exp. Sta.*)

Henbit (*Lamium amplexicaule* L.).

Description.—This is a winter annual or biennial weed, which is becoming too common in states east of us. It has low stems and rounded crenate marginal leaves clasping the stem. Flowers are bright red purple, in whorls. An early flowering plant.

Distribution.—Rare as yet in Iowa. In both waste and cultivated grounds at Keokuk and Boone.

Extermination.—Thorough cultivation will eradicate it. Treat the same way as peppergrass.

FIG. 159. Henbit, Lamium *(Lamium amplexicaule).*
(Photograph by Photo Section, Ia. Agr. Exp. Sta.)

Dead Nettle (*Lamium album* L.).

Description.—A medium sized hairy perennial, with ovate heart-shaped petioled leaves. Flowers with slender spreading calyx teeth, corolla, a whitish tube upwardly curved, obliquely contracted near the base, lateral lobes of lower lip with a long slender tooth.

Distribution.—Not uncommon in the eastern states. Escaped in some places in Iowa, found in the streets of New Hampton.

Extermination.—Easily exterminated by cultivation.

Motherwort (*Leonurus Cardiaca* L.).

Description.—Tall perennial herb with erect stem, 2 to 6 feet high; leaves long-pointed, the lower round and palmately lobed, the upper crenate at the base, 3-cleft; flowers pale purple, in close axillary whorls; corolla bearded. The calyx lobes sharp pointed.

FIG. 160. Motherwort *(Leonurus Cardiaca).* A common weed in waste places and gardens.
(Photographs by Colburn and Ada Hayden.)

FIG. 160-A.   Distribution of Motherwort.

Distribution.—The weed is native to Europe. It is widely naturalized in the northern states and is common in waste places in Iowa, Story, Polk, Clayton and Allamakee counties.

Extermination.—This perennial weed can be exterminated by plowing, followed by frequent cultivation.

Hedge Nettle, Woundwort (*Stachys palustris* L.).

Description.—A leafy perennial 1 foot to 3½ feet tall, with thickened root-stocks freely stolon-bearing. Stems hirsute in the angles, leaves mostly sessile, crenate-serrate, downy or hairy. Whorls 6 to 10 flowers, pale purplish in color.

Distribution.—Found in wet grounds, borders of ditches, etc.

FIG. 161.   Hedge Nettle (*Stachys palustris*).
(*Photograph by Ada Hayden.*)

Extermination.—The plant may be killed after drainage, by cutting and cultivation.

Fig. 162.   Smooth Hedge Nettle (*Stachys tenuifolia*) showing root system.
(Photograph by Photo Section, Ia. Agr. Exp. Sta.)

Smooth Hedge Nettle (*Stachys tenuifolia* Willd.).

Description.—A perennial, smooth, slender branching plant 1 foot to 2½ feet in height. Leaves lanceolate, thin, tapering. Flower clusters in terminal spikes and in upper leaf axils. Flowers pale red.

Distribution.—In moist grounds.

Extermination.—By cultivation, after drainage.

Lance-leaved Salvia, Blue Sage (*Salvia lanceaefolia* Poir.).

Description.—A slightly pubescent or nearly smooth annual, 1 foot to 2½ feet high; leaves petiolate, lanceolate serrate or nearly

FIG. 163.   Lance-leaved Salvia, Blue Sage *(Salvia lanceaefolia).*
(Drawn by Ada Hayden.)

entire; flowers in interrupted, erect spike like clusters; calyx bi-labiate, upper entire, the lower 2-cleft; corolla blue, slightly ex-serted; stamens with long connective, attached to a sterile anther which blocks the throat of the corolla; pistil 1, deeply 4-lobed. This plant is related to the cultivated garden salvias.

Distribution.—Blue sage is found chiefly west of Missouri river, in Kansas, Nebraska, Arizona, Missouri and Texas, and is introduced also in Ohio and Indiana. It is common in Iowa in Pot-tawattamie, Fremont, Monona and Woodbury counties, less common in Story, Boone, Polk and Muscatine counties.

Extermination.—This weed is easily exterminated by culti-vation. The plant should not be allowed to produce seeds.

FIG. 163-A.   Distribution of Lance-leaved Salvia.

Horsemint (*Monarda mollis* L.).

Description.—A tall branching plant with ovate canescent leaves. Flowers in large attractive terminal clusters, lilac in color. The calyx of the flower is hairy in the throat. A very odorous plant.

Distribution.—General over the state, in dry soils.

Extermination.—The plant is killed when land is cultivated.

FIG. 164. Horsemint *(Monarda mollis)*.
(Photograph by Photo Section, Ia. Agr. Exp. Sta.)

Peppermint (*Mentha piperita* L.).

Description.—A glabrous, fragrant perennial; leaves ovate-oblong, serrate, acute; spikes loose. A smooth pungent tasting herb.

Distribution.—This plant is frequently found along brooks.

Extermination.—The effectual means of killing it is to clear the ground of the root-stocks by digging.

FIG. 165. Peppermint *(Mentha piperita)*. In some gardens.
(Photograph by Colburn.)

Mint *(Mentha arvensis* L.).

Description.—This perennial weed has freely branching stems 1 foot to 1½ feet high, retrorsely pubescent, leaves oblong to ovate, rounded at the base, minutely pubescent, closely serrate, petioled or nearly sessile; flowers white, pink or violet. The variety *canadensis* has lanceolate to oblong-lanceolate, pubescent leaves and is the common form in Iowa in low grounds. Several other mints occur in Iowa, as spearmint *(Mentha spicata)* with oblong or ovate-lanceolate unequally-serrate leaves.

Distribution.—This Eurasian species occurs from Newfoundland to Nebraska and the Pacific coast.

Extermination.—Easily exterminated by giving thorough cultivation and dragging the soil to bring the root-stocks to the surface of the ground.

FIG. 166.   Mint *(Mentha arvensis* var. *canadensis)*.   Common in low meadows;
whitish flowers.   Plant with odor of peppermint.
(Photograph by Colburn.)

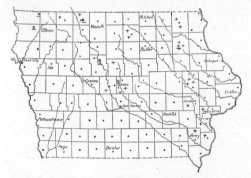

FIG. 166-A.   Distribution of Mint.

SOLANACEAE, NIGHTSHADE FAMILY.

Potato, tomato, tobacco, ground cherry, jimson weed, flowering
tobacco and black henbane belong to this family.

Common Nightshade or Stubbleberry (*Solanum nigrum* L.).

Description.—Annual, low-branched and often spreading; glab-

Fig. 167.   Black Nightshade *(Solanum nigrum)*.   Shady places, gardens and fields.
(*Photograph by Colburn.*)

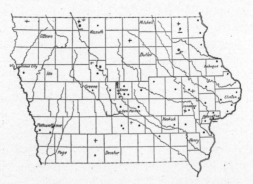

Fig. 167-A.   Distribution of Black Nightshade.

FIG. 167-B. Black Nightshade *(Solanum nigrum)*.
(Drawn by C. M. King.)

rous or hairy, hairs roughened on the angles; leaves ovate, petioled, flowers white in small, umbel-like, drooping, lateral clusters; calyx spreading, the lobes obtuse, much shorter than the white corolla; berries glabrous, globose, black; occasionally large.

Distribution.—It is found in northern United States; abundant everywhere in Iowa in shady grounds and fields. A cosmopolitan weed.

Extermination.—It is easily exterminated by cultivation.

Horse Nettle *(Solanum carolinense* L.).

Description.—A deep-rooting perennial, propagating freely by its underground root-stocks and roots, the running roots often being 3 feet long; stem 1 foot to 2 feet high, somewhat straggling, half shrubby at the base; stem hairy or merely roughish with minute hairs which are star-shaped, also armed with numerous stout, subulate, yellowish prickles; leaves oblong or sometimes ovate, obtusely sinuate-toothed or lobed, or deeply cut, 2 to 4 inches long; flowers borne in one-sided racemes; calyx consists of slender lobes, corolla light blue or white, an inch or less in diameter; flowers followed by yellow globose berries one-half to three-fourths inch in diameter; small yellowish seeds, a little less than one-twelfth inch long, minutely roughened. Flowers and yellow berries resemble those of the potato. The berries have a very disagreeable odor. The spiny character of the leaves and the further resemblance of the flower to the potato should render it easy of recognition.

Distribution.—Horse nettle is indigenous to the southern states, but now occurs from Connecticut to northern Iowa. This weed is abundant in southern Iowa and has been reported from Floyd, Story, Boone and Linn counties; in the north half of the state, however, it is a recent introduction. It is spreading rapidly.

Extermination.—There are two methods of propagation; one by seeds, the other by perennial roots. The weed is so exceedingly tenacious that it is almost impossible to remove it when fully established. The following methods have been suggested:

Smothering. This is an effective method of removing the plant. For this purpose sudan grass or sorghum is the most suitable crop. If the soil is not already rich, a liberal dressing of barnyard manure should be applied during the winter or spring. The soil should be harrowed or cultivated frequently until the time of seeding, which may be any time during the months of May or June. This cultivation will prevent the weed growth, and will also assist in the retention of moisture. If the seed is sown in drills about two pounds of seed per acre is sufficient quantity and three pounds if sown broadcast. When the crop has attained a rank growth it may be pastured or removed and fed to stock. Where land is lacking in vegetable matter it is good practice to plow the crop under when it is properly matured. The latter is not necessary when the object is to destroy the nettle, as the rank growth of the crop is very effective in smothering the weed.

Hoed crops. Planting of corn or roots is a method much in vogue for the destruction of this vile intruder. As in the previous method the plant should be kept down before seeding time. When the crop appears above the ground the use of horse and hand hoe should not be sparing. When the welfare of the crop prohibits the use of the horse hoe, the hand hoe should be used at intervals until the crop is removed; even after this, it is sometimes necessary to give attention to the pest. There is no question about the effectiveness of this mode of treatment if properly carried out, but negligence during the latter part of the season often results in failure.

FIG. 168.   Horse Nettle *(Solanum carolinense)* showing root system.
(Photograph by Photo Section, Ia. Agr. Exp. Sta.)

The Iowa Homestead suggests the following treatment: "Corn land that has grown up to horse nettles this year should be burned over, if possible, next spring, as this will destroy many of the seeds. Afterwards the land should be plowed lightly and kept cultivated at intervals until somewhat late in the season. A surface cultivator will be all that is necessary, and this need not be run deeper than two or three inches, just enough to effectively cut the plants off below the surface. By checking the growth several times before planting corn the root system becomes much weakened, so that ordinary cultivation the remaining part of the season will often keep them completely in check. Where nettles have been going to seed for a number of years it may require considerable time to free

FIG. 168-A. Horse Nettle *(Solanum carolinense)*. Deep rooted perennial, roots sometimes extend 3 to 4 feet in the soil. Flowers and berries somewhat like those of
the potato. Common in southern Iowa.
(Photograph by Colburn.)

the land because these will germinate as they are brought near the
surface by the various plowings. However, it should be kept in
mind that any perennial root system may be killed outright in one
season if it is not allowed to develop roots or stems.''

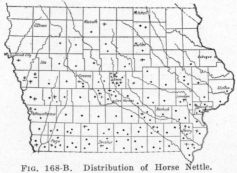

FIG. 168-B. Distribution of Horse Nettle.

Dr. C. E. Bessey in Breeder's Gazette recommends as follows: "To get rid of it the best thing is first not to allow the weed to get a good start, as its deep roots are hard to get out. Second, if it has a good start, the plants must be cut down frequently so as to prevent their seeding and thus starting new plants. In the third place, the deep roots must be killed by digging out or by smothering. This can be done by using a very heavy dense crop like some of the sorghums, or by covering the patch with wet manure. Of course constant stirring of the soil will kill them. It will pay to watch this weed wherever it appears."

Buffalo Bur (*Solanum rostratum* Dunal.).

Description.—Herbaceous; woody when old, somewhat hoary or yellowish, 8 inches to 2 feet high, covered with copious stellate pubescence; branches and main stems, where it begins to branch, covered with sharp yellow prickles; leaves somewhat melon-like, 1 to 3 times pinnatifid, lobes roundish or obtuse and repand, covered with soft pubescence; hairs stellate, flowers yellow, corolla gamopetalous, about an inch in diameter, nearly regular, the sharp lobes of the corolla broadly ovate; stamens 5, declined, anthers

FIG. 169. Buffalo Bur *(Solanum rostratum)* showing root system.
(Photograph by Photo Section, Ia. Agr. Exp. Sta.)

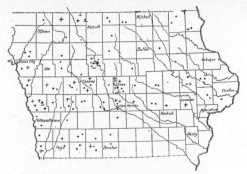

FIG. 169-A.   Distribution of Buffalo Bur.

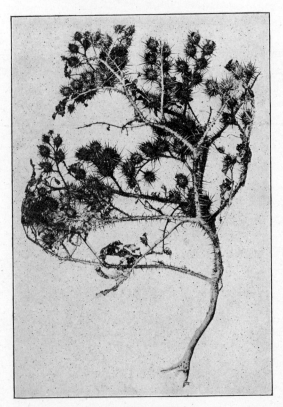

FIG. 169-B.   Buffalo Bur (*Solanum rostratum*).   Pastures, gardens, railways, etc.
(*Photograph by Colburn.*)

tapering upward, linear-lanceolate, dissimilar, the lowest much larger and longer, with an incurved beak, hence the technical name *rostratum;* style much declined; fruit a berry but enclosed by the close-fitting or prickly calyx, which has suggested the common name buffalo bur; pedicels in fruit erect; seeds thick, irregular, round or somewhat longer than broad, wrinkled, showing numerous small pits and surrounded by a gelatinous substance.

Distribution.—Buffalo bur is originally native of the plains region, between the Missouri river and the Rocky Mountains. It has spread eastward in the northern states and extensively in Texas, Mississippi and Arkansas. It is not infrequent from Tennessee to New York. This weed is widely scattered in small patches in many parts of the state of Iowa. It is spreading rapidly in Story, Polk, Linn, Pottawattamie and Marshall counties, and at Sidney, Hamburg, Glenwood, Missouri Valley and Sioux City.

It is the original host of the potato beetle.

Extermination.—Inasmuch as this weed is an annual, it can be

FIG. 170. Ground Cherry (*Physalis pubescens* L.).
(*Photograph by Ia. Agr. Exp. Sta.*)

easily exterminated by cutting off the young plants at the ground and this should be done before the pods are formed. If plants are older they should be cut off and burned.

The Iowa Homestead says concerning this weed: "On account of the fact that the buffalo bur is an annual its destruction or eradication is simply a matter of preventing it from maturing its seed. Corn fields that are badly infested may need but little attention after the regular time for laying the corn by, for which purpose the one horse cultivator may be pressed into use."

Ground Cherry (*Physalis pubescens* L.).

Description.—This ground cherry is pubescent, with viscid hairs. It is an annual branching plant, with somewhat angled leaves. The flower has a purple spot about the center; anthers violet. The berry is greenish or yellow.

Distribution.—In open rich grounds and gardens.

Extermination.—Controlled by cultivation and by cutting before seeds ripen.

Virginia Ground Cherry (*Physalis lanceolata* Michx.).

Description.—A hirsute perennial with short, stiff hairs, sometimes nearly smooth; forms short, stout underground stems; leaves oblong-ovate to lanceolate, sparingly angulate-toothed or more often entire; flowers in axillary peduncles, calyx hirsute, corolla

FIG. 171. Virginia Ground Cherry (*Physalis lanceolata*).
(Photograph by Photo Section, Ia. Agr. Exp. Sta.)

yellowish with a dark eye; berry reddish. The *P. virginiana* Mill., is also an erect perennial with narrowly ovate acutish leaves or acutish or rounded teeth, corolla pale yellow. The *P. subglabrata* MacKenzie and Bush, has ovate or ovate-oblong leaves, oblique at the base, entire or repand, and brownish corolla; berry large, reddish or purple. The *P. heterophylla* is perennial, leaves obtuse repand, or obtusely toothed; trichomes several-celled, glandular and non-glandular.

Distribution.—The *P. lanceolata* is found in southern Iowa and southward; the *P. virginiana* is common everywhere in Iowa, in dry gravelly soil, from Connecticut to Iowa and southward; the *P. subglabrata* is distributed from Rhode Island to Minnesota and southward.

Extermination.—All of the perennial ground cherries are diffi-

FIG. 171-A. Distribution of Virginia Ground Cherry (*Physalis virginiana*).

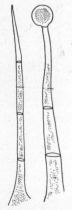

Fig. 171-B.   Figure 171-C.
FIG. 171-B. Trichome or plant hair from leaf of Ground Cherry (*Physalis heterophylla*).
(*Drawing by Charlotte M. King.*)
FIG. 171-C. Distribution of Ground Cherry (*Physalis heterophylla*).

cult to destroy because of the strong underground root-stocks which freely spread the weed. These plants are also scattered by seed. To exterminate them, plow shallowly and expose the roots to the sun; give frequent cultivation.

Jimson Weed, Thorn-apple (*Datura Stramonium* L.).

Description.—A glabrous annual with green stem, sinuate-toothed leaves and white corolla.

Purple Thorn-apple, Purple Stramonium, or Jimson Weed (*Datura Tatula* L.).

Description.—A glabrous annual from a few inches to 5 feet high; stem purplish; leaves thin, ovate, acute or acuminate; flowers consisting of a 5-toothed calyx and a 5-lobed funnel form corolla, with stamens included; filiform filaments inserted below the middle of the corolla tube; capsule globular, prickly, 4-valved and 2-celled. The plant has a strong odor.

FIG. 172. Jimson Weed (*Datura Stramonium*).
(*Photograph by Ada Hayden.*)

Distribution.—Both species are abundant in fields and waste places from New England to North Dakota and Texas. The Jimson weeds are originally native to India and were naturalized from Europe.

Extermination.—Both of the Jimson weeds are easily destroyed by cultivation. They produce an enormous amount of seed, which

Figure 172-A.   Figure 172-B.

FIG. 172-A. Jimson Weed or Thorn-apple *(Datura Stramonium).* *a,* flowering spray;
b, fruiting capsule.
(U. S. Dept. Agr.)
FIG. 172-B. Jimson Weed *(Datura Stramonium)* fruit.
(Photograph by Photo Section, Ia. Agr. Exp. Sta.)

retains its vitality for a considerable length of time. The seeds
have been found to germinate after lying buried in the ground a
number of years.

FIG. 172-C. Distribution of Thorn-apple *(Datura Stramonium).*

FIG. 172-D.   Purple Jimson Weed *(Datura Tatula)*.   Barnyards, roadsides.
(Photograph by Colburn.)

FIG. 172-E.   Distribution of Purple Jimson Weed *(Datura Tatula)*.

FIG. 172-F.   Jimson weed in corn field.
(Photograph by Victor Felter).

SCROPHULARIACEAE, MULLEIN FAMILY.

The Snapdragon and the Simpson honey plant belong to this family.

Mullein (*Verbascum Thapsus* L.).

Description.—A tall, densely woolly annual or biennial herb 2 to 6 feet high; leaves oblong, thick, covered with branched hairs, the basal leaves margined, petioled; flowers in long dense spikes; corolla rotate, yellow or rarely white; stamens unequal, the three upper shorter, woolly, with short anthers; the two lower smooth with larger anthers; trichomes many-celled, branched with central axis.

FIG. 173.   Figure 173-A.

FIG. 173.   Glandular trichome from viscid pod of Moth Mullein (*Verbascum Blattaria*).
(Drawing by L. H. Pammel and Charlotte M. King.)
FIG. 173-A. Distribution of Mullein (*Verbascum Thapsus*).

Fig. 173-B. Mullein (*Verbascum Thapsus*).
(*Photographs by Colburn and Featherly.*)

Distribution.—This plant is distributed from Nova Scotia west across the continent and southwest to Missouri and Kansas and Utah. It is common in waste places throughout Iowa. Mullein is especially common in limestone talus, other rocky places, in pastures and along roadsides in Winneshiek, Clayton, Dubuque, Fayette and Jones counties.

Moth Mullein (*Verbascum Blattaria* L.).

Description.—A green smoothish slender plant. The lower leaves petioled oblong, serrate, the upper partly clasping. Raceme loose; the filaments bearded with violet wool.

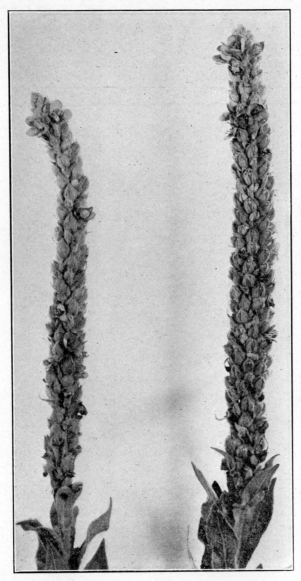

FIG. 173-C. Mullein (*Verbascum Thapsus*). A hairy biennial common roadside weed; on gravel hills along Mississippi river and in old fields.
(Photograph by Photo Section, Ia. Agr. Exp. Sta.)

Distribution.—This plant was naturalized from Europe. Waste places, Maine southward and westward.

Extermination.—Both species of mullein are easily destroyed by cutting the plants off a few inches below the surface of the ground.

This may be done in the autumn after the appearance of the root leaves, or in the second season when the plants send up the flowering shoots.

Toadflax, Butter and Eggs (*Linaria vulgaris* Hill.).

Plate 50

TOADFLAX or BUTTER AND EGGS
(Linaria vulgaris *Mill.*)

FIG. 174. Toadflax or Butter and Eggs (*Linaria vulgaris*). Roadsides, gardens, etc. (*After Clark and Fletcher.*)

Description.—A persistent, deep-rooted perennial, 1½ to 2½ feet high, with erect, slender stem; leaves smooth, sessile, crowded, alternate-linear, somewhat fleshy; flowers in racemes, showy, pale

FIG. 174-A. Toadflax or Butter and Eggs (*Linaria vulgaris*).
(Photograph by Photo Section, Ia. Agr. Exp. Sta.)

yellow and orange lips; corolla 2-lobed, closed; seeds small, dark brown to black and roughened; flowers from June to October.

Distribution.—Toadflax was introduced from Europe as a cultivated plant, from whence it has spread to roadsides, meadows and waste places. It is somewhat widely distributed in this state, but particularly common in Clayton, Allamakee and Winneshiek counties. It is in places the most common weed along roadsides and in fields in the above counties. It is local in Story county.

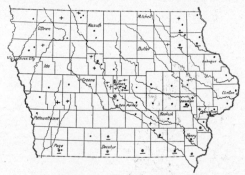

Fig. 174-B. Distribution of Toadflax.

Extermination.—Fletcher and Clark recommend as follows: "Short rotation of crops with deep, thorough cultivation in spring and fall will suppress it. Hand-pulling when the soil is wet is effective in pasture lands that cannot be cultivated. Badly infested meadows or pasture lands should be brought under cultivation by plowing in July, summer-fallowing until autumn, and planting with hoed crop the following spring."

Simpson Honey Plant (*Scrophularia marilandica* L.).

Description.—A glabrous, somewhat glandular, pubescent perennial, 3 to 5 feet high; stems 4-angled; leaves thin, ovate, or ovate-lanceolate, sharply serrate; flowers cymose; calyx lobes ovate, about the length of the tube, corolla brownish purple; capsule subglobular; seeds small, numerous.

Distribution.—This plant is common in woods and thickets from Maine to the Rocky mountains. Abundant in woods and adjacent fields in Iowa, especially in Story, Boone, Marshall, Hardin, Clayton and Allamakee counties.

Extermination.—Simpson honey plant produces a large number of small seeds. However, but little is known of their vitality. The weed is easily killed by cultivation and easily crowded out by clover and small cereals.

Scrophularia leporella Bicknell is similar as regards the foliage. The rudimentary stamen is, however, yellowish green instead of brownish purple as in *S. marilandica*.

FIG. 175. Simpson Honey Plant (*Scrophularia marilandica*). Woods and waste places.
   (*Photograph by Colburn.*)

FIG. 175-A.   Distribution of Simpson Honey Plant.

Purslane Speedwell, Neckweed (*Veronica peregrina* L.).

Description.—A glabrous, glandular, or nearly smooth, branching annual 4 to 9 inches high; leaves petioled, upper oblong, linear and entire; floral leaves like those of the stem but reduced; flowers axillary and solitary, white; capsule orbicular.

Distribution.—This cosmopolitan weed is common in fields in Iowa and in eastern North America from Nova Scotia southward; also west to Texas and the Pacific coast. It is one of the common early spring weeds in fields. *Veronica arvensis* occurs sparingly.

Extermination.—The seeds of neckweed are produced abundantly but it is not troublesome because young as well as older plants are easily killed by cultivation.

FIG. 176. Speedwell *(Veronica peregrina)*. Common in gardens and fields in early spring.
(Photograph by Quade.)

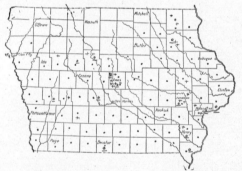

FIG. 176-A. Distribution of Speedwell.

PLANTAGINACEAE, PLANTAIN FAMILY.

The family contains few species of economic importance. The seeds of a few species are used as medicine.

Common Plantain *(Plantago major L.)*.

Description.—A smooth, glabrous perennial with short rootstocks; leaves with a long channeled petiole, ovate, oblong or oval;

spike long, linear, cylindrical, capsule circumscissile near the middle; flowers proterogynous; seed smooth, angled, reticulated; trichomes short, several-celled, from a broad base.

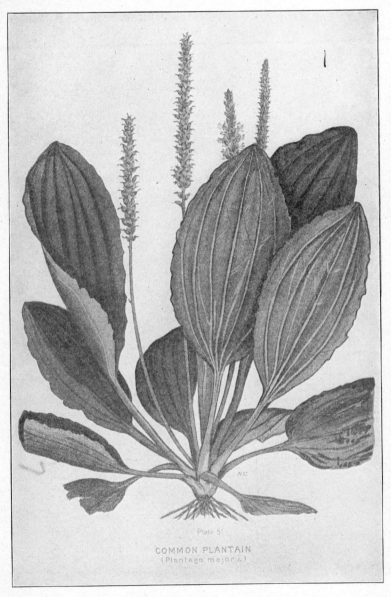

COMMON PLANTAIN
(Plantago major L.)

FIG. 177. Common Plantain (*Plantago major*). Common in dooryards, waste places, etc.
(*After Clark and Fletcher.*)

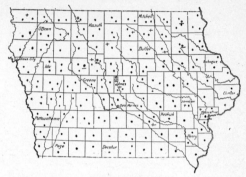

Fig. 177-A.   Figure 177-B.
FIG. 177-A.   Hairs of Common Plantain.
(*Drawing by L. H. Pammel and Charlotte M. King.*)
FIG. 177-B.   Distribution of Common Plantain.

Distribution.—Common plantain is widely distributed in North America from the Atlantic to the Pacific. Probably it is native far northward and naturalized in Iowa. It is found in every county in the state, and frequently in dooryards, fields and pastures.

Extermination.—This weed is usually not difficult to exterminate in cultivated fields.

Clark and Fletcher recommend the following treatment: ''Hoed crops every four years will keep this weed in check. Working with a broad-shared cultivator, followed by a harrow, to drag the plants with their fibrous roots to the surface, is recommended for spring cultivation. Plantain in lawns may be weeded out when the soil is firm by forcing a small implement like a chisel, with a half-round blade having a point like the tip of a spoon, between the soil and the fleshy crown of the weed to a depth sufficient to break the plant away from its fibrous roots without disfiguring the turf. A teaspoonful of salt applied to the crown of small plants in hot dry weather will kill them without seriously injuring the grass.''

Chemical Composition.—According to the report of the Bussey Institution* the chemical composition is as follows:

FRESH OR AIR DRY MATERIAL

Water	Ash	Protein	Fiber	Nitrogen free extract	Fat
81.44	2.16	2.65	2.09	11.19	0.47

WATER FREE SUBSTANCE

	11.7	14.3	11.7	60.2	.25

*Bull. 1877:117. Jenkins & Winton. Office of Experiment Stations, Bull. 11.

Rugel's Plantain (*Plantago Rugelii* Dcne.).

Description.—Perennial, much like the preceding, but leaves and petioles commonly purplish; spikes less dense; sepals oblong; capsule about twice as long as the sepals; circumscissile much below the middle; flowers proterogynous; seed oval or oblong, not reticulated.

Distribution.—Rugel's Plantain is common in fields and waste places from Maine to Texas, South Dakota and Ontario. It is very common in Iowa.

Extermination.—This weed may be exterminated in the same manner as the preceding species.

FIG. 178. Rugel's Plantain (*Plantago Rugelii*) showing root system.
(*Photograph by Photo Section, Ia. Agr. Exp. Sta.*)

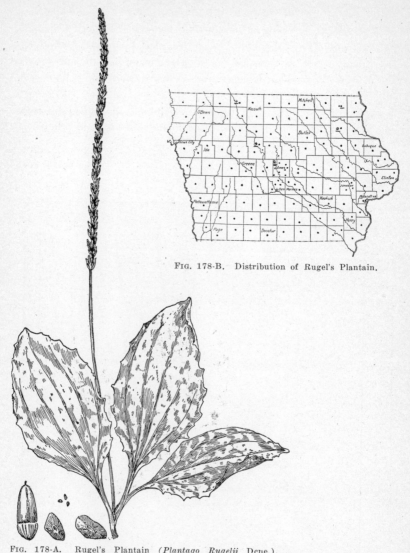

FIG. 178-B. Distribution of Rugel's Plantain.

FIG. 178-A.   Rugel's Plantain *(Plantago Rugelii* Dcne.).
(Mich. Agr. Exp. Sta.)

Buckhorn Plantain or Rib Grass *(Plantago lanceolata* L.).

Description.—A hairy, scapose perennial with flowering heads,
1 foot to 2½ feet high; leaves lanceolate or lance-oblong; spike
thick, at first capitate, becoming cylindrical; bracts and sepals
scarious; seed smooth, brownish, hollowed on the face; trichomes
simple, long, slender-pointed.

Distribution.—Buckhorn or rib grass is native to Europe and has long been known as a troublesome weed in the eastern states; it is particularly abundant in Ohio and New York and is frequent in the east; it is found in the Rocky mountains and on the Pacific coast. In Iowa it has been distributed widely with clover seed and will be found in clover meadows in many parts of the state, especially in Story, Boone, Jones, Linn, Marshall, Polk, Clinton, Jackson, Johnson, Ida, Sac, Lyon and Woodbury counties.

Extermination.—This weed is a persistent perennial in fields, lawns and clover meadows. Nothing but thorough cultivation will destroy it. In seeding to clover use only clean seed.

FIG. 179. Buckhorn Plantain *(Plantago lanceolata).*
(Photograph by Photo Section, Ia. Agr. Exp. Sta.)

Clark and Fletcher recommend as follows: "Sow clean seed. In common with other species of plantain, this weed is easily suppressed by hoed crop and short rotation. It is prevalent almost exclusively in clover crops, in which it increases rapidly by the

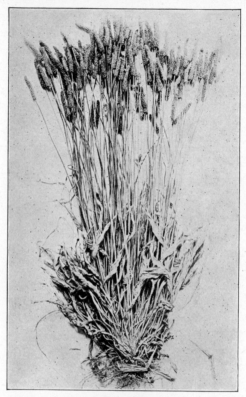

FIG. 179-A. Buckhorn Plantain or Rib Grass *(Plantago lanceolata)*. Common in clover meadows.
(Photograph by Colburn.)

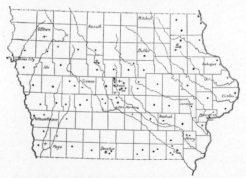

FIG. 179-B. Distribution of Buckhorn Plantain.

distribution of its seeds with commercial clover seed, the market value of which is depreciated by this impurity. Farmers who use only first quality red clover seed and who pull the first plants of this weed that occur in the clover seed crop will soon rid their farms of this pest.''

Chemical Composition.—The chemical composition of rib grass, grown in New Hampshire, according to the Report of the U. S. Department of Agriculture, 1879, page 121, is as follows:*

FRESH OR AIR DRY MATERIAL

Water	Ash	Protein	Fiber	Nitrogen free extract	Fat
7.85	6.90	9.80	20.24	51.10	4.11

WATER FREE SUBSTANCE

7.4	10.7	21.9	55.5	4.5

Prairie Plantain (*Plantago Purshii* R. & S.).

Description.—A silky, green annual with slender scapes; leaves linear, acute, with marginal petioles; spikes of flowers usually cylindrical, villous with rigid bracts; the two kinds of flowers on different plants; most of the flowers cleistogamous; sepals oblong, obtuse; corolla lobes broadly ovate; stamens 4; capsule oblong, obtuse, circumscissile at about the middle; seeds convex on the back, deeply concave on the face.

FIG. 180.   Distribution of Prairie Plantain.

Distribution.—Prairie plantain is common westward from Ontario and Illinois to British Columbia, Texas and Mexico. It is

*Jenkins and Winton. Bull. Off. Exp. Sta. 11:79.

sometimes a troublesome weed in Missouri and Nebraska. The
plant is found along railways in Iowa, especially in Story, Boone,
Greene, Carroll and Woodbury counties. It is commonly found

FIG. 180-A. Prairie Plantain (*Plantago Purshii*).
(*Drawing by Ada Hayden.*)

along railroads where it has been introduced; native from western Minnesota and Iowa to the Pacific coast.

Extermination.—This little plantain is not likely to give much trouble. The plant is easily destroyed by cultivation.

Bracted Plantain (*Plantago aristata* Michx.).

Description.—A loosely hairy, green annual, becoming glabrous with age, leaves 1 to 3-nerved, oblong, linear, or filiform; spike slender, cylindrical, with narrow linear bracts, much longer than the flowers. Flowers of two kinds with reference to the length of anthers and filaments on different plants, mostly cleistogamous; corolla lobes broad and rounded; seeds 2, smooth, light brown, with a ring on the hollowed portion. The *P. Purshii* is much like bracted plantain except that its leaves are silky villous and slender; spike dense.

FIG. 181. Bracted Plantain *(Plantago aristata)*. A common weed in clover fields in southern Iowa and in waste places.
(Photograph by Colburn.)

Distribution.—The bracted plantain is common in southern Iowa and is spreading to many other parts of the state with clover seed; on prairies, Illinois to Louisiana, naturalized eastward. In Iowa it is especially abundant in Story, Boone, Carroll, Warren, Taylor, Lucas, Van Buren, Appanoose, Lee and Guthrie counties.

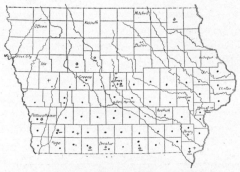

FIG. 181-A.   Distribution of Bracted Plantain.

Extermination.—The plant is easily exterminated by cultivation. Only clean clover seed should be used. Practice rotation of crops, oats, corn and clover.

Wallaces' Farmer says concerning its extermination: "The entire southern country seems to be infested with bracted or lance-leaved plantain, and seed coming from the south should always be regarded with suspicion. It is one of the worst weeds that can get on the farm. Cut the hay, plow up the land, put it in wheat, and don't undertake to take a crop of clover seed from that land. When this weed grows over the whole field the only thing to do is to put it through a course of rotation. Where there is only a stalk here and there it may be taken out with a 'spud,' which is simply a two-inch chisel with a handle, by means of which the farmer can cut out rapidly many of these weeds, but where it is scattered over the field the only way is to put it through a course of rotation."

Dwarf or White Plantain (*Plantago virginica* L.).

Description.—A hoary-pubescent plant, 1 foot to 2 feet high; leaves oblong, 3 to 5-nerved, coarsely toothed; spikes dense.

Distribution.—Dwarf plantain is found in sandy grounds in Story, Warren, Appanoose, and Van Buren counties.

FIG. 181-B. Dwarf or White Plantain *(Plantago virginica)*.
(Photograph by E. H. Richardson.)

CAPRIFOLIACEAE, HONEYSUCKLE FAMILY.

This family contains a number of cultivated ornamental plants like the coral honeysuckle, bush honeysuckle, elder, etc.

Indian Currant, Coral-berry *(Symphoricarpos orbiculatus* Moench.).

Description.—A shrub 2 to 4 feet high; purplish, usually pubescent branches; leaves oval or ovate, entire or undulate, nearly glabrous above, pubescent underneath; flowers in short axillary clusters; corolla bell-shaped, sparingly bearded, pinkish, stamens included; fruit a purplish berry.

Distribution.—Indian currant is found in rocky woods and along streams from New Jersey, Illinois, South Dakota, Nebraska to Texas and Georgia. This weedy shrub is common throughout the southern part of the state of Iowa where it is often most trouble-some.   It occurs in Polk, Lucas, Warren, Madison, Van Buren, Appanoose, Monona and Lee counties.

Extermination.—Fields that are infested with this weed must be broken up with a breaking plow and subsequently disked so that the roots may be brought to the surface and exposed to the sun.   It may be necessary to disk once or twice more before plant-ing the crop.

Fig. 182.   Indian Currant *(Symphoricarpus orbiculatus).*
(Drawn by Ada Hayden.)

FIG. 182-A.   Distribution of Indian Currant.

COMPOSITAE, SUNFLOWER FAMILY.

This family includes some economic plants, such as lettuce, artichoke, pyrethrum, sunflower; quite a number, such as gumweed (Grindelia), tansy and absinth, are used in medicine; several, like daisy, cosmos, coreopsis, aster and goldenrod, are ornamental.

Western Ironweed (*Vernonia fasciculata* Michx.).

Description.—A bushy perennial 3 to 5 feet high; leaves linear to oblong-lanceolate, long, acuminate, smooth or nearly so, denticulate; heads short-peduncled, 20 to 30-flowered, bracts of the involucre appressed, ovate or oval, acute, ciliate, the uppermost somewhat mucronate.

Distribution.—Western ironweed is common in the Mississippi valley, especially on low, alluvial grounds from Ohio to North Dakota, south to Kentucky and Texas; frequent in all parts of Iowa, especially in Story, Boone, Polk, Clayton, Warren, Madison, Webster, Marshall, Linn, Cedar, Jones, Jackson, Clinton and Allamakee counties.

Extermination.—This perennial weed, though abundant in pastures and low meadows, soon succumbs to cultivation.

Wallaces' Farmer says concerning its destruction: "An occasional cutting of ironweed is useless. If you are to keep it down by strangulation, then you must keep at it until the weed is strangled.

"If we had some permanent pasture that was covered with ironweed, we would try sheep. There are a few weeds that sheep will not eat. They will probably not make a very good living on ironweed alone, although we recently saw some sheep that apparently had nothing else to live on trimming up ironweed alone. But sheep

FIG. 183.　Western Ironweed (*Vernonia fasciculata*).
(*Photograph by Photo Section, Ia. Agr. Exp. Sta.*)

FIG. 183-A.　Distribution of Western Ironweed.

will eat almost any weed that grows out of the ground, barring thistles, mullein and buffalo berry. It requires about two years of sheep pasturing to get rid of ironweed. We know of no other way in which it can be done so easily.''

Ironweed (*Vernonia Baldwini* Torr.).

Description.—A roughish, pubescent perennial 3 to 5 feet tall; leaves lance-oblong or ovate, denticulate; heads in open, cymose clusters, about 25-flowered; involucre hairy-tomentose; bracts squarrose, purplish or greenish; involucre acuminate.

Distribution.—This ironweed is common from Maine to Missouri and southward. It is found in central Iowa, from Webster county southward and along Missouri river.

Extermination.—This plant is frequently a troublesome weed, but it is usually not difficult to exterminate in cultivated fields.

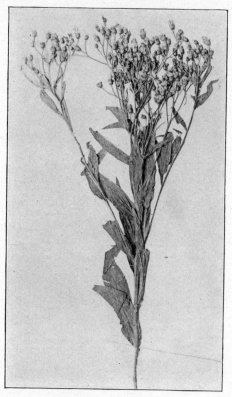

FIG. 184. Ironweed *(Vernonia Baldwini)*. Common in low pastures. Flowers in heads.
(Photograph by Colburn.)

FIG. 184-A.   Distribution of Ironweed.

Boneset or White Snakeroot (*Eupatorium urticaefolium* Reich.).

Description.—Perennial, with smooth, branching stem 15 to 40

FIG. 185.   Boneset or White Snakeroot (*Eupatorium urticaefolium*). Woodland
pastures.
(*Photograph by Quade.*)

inches high; broad, ovate, coarsely and sharply toothed, pointed, long-petioled leaves; flowers in compound, cymose clusters, white.

Distribution.—White snakeroot is found in Pennsylvania, Virginia, westward; reported from many places in Iowa in woodland pastures. It is common in Story, Hamilton, Marshall, Linn, Polk, Clinton, Johnson, Jones, Dubuque, Allamakee, Clayton and Van Buren counties.

Extermination.—This perennial weed is easily killed by cultivation. It is common in woodlands. It is mentioned here because of its supposed poisonous nature. Many cases of poisoning were reported last year, 1925.

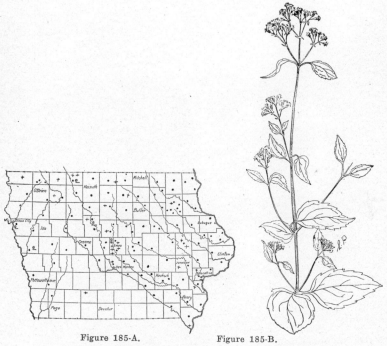

Figure 185-A.   Figure 185-B.

FIG. 185-A. Distribution of Boneset or White Snakeroot.
FIG. 185-B. Boneset or White Snakeroot (*Eupatorium urticaefolium*).
(*Drawing by Lois Pammel.*)

Canadian Goldenrod (*Solidago canadensis* L.).

Description.—A rough, hairy, pubescent perennial 3 to 6 feet high; lanceolate, pointed, sharply serrate leaves, pale in color, pubescent beneath and rough above; heads in recurved racemes forming panicles; ray flowers yellow; trichomes several-celled; cells short, with pitted walls.

Distribution.—This is the most widely distributed of the goldenrods from the Atlantic to the Rocky mountains. It is common in every part of Iowa, especially in Story, Boone, Clinton, Linn, Allamakee, Pottawattamie, Woodbury, Cerro Gordo, Kossuth, Clayton, Polk, Winneshiek, Monroe, Van Buren, Madison, Warren, Guthrie, Greene, Iowa, Dallas, Lucas and Marshall counties.

Extermination.—This weed is quite largely spread by "seeds," but is not difficult to kill by cultivation, although it sometimes per-

FIG. 186.   Canadian Goldenrod *(Solidago canadensis)*.
(Photograph by Photo Section, Ia. Agr. Exp. Sta.)

sists in fields for some years. The distribution of "seeds" should be prevented and thorough cultivation given.

FIG. 186-A. Canadian Goldenrod (*Solidago canadensis*). Roadsides and woods. *a*, hairs of leaf.
(*Photograph by Colburn, drawing by Charlotte M. King.*)

FIG. 186-B. Distribution of Canadian Goldenrod.

Smooth Goldenrod (*Solidago serotina* Ait.).

Description.—A tall, stout perennial 4 to 6 feet high; often glaucous; leaves smooth on both sides, lanceolate to oblanceolate, taperpointed, sharply serrate; heads in open panicles, pubescent, bracts linear; ray flowers 7 to 14, yellow.

Distribution.—This goldenrod is common from New England southward and westward to the Rocky mountains and Colorado. It is common in all parts of the state of Iowa, particularly in Story, Johnson, Greene, Jackson, Boone, Clinton, Polk, Kossuth, Emmet, Carroll, Dallas, Lucas, Warren, Woodbury, Monona, Madison and Lee counties.

Extermination.—This plant spreads by its seeds and root-stocks. It is, however, easily killed by cultivation.

FIG. 187.   Smooth Goldenrod *(Solidago serotina)*.   Abundant in low grounds along streams.
(Photograph by Colburn.)

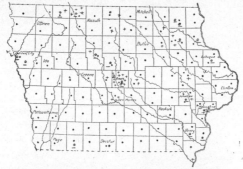

Fig. 187-A. Distribution of Smooth Goldenrod.

Large Yellow-flowered or Stiff Goldenrod (*Solidago rigida* L.).

Description.—A rough and somewhat hoary perennial, minutely pubescent; stems stout, 2 to 5 feet high, very leafy; leaves oval or

Fig. 188. Large Yellow-flowered or Stiff Goldenrod (*Solidago rigida*). In pastures and roadsides.
(*Photograph by Colburn.*)

oblong, feather-veined, thick and rigid; the upper sessile; heads large, collected in a large compound corymb, terminating the stem.

Distribution.—This goldenrod is abundant in dry soils from New England to Manitoba, Dakota, Nebraska and Missouri. It is common in pastures in Iowa, in Story, Boone, Polk, Linn, Marshall,

FIG. 188-A. Large Yellow-flowered or Stiff Goldenrod *(Solidago rigida)*.
(Photograph by Photo Section, Ia. Agr. Exp. Sta.)

Hardin, Cerro Gordo, Winnebago, Emmet, Clayton, Allamakee, Madison, Dallas, Greene, Carroll, Johnson, Fremont, Ida, Sac, Lyon, Plymouth and Woodbury counties.

FIG. 188-B. Distribution of Large Yellow-flowered Goldenrod.

Extermination.—Though the stiff goldenrod is often a very troublesome weed in pastures, it is easily killed by cultivation. It is spread largely by "seeds."

White or Many-flowered Aster (*Aster multiflorus* Ait.).

Description.—A pale or hoary pubescent, branched perennial, 9 inches to 1½ feet high; heads on spreading, racemose branches; leaves rigid, crowded, spreading, with ciliate margins; ray flowers white, small.

Distribution.—Many-flowered aster is frequent along roadsides and fields, on gravelly knolls, etc.

Extermination.—Though the aster is abundant in fields, it readily succumbs to cultivation.

Willow-leaved Aster (*Aster salicifolius* Ait.).

Description.—A branched, leafy perennial 2 to 8 feet high; leaves oblong to narrowly lanceolate, pointed, entire, or slightly serrate, firm, often scabrous; heads racemose, clustered; ray flowers purplish.

Distribution.—This aster is common in low grounds, thickets or borders of fields from New England to Wisconsin and Minnesota. An allied species, *A. paniculatus* Lam., is much like *A. salicifolius* except that the leaves of the former are more pointed, serrate and less scabrous than the leaves of the latter. It is a very variable species, with distribution similar to that of *A. multiflorus.*

Extermination.—Easily exterminated by cultivation.

FIG. 189.   White or Many-flowered Aster (*Aster multiflorus*). Common on roadsides.
(Photograph by Quade.)

The *Aster Tradescanti* L., is closely related to *A. paniculatus,*
but has smaller leaves and shorter rays.   The leaves are lanceolate
to linear.   The bracts are linear or acutish.

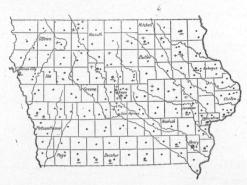

FIG. 189-A.   Distribution of White or Many-flowered Aster.

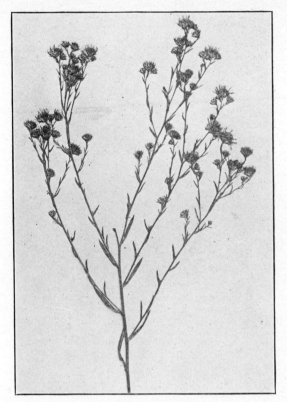

FIG. 190.   Willow-leaved Aster (*Aster salicifolius*).   Common in low grounds.
(*Photograph by Quade.*)

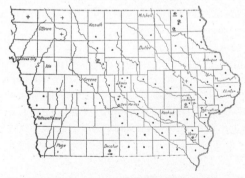

FIG. 190-A.   Distribution of Willow-leaved Aster.

Whiteweed or Fleabane (*Erigeron annuus* (L.) Pers.).

Description.—A sparingly pubescent annual 3 to 5 feet high;

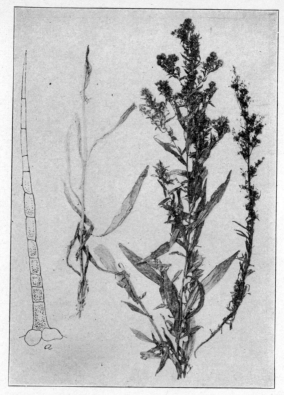

FIG. 190-B. *Aster paniculatus.* *a,* Plant hair. Common in low grounds everywhere in Iowa. Ray flowers white, in some cases purplish.
(Photograph by Colburn.   Drawing by Charlotte M. King.)

leaves thin, coarsely and sharply toothed, the lower one ovate, or ovate-lanceolate, acute, and entire on both ends; heads corymbed; rays white, tinged with purple.

Distribution.—This weed occurs from New England to Texas, and it is also frequent in the Mississippi valley. It is common throughout the state of Iowa, particularly in timothy and clover meadows of the following counties: Polk, Dallas, Story, Marshall, Warren, Madison, Lucas, Fremont, Lee, Van Buren, Appanoose, Scott, Muscatine, Clinton, Jackson, Jones, Dubuque, Clayton, Allamakee and Winneshiek. This weed is also naturalized in Europe.

Extermination.—Both this and *E. ramosus* are easily exterminated by thorough cultivation. They are seldom troublesome outside of meadows, but in some parts of Iowa the meadows and pastures are white with flowers of these species.

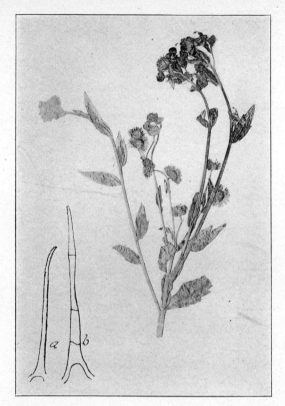

Fig. 191. Whiteweed or Fleabane *(Erigeron annuus).*   Common in clover and
timothy meadows.
(Photograph by Colburn. Drawings of plant hairs a and b by Charlotte M. King.)

Wallaces' Farmer states concerning its eradication: ''One of
the worst enemies of the meadow, and especially the timothy

Fig. 191-A. Distribution of Whiteweed.

meadow in the west, is a peculiar form of daisy to which farmers give the name of whiteweed. It may be seen in full bloom about the time timothy heads out, and if not dealt with on its first appearance in the timothy field it is only a question of time when the hay will be from one-fourth to one-half whiteweed. If the farmer is vigilant and goes through and pulls out these weeds on their first appearance, he can protect his timothy meadows. If he fails to do this, it is only a question of time when he will have to plow them up.''

FIG. 192. Daisy Fleabane (*Erigeron ramosus*). (*Mich. Agr. Coll. Exp. Sta. Bull.*)

Daisy Fleabane (*Erigeron ramosus* (Walt.) BSP.).

Description.—This resembles the preceding species except that the stem and leaves are somewhat more hirsute and hairy; leaves roughish, entirely or nearly so, the upper lanceolate, the lowest oblong or spatulate; flowers white and smaller than in the preceding species.

Distribution.—Daisy fleabane is native from New England to Arkansas. It is common in Iowa, particularly in drier situations and especially in clover meadows and timothy fields of Clayton, Allamakee, Winneshiek, Clinton, Dubuque and Story counties.

Extermination.—This weed is common in timothy and clover meadows. The seed often occurs in clover and timothy seed, and care should be used to sow only clover and timothy seed that does not contain these weed seeds. This weed is easily destroyed by cultivation. As meadows are infested by seed coming from fleabane plants along the neighboring roadside or field, weeds in these waste plaecs should be kept down by cutting.

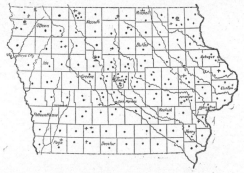

FIG. 192-A. Distribution of Daisy Fleabane.

Mare's-tail or Horse-weed (*Erigeron canadensis* L.).

Description.—A plant with bristly, hairy, or sometimes glabrate stem, 1 foot to 6 feet high, simple or paniculately branched; leaves usually pubescent or ciliate, the lower spatulate, incised or entire, obtuse or acutish, the upper generally linear and entire; heads numerous, with inconspicuous white ray flowers shorter than the pappus; pappus simple; trichomes several-celled, straight with long cells, curved with short cells.

Distribution.—Horse-weed is common throughout eastern North America; it is naturalized in Europe, the Rocky mountains and along the Pacific coast. It is abundant everywhere in Iowa in waste places and in cultivated fields, particularly in the following

FIG. 193. Distribution of Horse-weed.

counties: Johnson, Polk, Iowa, Lee, Scott, Van Buren, Marshall, Linn, Story, Boone, Carroll, Fremont, Woodbury, Ida, Sac, Emmet, Webster, Kossuth, Jones, Bremer, Winnebago, Hancock, Howard,

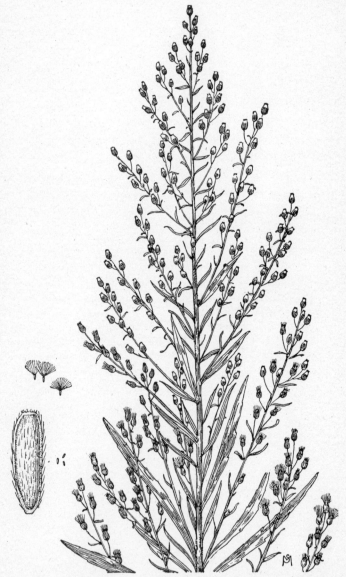

FIG. 193-A.   Horse-weed (*Erigeron canadensis*).   In fields and waste places.
(Mich. Agr. Exp. Sta.)

Jones, Winneshiek, Allamakee, Clayton, Dubuque, Jackson and Clinton counties.

Extermination.—This weed is an annual or winter annual and is very easily destroyed. Cutting off just below the surface of the ground will exterminate it, provided, of course, that the new seeds are not permitted to reseed the soil. Since the weed is common everywhere and its seeds are carried by the wind it is difficult to keep in check.

Diffuse Horse-weed (*Erigeron divaricatus* Michx.).

Description.—This weedy plant is spreading and low growing, 6 inches to 1½ feet in height. The heads are in loose corymb-like clusters. Rays are purplish.

Distribution.—The general distribution is throughout the western part of the middle states. It is found more particularly in the southern part of Iowa, as in Van Buren, Lee, Appanoose, Wapello, Warren, Clarke, Polk and Story counties.

Extermination.—It may be disposed of by cultivation.

Marsh Elder, Half-breed Weed (*Iva xanthiifolia* Nutt.).

Description.—An annual 1 foot to 8 feet high; stem in many cases pubescent when young; leaves opposite, rhombic, ovate, or lowest heart-shaped, doubly serrate, or cut-toothed, obscurely lobed; upper surface minutely scabrous, canescent beneath, especially when young; petiole in many cases ciliate at its upper end; flowers borne in spikelike clusters forming a compound panicle;

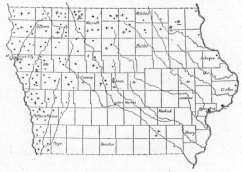

FIG. 194. Distribution of Marsh Elder.

heads small, crowded; outer bracts of the involucre broadly ovate, greenish; inner membranaceous; achenes glabrate.

Distribution.—The weed is common in regions from the eastern Rockies to Saskatchewan and western Wisconsin. It is very abundant in Iowa along the Missouri river, where it is troublesome in fields, along highways, and in yards. It is also spreading into north and northeastern Iowa, as, for instance, Mason City and Allamakee county. It also occurs in Boone, Story, Clayton, Winnebago, Howard, Winneshiek, Harrison, Clinton, Marshall, Hardin, Monona, Fremont and Pottawattamie counties.

Extermination.—Since marsh elder is an annual thorough cultivation for a single season will destroy it, provided it is not allowed to form seeds.

Fɪɢ. 194-A.   Marsh Elder, Half-breed Weed (*Iva xanthiifolia*).   Common in western fields and roadsides.
(Photograph by Colburn.)

FIG. 194-B.   Marsh Elder (*Iva xanthiifolia*) in corn fields.
(Photograph by Ada Hayden.)

Great Ragweed (*Ambrosia trifida* L.).

Description.—A stout, scabrous, hispid or nearly glabrous annual, 3 to 12 feet high; leaves all opposite and petioled, 3-nerved, deeply 3 to 5-lobed; lobes ovate-lanceolate and serrate, upper leaf sometimes ovate and undivided; flowers monoecious, staminate, borne in spikes surrounded by the larger bract-like leaves; involucre turbinate to obovoid, 5 to 7-ribbed, beaked, each rib bearing a tubercle near the summit; involucre enclosing a single oily seed.

Distribution.—This North American weed is most abundant in the Mississippi valley from Texas to Minnesota and in the Dakotas; however, it also occurs east from New England to Quebec. It is abundant in every part of Iowa, especially along highways, in grain fields and corn fields, and is found freely growing in Clayton, Allamakee, Winneshiek, Howard, Clinton, Cerro Gordo, Bremer, Lee, Jones, Jackson, Iowa, Johnson, Lucas, Appanoose, Polk, Marshall, Linn, Story, Boone, Greene, Webster, Kossuth, Carroll, Emmet, Palo Alto, Ida, Sac, Harrison, Fremont, Pottawattamie, Woodbury, Lyon, Plymouth and Monona counties.

Extermination.—Cultivating the young plants several times will remove the weed in a single season.

FIG. 195. Great Ragweed *(Ambrosia trifida)*, sometimes, but incorrectly, called Ironweed. Common in fields, along roadsides, etc.
(Photograph by Photo Section, Ia. Agr. Exp. Sta.)

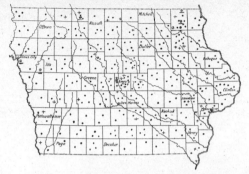

FIG. 195-A. Distribution of Great Ragweed.

Small Ragweed (*Ambrosia artemisiifolia* L.).

Description.—A puberulent or hirsute annual, branched, 1 foot to 3 feet high; leaves thin, 1 to 2-pinnatifid; upper leaves alternate, lower usually opposite, pale or canescent beneath; flowers monoecious, staminate above and pistillate in lower axils of the upper leaves; fertile heads obovoid or globose; short-beaked, 4 to 6-spined; trichomes several-celled, cells short or long.

Distribution.—Ragweed or hog-weed came originally from Europe but is common throughout eastern North America; it is also found in the Rocky mountains, the Pacific northwest and in Mexico, West Indies and South America. It is common throughout the state of Iowa in gardens and fields and is abundant in pastures in Woodbury, Lyon, Emmet, Plymouth, Ida, Sac, Greene, Carroll, Harrison, Crawford, Monona, Fremont, Taylor, Page, Lucas, Polk, Warren, Madison, Dallas, Appanoose, Monroe, Lee, Scott, Muscatine, Louisa, Clinton, Johnson, Jones, Clayton, Allamakee, Cerro Gordo and Winneshiek counties.

Extermination.—This weed is common in pastures, along roadsides and in waste places. It is easily exterminated by cutting the plants off below the surface of the soil. The commonly used cultivator will destroy most of the young plants in a corn field. In pastures the weed should be cut with a mower when the plant is in bloom.

Clark and Fletcher recommend the following treatment: "Sow clean red clover seed. Stubble lands where this weed is prevalent should be shallow plowed directly after harvest, or, if seeded, the autumn growth should be closely cut with a mowing machine within two weeks after the grain crop is cut."

Plate 57

COMMON RAGWEED or HOGWEED
(Ambrosia artemisiifolia L.)

FIG. 196. Small Ragweed or Hog-weed *(Ambrosia artemisiifolia)*. In pastures, waste
places, gardens and clover meadows.
(After Clark and Fletcher.)

The following article from Wallaces' Farmer concerning this
serious pest of the pasture suggests that feebleness of blue grass

may permit the spread of ragweed in a pasture and further suggests as remedy that grounds be reseeded with clover:

"The reason why the ragweed grows in the blue grass pastures is because for some reason the stand of grass has been weakened and thus the ragweed seeds, which are present in all cultivated soils in the west in great abundance, have a chance to grow. The stand of grass may have been weakened by overpasturing in a dry time, thus giving the sun opportunity to burn the roots and lower their vitality. Also it may have been weakened by the ravages of larvae of the various insects known as the white grub worms. We suggested still further that blue grass, not being able to obtain nitrogen from the atmosphere, was nitrogen hungry, and therefore weak.

"To meet all these various suggestions we proposed that farmers who have blue grass pastures of long standing should reseed them next year with one or other of the various kinds of clover, filling up the land with a preferred food for stock and at the same time restoring the nitrogen content to the soil, enabling the blue grass to make more rapid growth.

FIG. 196-A.   Small Ragweed *(Ambrosia artemisiifolia).*
(Photograph by Photo Section, Ia. Agr. Exp. Sta.)

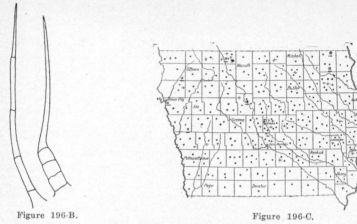

Figure 196-B.   Figure 196-C.

FIG. 196-B.   Plant hairs or trichomes of ragweed.
(Drawing by Charlotte M. King.)
FIG. 196-C.   Distribution of Small Ragweed.

"We did try it on a neighbor's farm under the most disadvantageous circumstances imaginable.   The field was a pasture of blue grass and wool grass with a very little white clover.   The ground

FIG. 196-D.   A weedy Iowa field; Ragweed, Foxtail, Barnyard Grass, etc.   The seeds
are sown in the field for next year.
(Photograph by Pammel.)

was dry, as dry as we have ever seen it at that time of the year. We found it easy even under these hard conditions to drill in clover on this tough sod and cover it from an inch to an inch and a half, using a Hoosier drill with two horses.

"We found that the clover was dropped in the very bottom of the slit made by the disk, a seed every two or three inches, using six pounds to the acre. It lay there until the 23d of May, apparently as dry as it came out of the drill, except in some of the lower spots, where it had sprouted. The 23d of May there was a two-inch rain on that field, and at once the clovers began to grow."

Perennial Ragweed (*Ambrosia psilostachya* DC.).

Description.—A branched hairy and rough perennial with slender running root-stock, 2 to 3 feet high; leaves once pinnatifid, acute lobes, lower leaves incised; monoecious flowers, staminate flowers with flattish involucres, involucre of fertile flowers obovoid, tubercles absent or very small.

FIG. 197.   Perennial Ragweed (*Ambrosia psilostachya*).   Pastures, drift soils, road-sides.
(*Photograph by Quade.*)

Distribution.—This ragweed is common on gravel hills and sandy plains from Illinois, Wisconsin and the Saskatchewan to the Rocky mountains. It occurs in Clinton, Muscatine, Carroll, Kossuth, Pottawattamie, Boone, Story, Clayton, Cerro Gordo, Howard, Woodbury, Monona, Fremont and Harrison counties.

Extermination.—The perennial ragweed succumbs readily to cultivation.

Cocklebur (*Xanthium commune* Britton).

Description.—A coarse, rough annual from 1 foot to 2 feet high, stem marked with brown punctate spots; leaves alternate, cordate or ovate, 3-nerved, long petioled; flowers monoecious, staminate and pistillate flowers in different heads, the pistillate clustered below; involucre of staminate flowers somewhat flat, of separate scales; receptacles cylindrical; scales of the fertile involucre closed; fruit 2-beaked, containing 2 achenes; bur densely prickly and hispid, achenes oblong, without pappus.

The spiny clotbur (*X. spinosum*) has spines in the axils of the lanceolate leaves. This weed has been found a few times in southeastern Iowa.

Distribution.—Cocklebur is common in the Mississippi valley from Texas to Minnesota and eastward. It is common in fields in many parts of Iowa, but more common in the southern than in the northern part. It is abundant in Lucas, Lee, Warren, Monroe, Madison, Taylor, Page, Guthrie, Fremont, Monona, Carroll, Story, Boone, Linn, Clinton, Clayton, Johnson, Jackson and Iowa counties.

Extermination.—The best means of combating this weed is by rotation of crops and clean culture. Corn fields, when infested with cocklebur, should be thoroughly cultivated and none of the weeds allowed to mature seed. After cultivation remaining cockleburs may be destroyed with a hoe or pulled by hand. The corn should be followed first by winter rye and then by oats, using the oats as a nurse crop for clover and timothy. The field should be left in meadow for at least two years and then turned into pasture.

Mr. E. B. Watson found that clover seed would not germinate well in soil badly infested with cocklebur, and this observation has been generally verified in practice.

The Homestead says concerning the eradication of cocklebur: "Needless to say there is no easy way of eradicating the pest. Where the winter wheat can be grown the following plan can be depended upon. Start on fields that have been in small grain and

FIG. 198.   Cocklebur *(Xanthium commune)*.
(Photograph by Photo Section, Ia. Agr. Exp. Sta.)

plow the land as soon as the crop is removed.   Harrow as often as necessary to kill weeds and put in wheat when the time comes. The next season as soon as the wheat is harvested remove from the field and go on with the mower.   This will clip all or most all of the young cocklebur plants, as well as other weeds, and following this operation the stubble should be plowed as rapidly as possible and prepared for another crop of wheat.   Another season's treatment of this sort will generally reduce the burs to such an extent that very few will be left and these can be pulled by hand.

"One of our Nebraska subscribers, Mr. J. J. Bishop, stated some time ago that he succeeded in almost clearing out a badly infested field of cockleburs in two years by employing the following method: just as soon as the removal of the oat crop the soil was plowed and prepared for winter wheat, this crop being sown at the proper time.   Mr. Bishop stated that before plowing this ground after removing the oats the surface was covered with burs just about as thick as they could grow.   After harvesting the first crop

FIG. 198-A. Cocklebur (*Xanthium commune*).
(*Photograph by H. I. Featherly.*)

of winter wheat the soil was again plowed and seeded for the
second time to winter wheat. After this it was followed by corn
and other crops, with the result that even in the corn crop a very
short time spent in pulling burs freed the field entirely of these
pests.''

Mr. Albert Wiltz says in Wallaces' Farmer: ''When I moved to
this farm nine years ago the land was very badly infested with
cockleburs, and farmers told me that each bur had two seeds, one
growing one year and the other one the next year. I left a patch
of ground where the cockleburs were lying thick without a crop,
plowed in June once, and again in August. That settled the cockleburs. That year was a good corn year, with plenty of moisture.
Now, would not that way be the cheapest way to deal with them—
to put three years, yes, sometimes ten years' fighting into one year?

FIG. 198-B.   Cocklebur *(Xanthium commune)*.   Corn fields, roadsides, alluvial bottoms.
(Photograph by Colburn.)

That is, take a field one year to fight cockleburs, and finish it; next year take another, and so on, if the farmer is a renter on a long term lease or owns the land.''

Wallaces' Farmer states concerning the extermination of cockle-

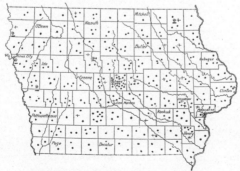

FIG. 198-C.   Distribution of Cocklebur.

bur: "If it is desirable to put some of this kind of land in alfalfa, we would not put it in corn, but disk it every week or two during the summer to sprout the burs, and then kill them by subsequent disking, and keep on that way all summer, missing the crop for the first year. Then in the fall, when the ground has sufficient moisture, say in August or in the first part of September, seed it to alfalfa alone. We would not sow alfalfa in the spring on that kind of land but by continuous summer cultivation it can be gotten in

FIG. 198-D. Spiny Clotbur *(Xanthium spinosum)*. Waste places from Maine to Kansas. Perhaps in southern Iowa.
(Photograph by Colburn.)

shape to grow alfalfa and thus avoid not only cockleburs but also crabgrass, another great foe to alfalfa in that part of the country.

"Speaking now on the subject of cockleburs generally. Where the land is not so badly infested with them as this farm seems to be, and it is not desirable to grow spring grains and seed to clover, we would make the stand of grain rather thin, put in a good seeding of clover, put the clover deep enough to insure germination, use as early a variety of grain as possible, get it off the land as soon as possible, and then keep the cockleburs mowed down by clipping the clover until a good stand is secured."

FIG. 199. Ox-eye (*Heliopsis scabra*). Common in orchards and waste places. Rather
large yellow heads and rough opposite leaves.
(Photograph by Photo Section, Ia. Agr. Exp. Sta.)

Ox-eye (*Heliopsis scabra* Dunal.).

Description.—A rough, pubescent perennial with opposite, petioled, triple-nerved leaves; heads large, peduncled; scales of involucre in 2 to 3 rows, nearly equal; ray flowers yellow, 10 or more, fertile; achenes smooth, thick, 4-angled, truncate; pappus chaffy or 2 to 3-toothed.

FIG. 199-A.   Distribution of Ox-eye.

Distribution.—Ox-eye is distributed from New York west to Wisconsin, Minnesota and British Columbia, and southwest to Missouri, Kansas and Arkansas.   It is common in Story, Boone,

FIG. 200.   Black-eyed Susan *(Rudbeckia hirta).*   Common in sandy fields.
(Photograph by Colburn.)

Clayton, Jones, Marshall, Linn, Lee, Jackson, Polk, Warren, Madison, Dallas, Guthrie, Greene, Emmet, and Palo Alto counties.

Extermination.—This weed is quite easily destroyed by cultivation.

Black-eyed Susan, Nigger-head, Cone-flower (*Rudbeckia hirta* L.).

Description.—A rough, hairy biennial 1 foot to 2 feet high, with stems simple or branched, bearing a long pedunculate head; leaves nearly entire, the upper sessile, oblong or lanceolate, the lower petioled and spatulate; heads many-flowered, radiate, neutral; receptacle columnar or conical; chaff hairy at tip, acutish; ray flowers yellow, disk dull brown; achenes 4-angled, pappus none.

Distribution.—This weed is indigenous to the northern Mississippi valley but has been naturalized eastward. It has been introduced into Iowa largely through clover seed and is common not only in meadows but in sandy fields in Linn, Muscatine, Story, Boone, Marshall, Webster, Palo Alto, Emmet, Kossuth, Jackson, Clayton, Cerro Gordo and Jones counties.

Extermination.—This weed succumbs readily to cultivation. Care should be used to sow clover seed free from the seed of this weed.

FIG. 200-A. Distribution of Black-eyed Susan.

Common Sunflower (*Helianthus annuus* L.).

Description.—A tall, rough annual, 6 to 8 feet high, leaves 3-ribbed, ovate or the lower cordate, serrate; large heads with yellow ray flowers, disk flowers brownish.

Distribution.—This weed has been widely distributed west of Missouri river from Saskatchewan to Texas, California and Mexico. It is of common occurrence in western Iowa, from Woodbury to Fremont county, in fields along highways, meadows, vacant lots and corn fields. It is widely scattered, but not abundant in Boone, Story, Polk, Cerro Gordo, Webster, Lyon, Linn and Muscatine counties. The common sunflower is becoming common in Calhoun, Pocahontas and Webster counties.

Extermination.—The seeds of this plant do not retain their vi-

FIG. 201. Sunflower *(Helianthus annuus)*.
(Photograph by Photo Section, Ia. Agr. Exp. Sta.)

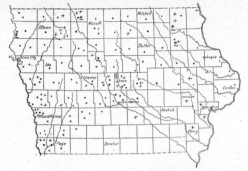

FIG. 201-A. Distribution of Common Sunflower.

tality very long. The young plants are easily destroyed by cultivation, and no plant should be permitted to go to seed.

FIG. 201-B. Common Sunflower (*Helianthus annuus*). Common in western Iowa, fields
and roadsides.
(*Photograph by Colburn.*)

FIG. 201·C. A patch of Wild Sunflowers (*Helianthus annuus*). Common in western
Iowa.
(Photograph by Pammel.)

Prairie Sunflower (*Helianthus petiolaris* Nutt.).

Description.—The prairie sunflower is an annual 1 foot to 3 feet
high; lower branches rough; stem leaves 1 inch to 3 inches long,
oblong to ovate-lanceolate, sparingly toothed, lower leaves abruptly
contracted into a long slender petiole; ray flowers yellow, disk
flowers brownish; bracts lanceolate or oblong-lanceolate, usually
not ciliate; head flowers smaller than in common sunflower; flowers
half an inch or more in diameter.

Distribution.—Prairie sunflower is very abundant in dry prairies
from Minnesota to Colorado, Wyoming, Montana and Oregon, and
southward to Missouri. It has become naturalized in Iowa and
it is not uncommon from Council Bluffs to Sioux City and around
Muscatine.

Extermination.—This weed is easily exterminated by cultivation.

FIG. 202.   Prairie or Western Sunflower *(Helianthus petiolaris)*.   In Muscatine Island and western Iowa.   Similar to Large Sunflower.
(Photograph by Colburn.)

FIG. 202-A.   Distribution of Prairie Sunflower.

Meadow or Saw-toothed Sunflower (*Helianthus grosseserratus* Martens).

Description.—A tall, glabrous perennial 6 to 10 feet high, bearing numerous short peduncled heads; lower stem leaves 8 to 10 inches long and petiole 1 inch to 2 inches long; leaves opposite or alternate with a slender petiole, oblong, lanceolate, acuminate with sharp teeth, or the upper merely denticulate, somewhat scabrous above, whitish below; heads one-half inch high with deep yellow rays about an inch long; bracts of the involucre slender.

Distribution.—The meadow sunflower is common in the central states and northward, also westward to Texas. It is abundant throughout the state of Iowa in corn fields, low swales and road-sides, particularly in the following counties: Lyon, Plymouth,

FIG. 203. Meadow Sunflower *(Helianthus grosseserratus)* showing root system. Common in meadows, pastures and fields.
(Photograph by Photo Section, Ia. Agr. Exp. Sta.)

Woodbury, Palo Alto, Calhoun, Kossuth, Webster, Hardin, Story, Boone, Greene, Winnebago, Hancock, Marshall, Linn, Clayton, Cerro Gordo, Allamakee, Jones and Jackson.

Extermination.—Clean cultivation will remove the weed in one

FIG. 203-A.   Distribution of Meadow Sunflower.

FIG. 203-B.   Meadow Sunflower *(Helianthus grosseserratus)*.   In meadows and fields. *(Photograph by Pammel.)*

or two seasons. It would be well to use clover, planted as a rotation after the field has had clean cultivation for a season.

Maximilian's Sunflower (*Helianthus Maximiliani* Schrad.).

Description.—Stem scabrous and hispid, 2 to 12 feet high, the latter height being attained in alluvial bottoms; leaves usually alternate, thick, becoming rigid, scabrous above, hairy beneath, lance-

Fig. 204-A. Distribution of Maximilian's Sunflower.

Fig. 204. Maximilian's Sunflower (*Helianthus Maximiliani*). Common in meadows and fields of northern Iowa. Yellow flowers, hairy elongated leaves.
(*Photograph by Colburn.*)

olate, narrowing at both ends, nearly sessile, entirely or sparingly denticulate; heads large, one-half to three-fourths inch high; short peduncle terminating the simple stem and later appearing in the axils of lower leaves; involucre consisting of rigid bracts about 1½ inches long; ray flowers golden yellow, disk flowers brownish, flowering in late summer and early autumn.

Distribution.—This weed is common in places from Alberta and

Manitoba to Texas. In Iowa it is most abundant in the northwestern and western counties, in the alluvial bottoms of Missouri river, in Lyon, Plymouth, Woodbury, Monona, Pottawattamie, Mills and Fremont counties, and on high prairies of Pocahontas, Dickinson, Emmet and Palo Alto counties. It is also found east in Worth, Howard and Cerro Gordo counties.

Extermination.—This perennial weed has the habit of the artichoke; the thickened underground stems freely propagate the plants. The infested field should be given a shallow plowing, then dragged. The roots should be exposed to the sun for a few days. This will destroy most of the plants. If the field is put into corn give thorough cultivation and follow corn first with a small-grain crop and then with clover.

Jerusalem Artichoke or Artichoke (*Helianthus tuberosus* L.).

Description.—A pubescent or hirsute perennial with tuberous underground stems; leaves oblong-lanceolate or ovate-acuminate, scabrous, minutely pubescent; flowers yellowish, large.

This sunflower is native. An improved form of it sometimes is cultivated in America for the tubers. It is extensively used in Europe.

Distribution.—This plant is common from New York to Minnesota. It is very abundant in the northern counties of Iowa, and particularly troublesome in Mitchell, Howard and Cerro Gordo counties. It is not infrequent along highways and fields in many other parts of the state including Story, Boone, Greene, Polk, Dallas, Madison, Warren, Lee, Lucas, Appanoose, Iowa, Poweshiek, Linn, Scott, Muscatine, Clayton, Allamakee and Winneshiek counties.

FIG. 205. Distribution of Jerusalem Artichoke.

Fig. 205-A.   Jerusalem Artichoke (*Helianthus tuberosus*).   In grain fields, roadsides and waste places.

Extermination.—This is a very troublesome weed in corn and small grain fields of northern Iowa.   The somewhat thickened underground stems spread the plant freely when the fields are cultivated.   The small-grain field should be plowed after the grain is removed, then dragged so as to expose the "roots" of the artichoke to the sun.   Before planting corn in the spring it is well to run a disk over the field, then harrow, plant to corn and give thorough cultivation.   It is well to get a field in which the weed is very troublesome into meadow or pasture.

Beggar-ticks or Tall Boot-jack (*Bidens frondosa* L.).

Description.—A diffusely branched annual with alternate, divided leaves and slender petioles; leaflets ovate-lanceolate, pointed, coarsely serrate, small heads of yellow flowers surrounded by a double involucre, the outer of 4 bracts; achenes linear, wedge-

shaped, smooth or tuberculate, bearing a pair of short, upwardly
barbed awns.

FIG. 206. Beggar-ticks *(Bidens frondosa).*
(Photograph by Ada Hayden.)

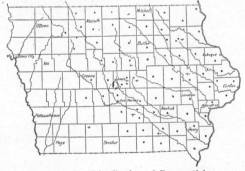

FIG. 206-A. Distribution of Beggar-ticks.

Distribution.—This plant grows in moist situations from New England to Missouri. Common in southern Iowa in Story, Polk, Boone, Dallas, Greene, Guthrie, Warren, Fremont, Mills, Taylor, Madison, Lee, Appanoose, Monroe, Linn, Clayton and Allamakee counties.

Extermination.—It succumbs readily to cultivation. The plants should not be allowed to go to seed as the seed is scattered by animals; its spreading can be prevented by cutting the plant off close to the surface of the ground when it begins to blossom.

Stick-tight, Boot-jack, Spanish Needle (*Bidens vulgata* Greene).

Description.—A branching, hairy or smooth annual 2 to 6 feet high; leaves petioled, 3 to 5-divided, terminal leaflet long-stalked, pointed, coarsely toothed, frequently divided again; rays small, yellow involucre double, the outer foliaceous; bracts ciliate, longer than the head; receptacles flattish with deciduous chaff; achenes narrowly acuminate, 2-awned, the awns downwardly barbed.

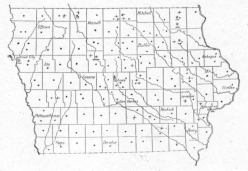

FIG. 206-B   Distribution of Boot-jack.

Distribution.—Boot-jack is widely distributed in moist places throughout the northern states. It is often a very troublesome weed in gardens. It is widely scattered by means of the "seeds" which adhere to clothing, pelts of animals, etc. It grows freely in Story, Boone, Greene, Webster, Kossuth, Palo Alto, Emmet, Lyon, Allamakee, Clayton, Winneshiek, Jones, Linn, Jackson, Dubuque, Clinton, Scott, Muscatine, Louisa, Lee, Appanoose and Monroe counties.

Extermination.—Boot-jack is easily exterminated by cultivation. It is well to cut off the plant, when it is in flower, close to the surface of the ground.

Fɪɢ. 206-C. Stick-tight, Boot-jack, Spanish Needle (*Bidens vulgata*). Common in gardens. The "seeds," more properly achenes, are scattered by animals.
(*Photograph by E. H. Richardson.*)

Swamp Beggar-ticks (*Bidens connata* Muhl.).

Description.—A tall branching plant 2½ to 4 feet high; bright green lanceolate leaves, some of the lower deeply parted, with slender petioles; awns half as long as the achene, retrorsely barbed. Rays of the flowers are yellow.

Distribution.—Common in swamps and ditches.

FIG. 207.   Swamp Beggar-ticks *(Bidens connata).*
(Photograph by Ada Hayden.)

Extermination.—Cut before seeds ripen.

Nodding Stick-tight (*Bidens cernua* L.).

Description.—A nearly smooth plant about 1 foot to 3 feet high, with short branches. Lanceolate leaves, sharp-pointed, irregularly serrate, connate at the base. Outer involucre longer than the head achenes, tuberculate on the angles. Flowers yellow.

Distribution.—Frequent in wet places.

Extermination.—Cut before seeds ripen.

FIG. 208. Nodding stick-tight *(Bidens cernua)*.
(Photograph by Ada Hayden.)

Tickseed (*Bidens aristosa* (Michx.) Britton).

Description.—A smoothish, slightly pubescent annual 2 to 4 feet high; leaves 1 to 2-pinnately 5 to 7-divided, petioled; leaflets lanceolate, cut-toothed or pinnatifid; heads panicled-corymbose; scales of the involucre in 2 series, the outer about as long as the inner, ciliate; ray flowers conspicuous, yellow; achenes obovate with ciliate margins, usually with 2 divergent teeth; a somewhat showy plant with yellow flowers.

Distribution.—Tickseed occurs from Michigan and southern Iowa to Kansas, Texas and Missouri. It is probably indigenous to southern Iowa; in recent years it has made its appearance in Wapello (Pammel), Marion (Pammel), Polk (Bakke), Story

FIG. 209. Distribution of Tickseed.

(Pammel) and Decatur (Anderson) counties. The weed is common in Madison, Warren, Appanoose, Monroe, Lee, Keokuk, Muscatine, Van Buren and Louisa counties.

Extermination.—This weed is easily exterminated by cultivation. Seeds should not be permitted to mature.

FIG. 209-A. Tickseed (*Bidens aristosa*).
(*Mich. Agr. Exp. Sta.*)

Sneezeweed (*Helenium autumnale* L.).

Description.—A smooth, angular, branching perennial, 1 foot to

5 feet high; mostly toothed, lanceolate-ovate oblong; heads yellow, appearing in autumn; involucre of the head or flower consists of small reflexed scales; ray and disk flowers yellow and fertile; seeds top-shaped and ribbed; pappus consisting of 5 to 8 thin, 1-nerved, chaffy scales.

Distribution.—Sneezeweed is native to the northern states, particularly from Missouri and Illinois to Wisconsin and Minnesota. It is found also in the Dakotas, the Rocky mountains, Utah and the northwest. Common in Marshall, Story, Boone, Carroll, Monona, Woodbury, Fremont, Ida, Sac, Lyon, Mills, Taylor, Page, Kossuth, Wright, Winnebago, Hancock, Bremer, Howard, Cerro Gordo, Jones, Linn, Jackson, Clinton, Scott, Lee, Louisa, Muscatine, Dubuque, Clayton and Allamakee counties.

Extermination.—This weed occurs only in low grounds. To

FIG. 210.   Sneezeweed *(Helenium autumnale)*.   Common in low grounds, pastures and along streams.
(Photograph by Colburn.)

eradicate it the soil should be drained; some useful leguminous crop like alsike clover should then be sown. The weed succumbs readily to cultivation.

FIG. 210-A. Distribution of Sneezeweed.

FIG. 210-B. Sneezeweed *(Helenium autumnale)*.

Fetid Marigold (*Dyssodia papposa* (Vent.) Hitchc.).

Description.—A nearly smooth or somewhat pubescent, branched annual with strong odor; 6 inches to 2 feet high; leaves opposite, sessile, pinnately parted, bristly-toothed, with large pellucid glands; heads many-flowered; disk and ray flowers small, yellow; involucre with a few scales at the base, one row of scales united to form a cup; achenes slender, 4-angled, pappus a row of chaffy scales finely divided into numerous rough bristles.

Distribution.—Fetid marigold is common from western Iowa and Minnesota to Illinois and the southwest. It is common along rights-of-way, streets, barnyards and fields in the following counties of western Iowa: Monona, Pottawattamie, Plymouth, Woodbury, Fremont, Crawford, Harrison, Clarke and Mills.

FIG. 211. Fetid Marigold *(Dyssodia papposa).* Pungent smelling herb. Roadsides, fields, waste places, etc., especially in western Iowa.
(Photograph by Hart.)

Extermination.—This weed is not difficult to destroy by cultivation. The seed of the weed sometimes occurs in clover and alfalfa seed.

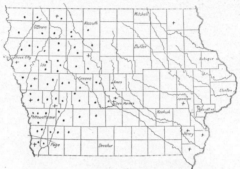

FIG. 211-A. Distribution of Fetid Marigold.

Yarrow (*Achillea Millefolium* L.).

FIG. 212. Yarrow (*Achillea Millefolium*). Common in pastures, especially
northeastern Iowa

Description.—A perennial with simple stem 1 foot to 2½ feet high; leaves twice-pinnately parted, the divisions linear; 3 to 5-cleft flowers in corymbose heads, flat-topped ray flowers usually white, 4 to 5, in some cases pink; plant with a somewhat pungent odor.

FIG. 212-A.   Distribution of Yarrow.

Distribution.—Yarrow is widely distributed in fields, especially on gravelly knolls and in drift soils throughout Iowa; particularly common in the northeastern part of the state. It is found from the Atlantic to the Pacific, also in Europe and Asia. Common in many counties: Clayton, Allamakee, Winneshiek, Howard, Jackson, Jones, Linn, Cerro Gordo, Kossuth, Hardin, Bremer, Marshall, Lee, Keokuk, Appanoose, Warren, Clark, Lucas, Scott and Muscatine.

Extermination.—The weed is not difficult to destroy by cultivation. Rotation of crops may be practiced to advantage. For removal of this weed when it becomes troublesome in pastures, cutting the roots off with a small spade is effective. In Europe it is sometimes recommended as a forage plant but it is of doubtful value for this use.

May-weed or Dog Fennel (*Anthemis Cotula* L.).

Description.—An acrid, branching, strong-scented perennial, white ray flowers; plants 1 foot to 2 feet high; leaves pinnately dissected; solitary and many-flowered, outer ray flowers pistillate, fertile or neutral; disk flowers yellow, small and tubular; involucre of numerous, small, dry scarious scales; achenes small, tuberculate; pappus roughened, none, or merely a minute crown.

Distribution.—This weed is native to Europe. It was early introduced in the United States and now is common from the

Atlantic to the Pacific. It is especially abundant in gardens and along roadsides of northeastern Iowa. This weed is common in barnyards or old hog lots. Cattle and hogs will not feed upon this plant. It is abundant in Story, Hamilton, Boone, Greene,

Plate 59

STINKING MAYWEED
(Anthemis Cotula L.)

FIG. 213. May-weed or Dog Fennel (*Anthemis Cotula*). Barnyards, roadsides, etc. (*After Clark and Fletcher.*)

Sac, Ida, Monona, Woodbury, Webster, Kossuth, Palo Alto, Emmet, Howard, Winneshiek, Clayton, Allamakee, Clinton, Jones, Linn, Scott, Louisa, Muscatine and Lee counties.

Clark and Fletcher recommend as follows: ''Clean up the waste places about the farmyards and seed to permanent grass that will take full possession of the soil to the exclusion of this and other weeds. This plant is usually prevalent in gardens fertilized with manure from city stables.''

FIG. 213-A. May-weed *(Anthemis Cotula)*.
(Photograph by Ada Hayden.)

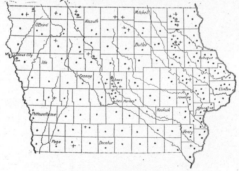

FIG. 213-B. Distribution of May-weed.

Ox-eye Daisy (*Chrysanthemum Leucanthemum* L. var. *pinnatifidum* Lecoq & Lamotte).

Description.—A perennial herb with erect stem; spatulate, petioled root leaves, those of the stem partly clasping, all leaves cut or pinnatifid-toothed; nearly simple stem bearing a large, many-flowered head with numerous white rays; scales of involucre with scarious margins, both disk and ray flowers producing achenes, marked with longitudinal lines; pappus absent.

OX-EYE OR WHITE DAISY
(Chrysanthemum Leucanthemum L. var. pinnatifidum Lecoq & Lamotte.)

FIG. 214. Ox-eye Daisy (*Chrysanthemum Leucanthemum* var. *pinnatifidum*). In pastures occasionally.
(*After Clark and Fletcher.*)

FIG. 214-A.   Ox-eye Daisy (*Chrysanthemum Leucanthemum* var. *pinnatifidum*).
(*Photograph by Photo Section, Ia. Agr. Exp. Sta.*)

FIG. 214-B.   Distribution of Ox-eye Daisy.

Distribution.—This European weed has long been known as a troublesome weed in New England and the central states. It is not abundant in Iowa except in a few places. In recent years the weed has spread, especially in Dubuque, Clayton and Allamakee counties. A small quantity has persisted for years in Story county, but it is not spreading rapidly.

Extermination.—This weed is not as yet troublesome in Iowa. There is much danger, however, that it may be introduced with clover seed, as it frequently occurs in eastern and European grown clover seed. To sow only clean clover seed is a practice which should be carefully observed. It succumbs quite readily to cultivation.

Clark and Fletcher make the following recommendations: "Shallow plowing of sod in August, with thorough cultivation from time to time until frost, will suppress it. This pest does not give trouble on lands worked under a short rotation of crops. Clover for hay in which this weed is plentiful should be cut early."

Chemical Composition.—Its chemical composition according to Maine Bulletin of Agricultural Experiment Station 26:6 (1888), is as follows.*

FRESH OR AIR DRY MATERIAL

Water	Ash	Protein	Fiber	Nitrogen free extract	Fat
9.63	6.85	8.44	29.00	51.72	4.36

WATER FREE SUBSTANCE

	7.6	9.3	32.1	46.2	4.8

Tansy (*Tanacetum vulgare* L.).

Description.—A bitter, acrid, strongly scented, poisonous herb or branched perennial 2 to 4 feet high; leaves pinnately divided into linear-pinnatifid divisions, lobes serrate; heads many-flowered, few ray flowers, disk yellow; marginal flowers fertile; scales of the involucre in several series; receptacle flat or convex, naked; branches of the style brushlike at the summit; achenes 5-angled or 5-ribbed, truncate or obtuse; pappus none or a short crown.

Distribution.—Tansy is common throughout the United States from the Atlantic to the Pacific but more common in eastern North America than in the southern part. It is frequent in many parts

*Compiled by Jenkins and Winton; Bull. Off. Exp. Sta. 11:78.

of the state of Iowa, especially in some communities, in gardens

FIG. 215. Tansy (*Tanacetum vulgare*).
(Photograph by Photo Section, Ia. Agr. Exp. Sta.)

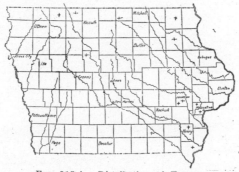

FIG. 215-A. Distribution of Tansy.

and along roadsides.   This weed is especially common in northeastern Iowa in Clayton, Allamakee, Winneshiek, Jones, Delaware,
Dubuque and Jackson counties.

Extermination.—Tansy is easily exterminated by cultivation.

FIG. 215-B.   Tansy (*Tanacetum vulgare*).   Common in old gardens, roadsides, etc.
(*Photograph by Colburn.*)

Western Mugwort (*Artemisia ludoviciana* Nutt.).

Description.—A branching perennial with inconspicuous flowers; leaves and stems white, woolly; leaves lanceolate, the upper
usually entire, the lower cut-toothed; heads in narrow panicles, ray
flowers absent; involucre of dry scarious scales; receptacle naked;
flowers small, yellowish; achenes obovoid; no pappus; trichomes
long, simple, cylindrical, tortuous.

Distribution.—This weed is common from Illinois north to
Saskatchewan, southwest to Texas, and west to Utah.   It is quite
widely distributed in the state of Iowa in Story, Linn, Marshall,
Iowa, Greene, Boone, Hamilton and Webster counties.

Extermination.—This weed is easily exterminated by cultivation. After the crop has been removed the field where the weed is troublesome should be plowed thus leaving the soil in good condition; this measure will check the growth of mugwort.

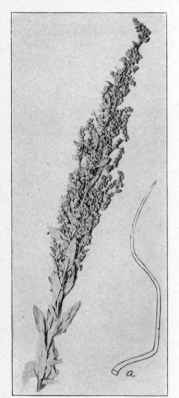

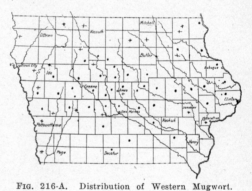

FIG. 216-A. Distribution of Western Mugwort.

FIG. 216. Western Mugwort, or White Wormwood *(Artemisia ludoviciana)*. Common in gravelly places, fields and pastures. *a*, plant hairs.
(Photograph by Colburn. a, Drawing by Charlotte M. King.)

Biennial Wormwood (*Artemisia biennis* Willd.).

Description.—An aromatic, somewhat bitter, smooth annual, or biennial herb, 1 foot to 3 feet high, with leafy stems and erect branches; lower leaves twice pinnately parted, the upper pinnatifid, the lobes linear or linear-oblong, serrate or cut-toothed; inconspicuous flowers; ray flowers absent; heads numerous in short axillary spikes; bracts of involucre green, scarious, margined.

Distribution.—Wormwood is common in the northern Mississippi valley and widely scattered east to Nova Scotia and south to Kentucky. It occurs in many parts of the state of Iowa, including

Boone, Greene, Story, Hamilton, Harrison, Ida, Calhoun, Woodbury, Monona, Sac, Johnson, Lee, Allamakee, Clayton and Winneshiek counties.

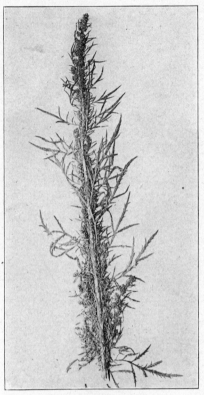

FIG. 217. Biennial Wormwood. *(Artemisia biennis)*. Pungent smelling herb, fields,
woods, etc.
(Photograph by Colburn.)

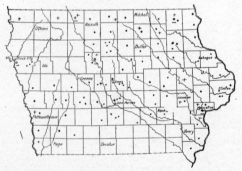

FIG. 217-A. Distribution of Biennial Wormwood.

Extermination.—This weed readily succumbs to cultivation. The plant should be cut off close to the surface of the ground.

Fireweed (*Erechtites hieracifolia* (L.) Raf.).

Description.—A coarse, annual weed of rank odor and grooved stem which in many instances is hairy; leaves simple, lanceolate or oblong, acute, cut-toothed, the upper with auricled base; heads many-flowered; receptacle naked; flowers tubular and perfect; achenes oblong, tapering; soft, white, capillary bristles.

Distribution.—This weed is common in moist woods of the north, especially in recent clearings which have been burned over, hence the common name fireweed. It also occurs in the Rockies and Kansas and is common in many parts of Iowa, especially along streams. It is common in northeastern Iowa: Clayton, Allamakee, Winneshiek, Jones and Howard counties.

FIG. 218. Fireweed *(Erechtites hieracifolia).* Common in clearings and woodland pastures.
(Photograph by Colburn.)

Extermination.—Fireweed is easily exterminated by cultivation. Plants should be cut off close to the surface of the ground.

FIG. 218-A.   Distribution of Fireweed.

Burdock (*Arctium minus* Bernh.).

Description.—A coarse, branched biennial 1 foot to 3 feet high;

FIG. 219.   Burdock (*Arctium minus*).   Common in waste places.   A biennial weed; "seeds" scattered by animals.
(Photograph by Gardner.)

hairy; leaves large, roundish or heart-shaped, thin, obtuse, entire or dentate, floccose, tomentose beneath; petioles deeply furrowed, heads of purplish or whitish flowers, clustered or somewhat corym-

FIG. 219-A.   Burdock (*Arctium minus*).
(Photograph by Photo Section, Ia. Agr. Exp. Sta.)

bose; involucre surrounding the flowers lengthened into hooked tips; glabrous or slightly cottony; trichomes simple, long, twisted.

Distribution.—Burdock has long been known as a troublesome weed in the northern states and in Europe. It is quite common from New Brunswick to Alabama and the Rocky mountains, the Great Basin country and on to the Pacific coast. Common in fields, roadsides, yards and waste places in the following counties of Iowa: Story, Boone, Greene, Ida, Sac, Harrison, Wright, Monona, Woodbury, Mills, Fremont, Plymouth, Lyon, Johnson, Iowa, Polk, Dallas, Guthrie, Madison, Warren, Lucas, Van Buren, Lee, Scott, Louisa, Appanoose, Clayton, Cerro Gordo, Howard, Winneshiek, Allamakee, Clinton, Jones, Linn and Bremer.

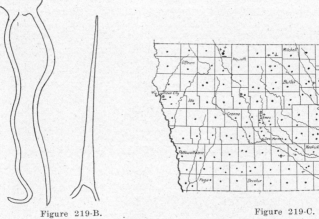

Figure 219-B.   Figure 219-C.

FIG. 219-B.   Trichome or plant hair from leaf of Burdock.
(Drawing by Charlotte M. King.)
FIG. 219-C.   Distribution of Burdock.

Extermination.—Burdock is easily destroyed. Since it is a biennial it should be cut off below the crown during spring or summer; if it comes up again cut off as often as may be necessary.

Doctor Vasey says: "It may also be killed by being mowed when the seed has fully formed, and the tops burned."

Professor Shaw says: "Farmers who go over their fields twice a year with the spade will soon have no burdock."

Professor Goff says: "During the first year of growth the plant is readily destroyed by pulling out by the roots when the ground is very wet."

The important thing in eradicating burdock is not to allow it to go to seed; the plants will soon die out, if not re-seeded. But we may always expect an abundance of the weed as long as it is allowed to grow in waste places, on account of its effective means of dispersal.

Bull Thistle (*Cirsium lanceolatum* (L.) Hill).

Description.—Branching biennial, 3 to 4 feet high, tomentose, becoming dark green and villous or hirsute with age, branchlets bearing large heads; leaves lanceolate, decurrent on the stem with prickly wings deeply pinnatifid, the lobes with rigid prickly points, upper face roughened with short hairs, lower face with a cottony tomentum; heads 1¾ to 2 inches high; bracts of the involucre lanceolate, rigid when young, more flexible with age, long-attenuated, prickly, pointed, spreading tips, woolly arachnoid; flower

Fig. 220. Bull Thistle (*Cirsium lanceolatum*). Common in woodland pastures, roadsides and waste places.
(*Photograph by Photo Section, Ia. Agr. Exp. Sta.*)

hermaphrodite; tube of the corolla 10 lines long; anther tips acute, filaments pubescent; achenes smooth, 1½ inches long; pappus of numerous plumose bristles.

FIG. 220-A. Bull Thistle *(Cirsium lanceolatum)*.
(Photograph by H. I. Featherly.)

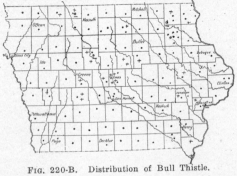

FIG. 220-B. Distribution of Bull Thistle.

Distribution.—Bull thistle is native to Europe. It has long been an inhabitant of the northern states and now extends across the continent. In Iowa it is abundant in every county, and it is frequently found in fields, and particularly in pastures and wood-lots. This weed is common in Clayton, Allamakee, Bremer, Howard, Winneshiek, Jones, Jackson, Linn, Johnson, Iowa, Lee, Scott, Mus-catine, Louisa, Appanoose, Van Buren, Lucas, Poweshiek, Polk, Warren, Madison, Dallas, Boone, Story, Greene, Hamilton, Hardin, Marshall, Wright, Kossuth, Calhoun, Carroll, Monona, Woodbury, Harrison, Mills and Fremont counties.

Extermination.—This weed should be treated like all other biennials. The most important point is to prevent the seeds from forming; therefore the plant should be cut off in early spring below the surface of the ground. During the first season, after germination, the plant produces a flattened mat of leaves, in the second season a flowering stem shoots up rapidly. The plant flowers from early August till frost.

The only successful method of eradication of the bull thistle is to cut down and remove all the "roots" as far as it is possible to do so. If this is done frequently and thoroughly the weed can be exterminated. If the patch is a small one, cutting off the leaves and stems several times during the season as soon as they appear above the ground will destroy this thistle. In treating larger patches plow the ground, harrow and remove the thistle and either burn the material or put it into compost heaps. This should be done five or six times during the season or as often as occasion may require.

Woolly Thistle (*Cirsium canescens* Nutt.).

Description.—Branching perennial, 2 to 4 feet high, woolly throughout, branches bearing single, medium-sized heads; stem angled, white-woolly; leaves, radical, 8 inches to 1 foot long, the division usually 2-lobed, prominently ribbed, ending in stout spines; stem leaves, except the lower, 1 to 4 inches long, pinnatifid, the upper sessile, slightly roughened, with a slight cottony down, the lower white-woolly; heads 1½-2 inches high; bracts of the involucre somewhat arachnoid; lower scales with a broad base, glutinous ridge and ending in a minutely serrated spine, inner scales long, attenuated, tips straw-colored; flowers purple.

Distribution.—This species is distributed from the vicinity of Mason City, Rockford and southwestern Minnesota, west to the

Rocky mountains. It was collected by Chas. A. Geyer in 1839 and described by Nuttall. The writer has seen it very abundant in both Wyoming and Colorado. The species occurs in Emmet, Dickinson, Sioux, Plymouth, Woodbury, Cerro Gordo, Worth, Ida and Carroll counties in Iowa. It has become naturalized in Hamilton, Story, Boone, Greene and Webster counties.

FIG. 221. Woolly Thistle (*Cirsium canescens*). Common in western Iowa fields and roadsides.
(*Photograph by Quade.*)

Extermination.—Correspondents sending this weed frequently refer it to Canada thistle. It occurs not only in pastures and meadows but also in corn and grain fields. Like the Canada thistle, it grows in patches which increase in size from year to year. It was described as a doubtful perennial by early botanical writers and so far as we have been able to determine, it is a perennial. It may be exterminated by thorough cultivation, plowing well and then following with the cultivator.

FIG. 221-A.   Distribution of Woolly Thistle.

FIG. 221-B.   Woolly Thistle *(Cirsium canescens)*. In pastures and fields of northwestern and western Iowa.
(Photograph by Pammel.)

Field Thistle (*Cirsium discolor* (Muhl.) Spreng.).

Description.—Tall, branching, leafy biennial, 5 to 7 feet high,
with heads larger than in Canada thistle; stem striate, slightly
hirsute; leaves radical, 12 to 14 inches long, deeply pinnatifid, the
divisions frequently divided, prickly-toothed, the upper surface
smoothish, and the lower white; woolly single heads terminating

FIG. 222. Field Thistle (*Cirsium discolor*). Common along border of woods, etc.
(Photograph by Photo Section, Ia. Agr. Exp. Sta.)

the branches, with purple flowers; heads 1 inch to 1½ inches long; bracts of the globose involucre somewhat suppressed, slightly arachnoid, lower bracts ovate with a broad base and a weak prickly recurved bristle, slight dorsal gland, inner linear-lanceolate with a nearly colorless entire appendage; flowers purple, tube of the corolla 11 to 12 lines long, lobes of the corolla terminating in clavate tips; anther tips acute, filaments pubescent; bristles of pappus plumose; achene 22 lines long, smooth, upper part yellow.

Distribution.—Cirsium discolor is common in many parts of

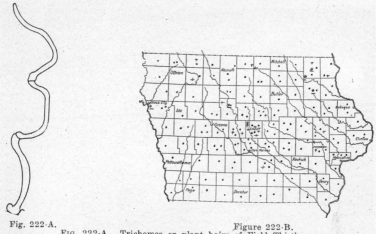

Fig. 222-A.   Figure 222-B.
FIG. 222-A. Trichomes or plant hairs of Field Thistle.
FIG. 222-B. Distribution of Field Thistle.

Iowa; it occurs in Marshall, Johnson, Winnebago, Lee, Winneshiek, Allamakee, Greene, Clayton, Clinton, Iowa, Johnson, Linn, Howard, Jones, Jackson, Scott, Story, Palo Alto, Calhoun, Webster and Emmet counties. It is abundant at Keokuk, Muscatine, Ames, Cedar Rapids, Carroll, Des Moines, Polk City, Steamboat Rock, Mason City, Belle Plaine and Iowa City.

Extermination.—This field thistle should be treated like all other biennial weeds. The flattened masses of leaves should be cut off below the ground in the spring and none of the plants should be allowed to go to seed. We have received numerous inquiries in regard to this weed from western and northwestern Iowa.

Iowa Thistle (*Cirsium iowense* (Pammel) Fernald).

Description.—Biennial with downy, branching stem; leaves roughly hairy above but white-woolly beneath, oblong-ovate to narrowly lanceolate, sinuate-toothed, or somewhat pinnatifid, lobes or teeth with weak prickles; rather large heads; involucre 1 inch to 1½ inches long; bracts with broad glandular back, the inner with a somewhat attenuated colorless tip.

Distribution.—The Iowa thistle is common in borders of woods and in fields from Iowa to South Dakota and Kansas. It is found in Story, Emmet, Kossuth, Marshall, Boone, Linn, Clinton, Webster and Carroll counties in prairie meadows.

Extermination.—This biennial is readily destroyed by cutting the plants off below the surface of the ground. When left to

FIG. 223.   Iowa Thistle *(Cirsium iowense).*
(Photograph by Photo Section, Ia. Agr. Exp. Sta.)

flower it dies, but in meadows where cut off above the surface of
the ground it acts in its method of growth like a perennial.

Canada Thistle *(Cirsium arvense* (L.) Scop.).

Description.—Smooth perennial, spreading by roots and root-
stocks, 1 foot to 3 feet high, corymbosely branched at the top;
stem smooth; leaves lanceolate, sessile, and deeply pinnatifid, lobes
and margins of leaf with spiny teeth; heads small, three-fourths
to one inch high, bracts appressed, the outer with a broad base,
inner narrow, all with an acute, never spiny, tip; somewhat arach-

FIG. 223-A. Iowa Thistle *(Cersium iowense)*. Common in pastures and meadows.
(Photograph by Colburn.)

noid flowers purple, dioecious; in staminate plant, flowers exserted
with abortive pistils, in pistillate less so, scarcely exceeding the
bracts; tube of the corolla 6 lines long; stamens with abortive

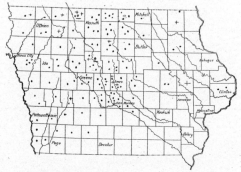

FIG. 223-B. Distribution of Iowa Thistle.

anthers, anther tips acute, filaments minutely pubescent; young
achene pubescent; all of the bristles of the pappus plumose; trichomes simple, long, floccose.

Distribution.—This European weed is widely distributed in
Canada to the Pacific coast. It is found in Iowa in many counties,
more commonly in northern counties than in the southern. It is
more or less abundant in Hardin, Pocahontas and Clinton counties
and it is especially common in Clayton, Allamakee, Winneshiek,
Jackson, Jones, Kossuth, Boone, Story, Marshall and Worth
counties, frequently in clover meadows and in pastures.

Extermination.—The Canada thistle can be treated with sodium
arsenite. No other chemicals, so far as our experiments extend,
will entirely destroy this weed. It is applied at the rate of $1\frac{1}{2}$ to
2 pounds to 52 gallons of water. Carbolic acid is used at the rate
of one part to one part water. However, it only partly destroys the roots and the plants shoot up again from below the
point of injury, but by repeating the application of the acid the
Canada thistle can ultimately be exterminated. A good method of
eradicating the weed is to plow shallowly and cultivate frequently
during the summer. The roots of the Canada thistle extend deeply
down into the soil; hence for this reason deep cultivation will be
of no avail. After plowing, the soil should be dragged and the
roots exposed to the sun and removed, when possible. It may be
necessary to run over the field with a hoe to cut off the stray plants
which appear. This method was tried on a patch several years ago
and no Canada thistles have since made their appearance in this
place. Various crops, such as clover and sorghum, are said to be
effective in subduing the thistles.

In response to circulars of inquiry sent out by the Iowa Experiment Station, the majority of correspondents recommend shallow plowing, disking and harrowing, continuing cultivation and
hoeing as long as the thistles make their appearance. Some report
successful treatment with salt scattered thickly about the thistles,
especially if cattle or sheep are given access to the plants. Some
report success with carbolic acid when it is applied directly to
the stem. Covering the thistle with tarred paper in a few cases
gave success, as did also covering thickly with straw or manure.
The depth of the straw covering was not, however, stated.

Clark and Fletcher recommended the following treatment: ''The
chief safeguard against the Canada thistle and all similar deep-
rooted perennials is undoubtedly a regular short rotation. A

FIG. 224.   Canada Thistle *(Cirsium arvense)*.   Common and widely distributed in Iowa.
(After Clark and Fletcher.)

three-year rotation, including two cuttings of early red clover for
the first year, followed by a deep fall plowing for hoed crops with
clean cultivation, and a cereal crop for the third year, will suppress it.''

A correspondent in The Prairie Farmer on the resistant qualities of Canada thistle says: ''I have been debating in my mind
and endeavoring to determine whether or not root-stocks or portions thereof have to some extent the hibernating qualities of the

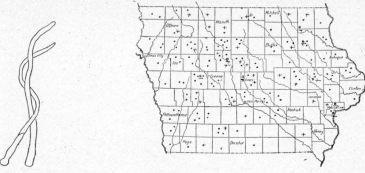

Figure 224-A.   Figure 224-B.
FIG. 224-A.   Trichome or plant hair from leaf of Canada Thistle.
(Drawing by Charlotte M. King.)
FIG. 224-B.   Distribution of Canada Thistle.

seed. For instance, take two seeds of the cocklebur—one hiber-
nates for one season and the other for two seasons, with growth
always present. Now the question is may not a Canada thistle
with its root-stock or a portion of it lie dormant for a season or
more? If this be true, then some of the best known methods of
extermination are useless.''

To this Prof. R. A. Moore says: ''In regard to Canada thistle
roots hibernating and retaining their vitality for several years,
will say, that I think your correspondent's version seems reason-
able, and it is quite conclusive from this fact that the eradication
of the pest is all the more difficult. It seems that many of the
seeds and plants are given this power of remaining dormant when
subjected to adverse conditions. In the lower order of plants,
many of the species of bacteria when subjected to adverse environments are transformed into resistant spores and will not vegetate
until the conditions are favorable.''

We find that the roots are perennial.

Wallaces' Farmer says concerning its eradication: ''We believe if we had a quarter of an acre of Canada thistles we would
let them alone until August, when the thistle will put forth its
utmost efforts to produce seed. While the thistles are in full
blossom we would mow them, rake them up and burn them, and
then plow the ground about eight inches deep, throwing the furrow flat. Letting them put forth their full strength to produce
seed and thwarting that by mowing and burning would weaken
the roots materially. Then by plowing them under eight inches
deep, if possible, you would attack them at their weakest point.''

Smooth Canada Thistle (*Cirsium arvense* var. *integrifolium* Wimm and Grab.).

Description.—This is a form of Canada thistle in which the leaves are chiefly plain and uncut, or the lowest somewhat pinnatifid.

Distribution.—This thistle is local from New England and New York westward. It has made its appearance in several localities in Iowa.

Extermination.—The means of eradication for this thistle are the same as used to remove Canada thistle.

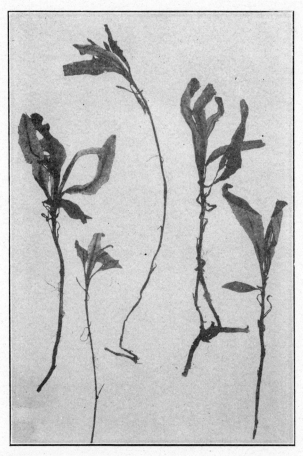

FIG. 225.   Smooth Canada Thistle *(Cirsium arvense* var. *integrifolium).*
(Photograph by E. H. Richardson.)

FIG. 226. Barnaby's Thistle or Star Thistle *(Centaurea solstitialis)*. In alfalfa fields.
(*Mich. Agr. Exp. Sta.*)

Barnaby's Thistle or Star Thistle (*Centaurea solstitialis* L.).

Description.—Annual erect, branched, cottony stem; lower leaves lyrate, deeply pinnatifid, upper leaves linear, entire or nearly so, decurrent wings on the stem; outer bracts with long spreading spines, those at base few and smaller; flowers yellow with soft pappus. A noxious weed on account of its spiny heads.

Distribution.—Barnaby's thistle occurs from Massachusetts to

FIG. 226-A. Distribution of Barnaby's Thistle.

Ontario and Iowa. It has been introduced with alfalfa seed into the western states.

Extermination.—Since this annual weed has been introduced largely with alfalfa seed only clean seed should be sown. Seed coming from the Rocky mountains or Kansas where the weed is not common, is likely to be free from the seed of this thistle. It is easily killed by cultivation.

Chicory or Succory (*Cichorium Intybus* L.).

Description.—A branching perennial with deep roots, alternate leaves; flowers blue or in some cases pink or purple; basal leaves spreading on the ground; stem leaves oblong or lanceolate, partly clasping.

FIG. 227. Distribution of Chicory.

Distribution.—Chicory is common along roadsides in fields and waste places from New England and Canada to Nebraska, espe-

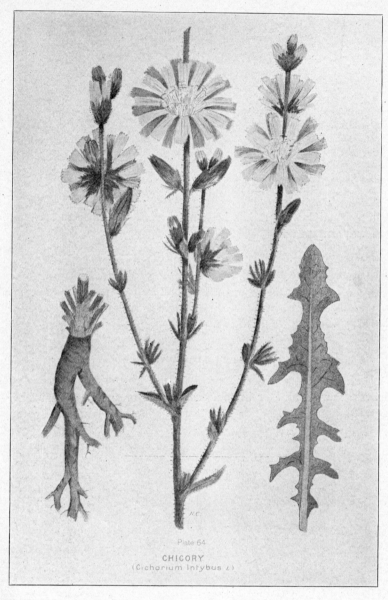

Plate 64

CHICORY
(Cichorium Intybus L.)

FIG. 227-A. Chicory (*Cichorium Intybus*).
(*After Clark and Fletcher.*)

eially common where it has been cultivated. The plant has become a troublesome weed in Wisconsin and Minnesota. This weed is becoming common in Hancock, Clayton, Allamakee, Winneshiek, Jones and Linn counties.

Extermination.—Chicory is not difficult to destroy where rotation of crops is practiced. Though a perennial, the roots are easily killed by repeated cultivation.

Clark and Fletcher recommend the following treatment: "A short rotation of crops will soon suppress it. Chicory is not often

FIG. 227-B. Chicory (*Cichorium Intybus*). In clover and alfalfa fields, sometimes in waste places.
(Photograph by Photo Section, Ia. Agr. Exp. Sta.)

seen in good farming districts except as a wayside weed. Individual plants may be destroyed by close cutting and applying salt to the root in hot, dry weather.''

Dandelion (*Taraxacum officinale* Weber).

Description.—A smooth, or at first pubescent biennial or perennial; the many-flowered head borne on a slender hollow scape; root leaves pinnatifid or runcinate; involucre double, the outer of short scales, the inner of long, linear, erect scales in a single row; after flowering the inner involucre closes, the fruit is ripened close to the ground, and when ripe the hollow scape elongates and the whole involucre is reflexed permitting the wind to scatter the "seeds;" "seeds" oblong, long-beaked, the beak being 2 or 3 times as long as the remainder of the achene, bearing at the end the pappus.

FIG. 228. Dandelion *(Taraxacum officinale)*. Long root, sometimes to a depth of three and one-half feet in the soil.
(Photograph by Gardner.)

FIG. 228-A.   Distribution of Dandelion.

Distribution.—The dandelion is cosmopolitan.   It is quite as common in Europe as in the United States, even being common and abundant at high elevations, as in the Rocky mountains.   Found everywhere in Iowa on lawns and pastures.   It is abundant in every county in Iowa.

Extermination.—Dandelions are not difficult to exterminate in cultivated fields but when occurring in garden crops, especially in strawberry beds, it is more difficult to remove them.   As the dandelions are perennial herbs, seed formation should be prevented.

FIG. 228-B.   A patch of Dandelion in a lawn, early in June.
(Photograph by Charlotte M. King.)

Where they occur in small patches a spud may be used successfully to cut them out. Where they are abundant in lawns it is only necessary to keep the lawn closely cropped and dig up the dandelions with a small spud to prevent seeding. Blue grass and clover, especially the latter, will crowd them out. It is rare that dandelions give trouble after the middle of June.

FIG. 228-C. Common Dandelion *(Taraxacum officinale).* *1,* head; *2,* single flower; *3,* achene; *4,* receptacle and seed with pappus.

Experiments have been made with herbicides. the one most commonly in use being iron sulphate, which is applied at the rate of 100 pounds to one barrel of water. The leaves of the weed where properly sprayed will be destroyed, but owing to the fact that the dandelion posseses a long perennial root, in some instances 4 feet long, it will sprout again. The spraying must be kept up until fall for permanent results.

Chemical Composition.—According to the report of the Bussey Institution the chemical composition of the dandelion is as follows:*

FRESH OR AIR DRY MATERIAL

Water	Ash	Protein	Fiber	Nitrogen free extract	Fat
85.54	1.99	2.81	1.52	7.45	0.69

WATER FREE SUBSTANCE

	13.8	19.4	10.5	51.5	4.8

*Bull. 1877. Compiled by Jenkins and Winton; Bull. 11, Off. Exp. Sta., U. S. Dept. Agr.

Red-seeded Dandelion (*Taraxacum erythrospermum* Andrz.).

Description.—This is a perennial weed with a long root; leaves deeply runcinate-pinnatifid or pinnately divided into narrow segments; heads somewhat smaller than in common dandelion, sulphur yellow; involucre glaucous, the inner bracts corniculate, appendaged at tip; the outer short, spreading or ascending; achene reddish, tuberculate above.

Distribution.—The red-seeded dandelion is a much more recent introduction than common dandelion. It occurs from Maine to Kansas. It was naturalized from Europe and grows in situations similar to those in which common dandelion is found in Iowa. It

Fig. 229.   Red-seeded dandelion (*Taraxacum erythrospermum*).   Common in lawns.
(*Photograph by Colburn.*)

is sometimes less abundant and sometimes more abundant than the latter. We have observed it at Ames and in Des Moines.

Extermination.—This weed may be exterminated by the means used for the common dandelion.

Clark and Fletcher recommend the following treatment: "It is important to prevent dandelions from seeding in lands adjacent to lawns. Though entailing much labor, the most satisfactory way to deal with them, when deeply rooted in lawns, is to loosen the soil with a digging fork and pull them up. The use of the fork may not be necessary in some wet and soft soils. The application of kerosene to the crown of the plant, in the centre of the rosette of leaves, is recommended. Sulphate of ammonia or sulphate of iron in excess is also recommended. A small tablespoonful of salt applied in the morning of a hot day, when the soil is dry, will kill them."

FIG. 230. Perennial Sow Thistle *(Sonchus arvensis)*. Plants with bright yellow flowers, milky juice. Not common in Iowa. A difficult weed to exterminate.
(Photograph by Colburn.)

FIG. 230-A.   Distribution of Perennial Sow Thistle.

Perennial Sow Thistle (*Sonchus arvensis* L.).

Description.—A perennial with creeping root-stock and milky juice; leaves runcinate, pinnatifid and spiny toothed, heart-shaped

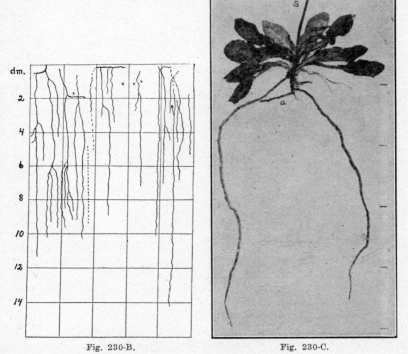

Fig. 230-B.   Fig. 230-C.

FIG. 230-B.   Representation of a section through roots of sow thistle patch.
(From N. Dak. Agr. Exp. Sta. Bull 181)
FIG. 230-C.   Sow thistle plant showing thickened vertical roots.
(From N. Dak. Agr. Exp. Sta. Bull. 181.)

base; flowers yellow; peduncle and involucre bristly; achenes ob-
compressed, wrinkled on the ribs.

Distribution.—Perennial sow thistle is common from Nova
Scotia west to Saskatchewan, North Dakota and Minnesota, and
southward to New Jersey and New England. This weed is a most
pernicious weed in northern Minnesota and common in pastures of
eastern Wisconsin. It has been noted in only a few localities in
Iowa, as at Spencer and Waukon; at the former place along the
right of way of the Chicago, Milwaukee & St. Paul Railway, at
Waukon on a dump heap. We also observed it this summer (1925)
at Postville, and Dr. B. Shimek reports that he found it the past
season (1925) at Clinton and Mason City. Dr. T. H. Macbride
writes that he has seen it on the Chicago, Rock Island and Pacific
Railway near Iowa City.

Extermination.—This is a most difficult weed to exterminate and
should be treated like the Canada thistle. Summer fallow with
frequent cultivation is the only successful method. Clark and
Fletcher of Canada recommend the following:

"Small patches may be eradicated by digging out the roots as
thoroughly as possible and destroying them. This may have to be
done several times during a season. Great care must be taken not
to distribute pieces of the root-stocks over the fields by harrows or
other implements. To exterminate perennial sow thistle some system must be adopted which will prevent the development of leaves
for a period sufficiently long to kill the roots by smothering them.
When a field is badly infested it requires special treatment for a
season and close attention for a number of years. One of the most
effective methods is to plow lightly immediately after the hay or
grain crop is removed and follow with frequent use of a broad-
shared cultivator. Late in the fall plow again, somewhat deeper.
In the spring give frequent cultivation, so as to prevent the development of any leaves, and thus weaken the roots to the greatest
possible extent. About the middle of June or first of July sow
rape in drills at the rate of about 1½ pounds per acre. Cultivate
between the drills as soon as possible and repeat at short intervals
until the rape completely covers the ground. Some hand hoeing
may be necessary to keep all the thistles down. This should pretty
well exterminate the pest but if some plants still remain when the
rape is cut or pastured off, the field may be fall plowed and put
into hoed crop the next season, when special attention can be given
to any small patches that may appear. Buckwheat is sometimes
used instead of rape for a smothering crop."

Summer fallow with frequent cultivation is the most successful
method of eradication. Small patches of the weed may be removed
by digging out the roots as thoroughly as possible several times a

FIG. 230-D. Field of Sow Thistle (*Sonchus arvensis*) on the right-of-way of the Chicago, Milwaukee & Saint Paul Railway near Postville. To the right, Evening Primrose; to the left of this, Sow Thistle.
(*Photograph by G. W. Bulman.*)

season. Care must be taken not to distribute portions of the root stocks over the fields by implements. The perennial sow thistle plants can be killed by some method which will prevent the development of leaves for a period sufficiently long to smother the roots.

FIG. 230-E.   Close-by view of Sow Thistle on the right-of-way of the Milwaukee Railway at the same place as figure 230-D.
(*Photograph by G. W. Bulman.*)

Annual Sow Thistle (*Sonchus oleraceus* L.).

Description.—An annual, succulent herb with leafy, smooth stems and pale yellow flowers in corymbose or umbellate clusters; leaves of stem dentate, runcinate-pinnatifid, terminal with a large segment; heads numerous; blossoms in late summer and fall.

Distribution.—This weed is common in fields and waste places throughout North America, especially in the north. It is common

Plate 67
COMMON or ANNUAL SOW THISTLE.
(Sonchus oleraceus z.)

FIG. 231.   Common or Annual Sow Thistle *(Sonchus oleraceus)*.   Waste places.
(After Clark and Fletcher.)

in Europe and also occurs in Mexico and South America.   It has
been observed in Story, Boone, Carroll, Dickinson, Emmet, Calhoun, Monona, Woodbury, Harrison, Mills, Fremont, Clay, Kos-

suth, Cerro Gordo, Clayton, Winneshiek, Allamakee, Jones, Jackson, Clinton, Scott, Poweshiek, Lee, Louisa, Muscatine and Iowa counties.

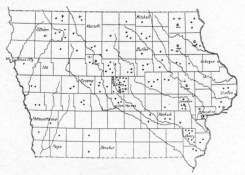

FIG. 231-A.   Distribution of Annual Sow Thistle.

Extermination.—Sow thistle is easily exterminated by cultivation. It can also be exterminated by the use of iron sulphate at the rate of 100 pounds to a barrel of water; where the weed is abundant it may be necessary to make two or three applications of the mixture.

Clark and Fletcher recommend as follows: "Prevent them from seeding in waste places by cleaning them up and seeding them to permanent, vigorous grasses. This annual weed, with its relatively small, pale yellow flowers, when compared with perennial species, is not difficult to control by ordinary methods of cultivation and alternation of crops. Sheep, if sufficient in numbers, will prevent sow thistles from seeding in pasture lands."

The Iowa Homestead says concerning its eradication: "We have seen the sow thistle take complete possession of a soil, growing so thickly that other crops were entirely choked out. Necessarily the best way to destroy it is to cultivate freely. If it makes its appearance in stubble ground we would advise plowing as early as possible after harvest and the cultivation of surface at intervals during the late summer and fall in order to keep the thistles below the ground."

Spiny-leaved Sow Thistle (*Sonchus asper* (L.) Hill).

Description.—This sow thistle resembles the preceding species except that stem leaves are less divided and more spiny-toothed and have the auricles of the clasping base rounded; achenes 3-nerved on each side and margined, smooth.

Distribution.—The spiny-leaved sow thistle is commonly found with the preceding species, in waste places.

FIG. 232. Spiny-leaved Sow Thistle *(Sonchus asper)*. Waste places, yellow flowers and milky juice.
(Photograph by E. H. Richardson.)

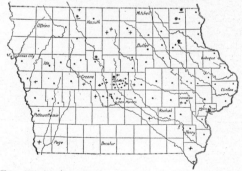

FIG. 232-A. Distribution of Spiny-leaved Sow Thistle.

Extermination.—This annual is not difficult to exterminate by giving thorough cultivation to the soil in which it occurs.

FIG. 233.   Prickly Lettuce (*Lactuca Scariola*).
(*Photograph by Photo Section, Ia. Agr. Exp. Sta.*)

Prickly Lettuce (*Lactuca Scariola* L.).

Description.—The lower part of the stem sparsely bristly; leaves pinnatifid, spinulose, denticulate, tending to turn to a vertical position. Midrib usually bearing stiff bristles; flowers in a loose panicle, pale yellow.

Distribution.—This weed is much more common than the variety; formerly the variety was the common type. The history of the variety is as follows: In the fifth edition of Dr. Gray's Manual of Botany, published in 1868, this statement is made with reference to Prickly Lettuce (*Lactuca Scariola*): "Waste grounds and roadsides Cambridge, Mass., adv. from Europe." In a paper on the distribution of some weeds in the United States, etc., which the senior author of this bulletin published in 1891 the statement is made that it was first observed near Hovey's Garden in 1863-64. In the next edition of Gray's Manual by Watson and Coulter the distribution is given "waste grounds and roadsides, Atlantic states to Missouri and Minnesota." In the next edition by Robinson and Fernald the *L. Scariola* L. is said to occur as follows; "roadsides, railway ballast, etc., s. N. E. to O., Mo., and Ky., chiefly west," but even then less common than the following variety *integrata* Gren. & Godr., which is said to occur in "waste grounds and roadsides, across the continent; westw. an abundant and pernicious weed."

The senior author has seen prickly lettuce for a great many years. The plant so common in St. Louis in 1889, at Madison in 1883, LaCrosse, Wisconsin, in 1886 and in Ames and elsewhere in Iowa

Fig. 233-A. Distribution of Prickly Lettuce (*Lactuca Scariola*)

in 1889 was the variety *integrata*. He saw the true *L. Scariola* common everywhere in California and the Salt Lake basin in 1898.

Plate 68
PRICKLY LETTUCE
(Lactuca scariola / var integrata Gren Gode.)

FIG. 233-B. Prickly Lettuce *(Luctuca Scariola* var. *integrata)*. Common roadsides and gardens.
(After Clark and Fletcher.)

Prickly Lettuce (*Lactuca Scariola* L. var. *integrata* Gren. & Godr.).

Description.—Tall, erect herbs, glaucous, green, 2 to 5 feet high, simple or branched except the lower part of stem which has stiff bristles; leaves glaucous, green, smooth except the midrib which is beset with weak prickles lanceolate to oblong in outline, with spinulose, denticulate margins, occasionally sinuate-toothed; flowers pale yellow. The leaves of *L. Scariola* are pinnatifid and more prickly; trichomes multicellular.

Distribution.—Prickly lettuce was introduced into Massachusetts about 1863 from Europe. It is quite widely distributed in northern Africa and Europe and has become frequent throughout the northern Mississippi valley to the Pacific coast. It is common everywhere in Iowa particularly along roadsides, highways and in gardens. The *L. Scariola* is becoming more frequent in Iowa, in Ames, Des Moines, Boone, etc.

Extermination.—The weed is easily exterminated from cultivated fields and in waste places by cutting off young plants below the ground. Where the stem is cut off below the surface of the ground it will give no trouble, but in meadows and lawns where the plants are cut off above the ground the weed will continually reappear, producing from three to six branches. The following excellent suggestions are made by L. H. Dewey:

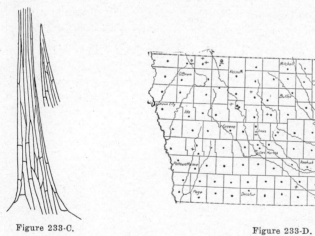

Figure 233-C.   Figure 233-D.

FIG. 233-C.   Bristles on Prickly Lettuce (*Lactuca Scariola* var. *integrata*).
(Drawing by Charlotte M. King.)
FIG. 233-D.   Distribution of Prickly Lettuce (*Lactuca Scariola* var. *integrata*).

"Sheep and sometimes cattle will eat the young prickly lettuce, and in some localities their services have been found very effective in keeping it down, especially in recently cleared land where cultivation is impossible. Repeatedly mowing the plants as they first begin to blossom will prevent seeding and eventually subdue them. Thorough cultivation with a hoed crop, by means of which the seed in the soil may be induced to germinate, will be found most effective. The plowing should be shallow so as not to bury the seeds too deep. Under no circumstances should the mature seed-bearing plants be plowed under, as that would only fill the soil with seeds buried at different depths to be brought under conditions favorable for germination at intervals for several years. Mature plants should be mowed and burned before plowing. The seed appears as an impurity in clover, millet and the heavier grass seeds, and the plant is doubtless most frequently introduced by this means. As the seeds may be carried a long distance by the wind, the plants must be cleared out of the fence rows, waste land and roadsides.''

Clark and Fletcher recommend as follows: ''The seed is short-lived and if the plant is kept closely cut and prevented from seeding in waste places for two or three years it will soon disappear from cultivated areas. Clean waste lands and seed to permanent vigorous grasses. Ordinary methods of cultivation will suppress it in the fields.''

Wild or Canadian Lettuce (*Lactuca canadensis* L.).

Description.—Stem leafy, glabrous or nearly so, glaucous; lower leaves sinuate, pinnatifid, upper entire; heads numerous, in a rather long open panicle; flowers yellow.

Distribution.—Wild lettuce is found from Nova Scotia to Ontario, Ohio and westward; frequently found in Iowa. This species

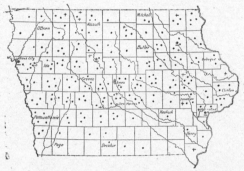

Fig. 234. Distribution of Wild Lettuce (*Lactuca canadensis*).

is common in Story, Boone, Marshall, Linn, Greene, Clayton, Allamakee, Iowa, Polk, Emmet and Kossuth counties.

Extermination.—This perennial is not difficult to destroy by
cultivation.

FIG. 234-A. Wild or Canadian Lettuce (*Lactuca canadensis*).
(*Photograph by Photo Section Ia. Agr. Exp. Sta.*)

FIG. 234-B. Wild or Canadian Lettuce (*Lactuca canadensis*). Fields, roadsides and meadows.

(*Photograph by Quade.*)

Blue Lettuce (*Lactuca pulchella* (Pursh.) DC.).

Description.—Perennial plant, deep-rooted, pale or glaucous; stem simple, about 1 foot high; leaves sessile, oblong or linear-lanceolate, glabrous, entire, or lower leaves somewhat pinnatifid; racemose heads large, erect; peduncles with scaly bracts; bracts of involucre imbricated in 3 to 4 ranks; flowers blue.

Distribution.—Northern Michigan and Ontario southward; reported from several localities in Iowa.

Extermination.—Prevent from distributing seed by continued cutting before flowering. If it becomes established in a field, try thorough summer fallow with deep cultivation so as to check growth of long rootstocks.

FIG. 235. Blue Lettuce *(Lactuca pulchella)*. Plant with blue flowers and milky juice. Common in western Iowa.
(Photograph by Quade.)

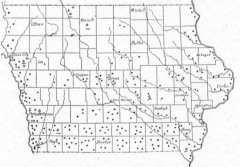

FIG. 235-A. Distribution of Blue Lettuce.

Rushlike Lygodesmia *(Lygodesmia juncea* (Pursh.) D. Don.).

Description.—A tufted, smooth, frequently glaucous perennial 1 foot or more high, coming from a thick woody root, with copious yellowish juice; lower leaves rigid, linear-lanceolate, small, entire, the upper scalelike; flowers purple in erect heads; achenes nar-

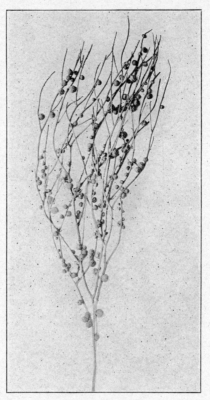

FIG. 236.   Rush-like Lygodesmia or Skeleton Weed *(Lygodesmia juncea).*   A deep rooted perennial with a yellowish milky juice.
(Photograph by Colburn.)

FIG. 236-A.   Distribution of Lygodesmia.

row-ribbed, pappus light brown. This weed is sometimes called
skeleton weed.

Distribution.—This weed is common from Missouri river to western Montana and east to Saint Croix river in Wisconsin. It is a
somewhat troublesome weed in western Iowa in Lyon, Plymouth,
O'Brien, Woodbury, Carroll, Crawford, Harrison, Mills and Fremont counties. It is easily recognized by the yellowish juice and
rushlike stems.

Extermination.—This plant spreads rapidly by a long root. It
also produces a large number of "seeds." Where the weed is
common, the field should be plowed after harvest and the plants
disked. It is a good plan to follow up this treatment with a hoe,
cutting off any plants which are left.

CHAPTER II.

THE GENERAL CHARACTERS OF SEEDS.
L. H. PAMMEL AND CHARLOTTE M. KING.

GRAMINEAE, GRASS FAMILY.

Johnson Grass (*Sorghum halepense* (L.) Pers.).

The spikelet lanceolate, acute, one-sixth to one-fifth inch long.
The scar light colored. The appendages of the seed are cup-shaped
and smooth at the ends. The seeds are of reddish brown to straw
color. The hulled seed is reddish brown and smaller than the
grain of Sudan grass.

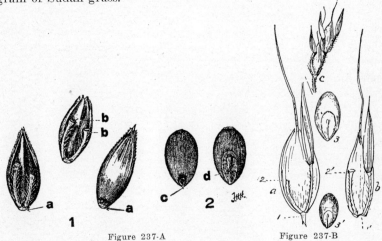

| Figure 237-A | Figure 237-B |

Fig. 237-A. Johnson grass seeds, enlarged. Unhulled seeds, spikelets (1); hulled
grains (2); a, a, scar of the hull; b, b, appendages of the seed with expanded cup-
shaped apexes; c, scar of the grain; d, embryo.
Fig. 237-B. a, Seed of Sudan Grass; 1, fragment of pedicel; 2, broken tip of pedicel;
3, hulled grain; b, 1—suture at base, 2—disk at tip of pedicel, 3—hulled grain;
c, Johnson Grass showing arrangement of sessile and pedicellate spikelets.

Sudan Grass (*Sorghum sudanense* Stapf.).

The seeds vary from one-fifth to one-fourth inch in length.
Most of the seeds retain a part of a short stem. The glumes are
usually straw colored, or tinged with brown. In general, Sudan
grass has fewer very dark seeds than Johnson grass has. The
hulled grains are light brown, larger than in Johnson grass.

Smooth Crab Grass (*Digitaria humifusa* Pers.).

Spikelets lanceolate or elliptical, one-twelfth inch in length,
acutish; glumes usually present, first glume wanting, sometimes

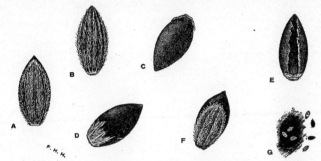

FIG. 238. Seeds of Smooth Crab Grass (*Digitaria humifusa*). A and B, spikelets; A showing the second glume, B showing the third glume. C, D and E, florets; D, bearing a portion of the second glume, E, the inner face, showing the edges of the flowering glume. F, a spikelet of *Digitaria filiformis*, showing the shorter second glume. G, the natural size of both of these species.
(*After Hillman, Bull. Nevada Agr. Exp. Sta.*)

rudimentary, 3-nerved; the first and second, hairy on the margins; the third, 7-nerved; the fourth, dark purplish brown. The occurrence of the seed is very frequent in alfalfa, clovers and commercial grass seed.

Crab Grass (*Digitaria sanguinalis* (L.) Scop.).

Spikelets one-seventh inch in length with usually persistent scale-like glumes, lanceolate, pedicellate; second glume usually ciliate on margins, short; fourth glume silky-villous along marginal nerves, 5-nerved, color pale. This seed frequently occurs in red and alsike clover, as well as in timothy.

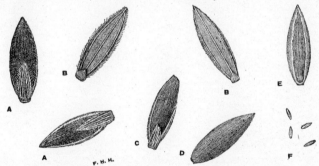

Fig. 239. Common Crab Grass (*Digitaria sanguinalis*). A, spikelets showing the second glume, floret and edges of the third glume. B, the opposite face, showing the minute first glume and third glume. D and E, the two faces of the floret. F, seeds, natural size.
(*After Hillman, Bull. Nevada Agr. Exp. Sta.*)

Tickle or Hair Grass (*Panicum capillare* L.).

Spikelets small, ovate or acute, one-fifteenth to one-twelfth inch long, acuminate-pointed, smooth, shining; sterile glumes usually

absent, when present not shining; first glume 1 to 3-nerved, obtuse
to acute; second and third glumes 5 to 7-nerved, tips acute; flowering glume shining, smooth, elliptical, obtuse, or subacute.   This
seed is often found in clovers and in timothy.

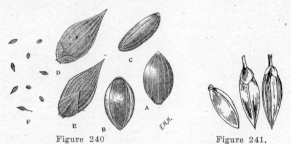

Figure 240   Figure 241.

Fig. 240.   Tickle or Hair Grass (*Panicum capillare*).   A, B and C, the outer, inner
and edge views, respectively, of a floret.   D and E are views of the spikelet, D
showing the second glume and the first in part, and E the first and third and
the second in part.   F, a group showing the natural size of the preceding.
FIG. 241.   Sprouting Crab Grass.   Various views of spikelets.
(*Fig. 240 after Hillman, Bull. Mich. Agr. Exp. Sta.; Fig. 241 drawn by Charlotte M. King.*)

. Sprouting Crab Grass (*Panicum dichotomiflorum* Michx.).

Spikelet lanceolate, ovate, acute, one-tenth inch in length,
smooth; lower glume obtuse, nerveless or 1 to 3-nerved; second and
third glume equal, acute, 5 to 7-nerved; flowering glume smooth
and shining; pedicels scabrous.   This seed is found rarely in clover.

Switch Grass (*Panicum virgatum* L.).

Spikelets ovate, acuminate, 3 to 5-nerved; flowering glume
shorter than the outer glumes, smooth, shining, minutely striated;
with outer glumes removed, the spikelet resembles a small jassid.
This seed is found rarely in clovers.

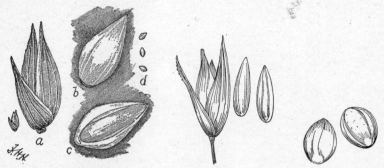

Figure 242-A.   Figure 242-B.   Figure 242-C.

FIG. 242.   A.   Switch Grass (*Panicum virgatum*).   a, b, c, various views of spikelet;
d, "seeds," natural size.
B.   A single spikelet.
C.   Millet (*Panicum miliaceum*).
(*A, after Hillman, Bull. Mich. Agr. Exp. Sta.; B and C, drawings by Charlotte M.
King.*)

Millet (*Panicum miliaceum* L.).

Spikelets acuminate, one-eighth to one-fifth inch long, lower glume acuminate, 5 to 7-nerved; third glume subtending the empty palet, 7 to 13-nerved; flowering glume indurated, obtuse, shining, minutely cross-striated; the hulled seeds ovoid, yellowish. This seed is found in clover and alfalfa seed.

Barnyard Grass (*Echinochloa crusgalli* (L.) Beauv.).

Spikelets with hispid or pubescent nerves; first glume shorter than the third, awned; second awnless or short-awned; third with long rigid awn; flowering glume generally ovate; one-tenth to one-ninth inch longitudinally striate; palet smooth. This seed is not infrequently found in clovers.

FIG. 243. Barnyard Grass (*Echinochloa crusgalli*). A, a floret, back view of the glume. B, front view of floret, showing the palea. C, edge view of the same. D, the spikelet, showing the small first glume, the awned third glume, and the tip of the second. E, a group showing the natural size of the preceding.
(*After Hillman, Bull. Nevada Agr. Exp. Sta.*)

Sandbur (*Cenchrus tribuloides* L.).

Burs with sharp, straight, pubescent prickles; each bur with 6 to 20 globose spikelets.

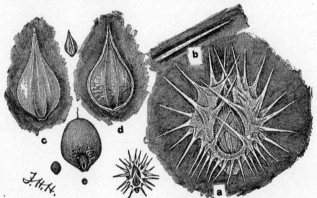

FIG. 244. Sandbur (*Cenchrus tribuloides*). a, bur enlarged; b, spine; c and d, spikelet; e, seed.
(*After Hillman, Bull. Michigan Agr. Exp. Sta.*)

Yellow Foxtail (*Setaria glauca* (L.) Beauv.).

"Seeds" about one-eighth inch in length, very variable; color yellowish, brownish, or even pale; perfect flower with flowering glume plano-convex, partly covering edges of palet; back of flowering glume with prominent transverse branching ridges; flowering glume minutely granular. The foxtail seeds occur in alfalfa, clovers and grass seed.

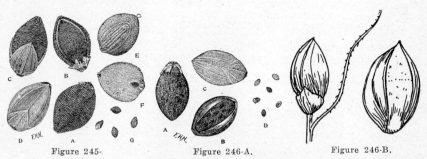

Figure 245.   Figure 246-A.   Figure 246-B.

FIG. 245.   Yellow Foxtail or Pigeon Grass *(Setaria glauca)*. A and B, the outer and inner faces, respectively, of a floret; B, showing the palea. C and D, the same showing the empty glumes of the spikelet; C, showing the second glume, and the first and third in part; D, showing the first and third glumes and the second slightly. E and F, the grain; E, the convex embryo-bearing face; F, the plane face. G, a group showing the natural size.

FIG. 246.   A. Green Foxtail *(Setaria viridis)*. A and B, views of the floret; A, the back of the glume; B. showing the palea, its shining edges partly covered by the edges of the glume. C, a floret covered by the empty glumes (a spikelet), the figure showing the first and third glumes. D, a group showing the natural size.

B.   Whorled Millet *(Setaria verticillata)*.

(A, after Hillman, Bull. Nevada Agr. Exp. Sta.; B, drawing by Charlotte M. King.)

Whorled Millet (*Setaria verticillata* (L.) Beauv.).

Spikelets elliptical-ovate, one-twelfth inch long; first glume triangular-ovate, acute or obtuse, 3-nerved; second glume ovate, obtuse, 5 to 7-nerved; third glume, 5 to 7-nerved, bears short palet in its axil; flowering glume about one-fifteenth inch in length, striate, nearly smooth; bristles about the flower 1 or 2, retrorsely scabrous, one-twelfth to one-third inch long. The whorled millet seed is found in clover seed.

Green Foxtail (*Setaria viridis* (L.) Beauv.).

"Seeds" about one-twelfth inch in length, rounding on both sides, color light green, or greenish; with flowering glume rounded, slightly granular, striate lengthwise and with cross-ridges; palea shining; commonly brownish or greenish. The seeds are found in alfalfa, clovers and grass seed.

Mexican Dropseed (*Muhlenbergia mexicana* (L.) Trin.).

Spikelet about one-twelfth inch long, on very short pedicel; empty glumes nearly equal, acuminate; flowering glume lanceolate, 3-nerved, scabrous on keel, pilose near base; sterile and flowering glumes marked by dark longitudinal lines; seed brown, about one-twelfth inch in length, marked at embryo by darker elliptical area. This seed occurs in alfalfa and the clovers.

Marsh Muhlenberg (*Muhlenbergia racemosa* (Michx.) BSP.).

Spikelets one-sixth to one-quarter inch long; lower glume acuminate-pointed; flowering glume acute, densely bearded at base, minutely pubescent and marked by black lines; seed slender, cylin-

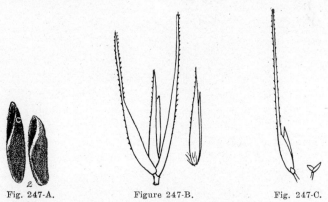

Fig. 247-A.   Figure 247-B.   Fig. 247-C.

FIG. 247. Dropseed Grasses. A. Seed of Dropseed Grass (*Sporobolus clandestinus*). B. Spikelet of Marsh Muhlenberg (*M. racemosa*). C. Nimble Will (*M. schreberi*). (*Drawings by Charlotte M. King.*)

drical, brown, with distinctly marked embryo at one end. This seed is found in timothy and clover seed.

Nimble Will (*Muhlenbergia schreberi* J. F. Gmel.).

Spikelet one-twelfth inch in length, as long as or longer than pedicel; empty glume minute; lower sometimes absent; flowering glume lanceolate, slender, awned, scabrous on nerves. This seed is found in clover seed.

Timothy (*Phleum pratense* L.).

Flowering glume or larger scale marked by several veins, truncate at top, shorter scale or palet also prominent; seed usually with flowering glume; one-sixteenth to one-twelfth inch long; color light gray; seeds somewhat transparent with darker elongated area at lower end, marking the location of the embryo.

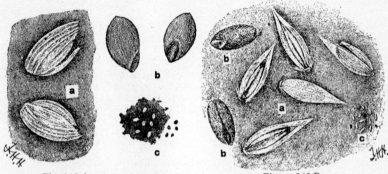

Fig. 248-A.   Figure 248-B.

Fig. 248. A. Seeds of Timothy (*Phleum pratense*): a, grains in the hull, or chaff; b, grains removed from the chaff; c, the same, natural size.
B. Red Top (*Agrostis alba*).
(*After Hillman, U. S. Dept. Agr.*)

Dropseed Grass (*Sporobolus clandestinus* (Spreng.) Hitchc.).

Spikelet about one-sixth inch long, slender, pointed, often marked by brownish spots. Glumes somewhat membranous. The achene is slender, somewhat translucent, with well marked dark area about the embryo. This seed and that of *Sporobolus vaginae-florus* are of quite common occurrence in clover seed.

Red Top (*Agrostis alba* L.).

Spikelet one-twelfth to one-eighth inch long, empty glumes lanceolate, acute; the first scabrous on the keel; the second a little shorter, and smooth or scabrous near the apex; flowering glume a little shorter than the empty ones, obtuse or truncate; palet one-half to three-quarters as long as glume; rachilla frequently present in seed, roughened; fruit brownish, ovate.

Velvet Grass (*Holcus lanatus* L.).

Spikelet one-sixth inch long and nearly as broad. Glumes flattened, hairy. The awn of the second floret is hooked. The achene is usually enclosed in its glumes. The seed is quite abundant in seed of grasses and alsike clover.

Wild Oats (*Avena fatua* L.).

Fruit spindle shaped and of a light yellow color on the tip, balance darker yellow to blackish brown; bears one long geniculate

awn with lower end twisted; basal scar oval, sloping, with a bunch
of soft hairs just above; size 15 millimeters.*

Figure 249-A.   Figure 249-B.

FIG. 249. Wild Oats *(Avena fatua)*. a, spikelet; b, floret; c, natural size.
(A, after Hillman, Bull. Nev. Agr. Exp. Sta.; B. Bull. Mich. Agr. Exp. Sta.)

Crowfoot or Goose Grass (*Eleusine indica* Gaertn.)
Spikelets closely imbricated, 1½ to 2 lines (3¾ to 5 millimeters)

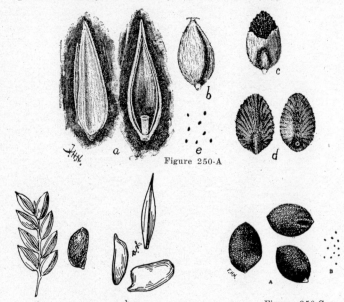

Figure 250-A.

Figure 250-B   Figure 250-C.

FIG. 250. A. Crowfoot or Goose Grass *(Eleusine indica)*. a, florets; b, c, d, **views**
of seed.
B. Tufted Eragrostis *(Eragrostis pilosa)*, a, spikelet; b, fruit.
C. Candy Grass *(Eragrostis megastachya)*. A. Seeds enlarged. B. Seeds natural
size.

*1 millimeter=0.0394 inch or nearly one-twenty-fifth inch.

long, 3 to 6-flowered; glumes obtuse, the first small, 1-nerved, the
second larger, with flowering glumes, 3 to 5-nerved; seeds rugose,
enclosed within a thin, loose pericarp.

Tufted Eragrostis, Southern Spear Grass (*Eragrostis pilosa* (L.) Beauv.).

Spikelet narrow, lanceolate, 3 to 15-flowered, equaling or exceeding the capillary pedicels, one-sixth to five-twelfths inch long;
empty glume ovate, acute, scabrous on keel; flowering glume
broadly ovate, obtuse, 3-nerved, scabrous on keel, one-seventh inch
in length; palet ciliate on keel; seeds small, elliptical or ovoid;
one-twenty-eighth inch in length. This seed is found in commercial grass seed.

Candy Grass (*Eragrostis megastachya* (Koeler) Link.).

Spikelets ovate to linear, many-flowered, one-sixth to two-thirds
inch long; empty glumes nearly equal, ovate-lanceolate, one-twelfth
inch long, prominently nerved, scabrous on keel; palet ciliate on
keel; seed small, ovoid to elliptical, one-thirty-second inch in
length, color brown. This seed is found in commercial grass seed
and alsike clover.

Orchard Grass (*Dactylis glomerata* L.).

Spikelets compressed, 3 to 5-flowered, in crowded, 1-sided
clusters; flowering glumes lanceolate, acute or awn-pointed, one-
sixth to one-quarter inch in length, ciliate on keel, and otherwise
minutely pubescent; callus at base; palet serrate on margin near
upper end and minutely pubescent.

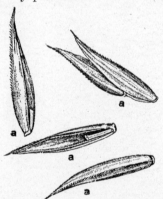

Fig. 251.   Orchard Grass *(Dactylis glomerata).*
(After Hillman. U. S. Dept. Agr.)

Wire Grass (*Poa compressa* L.).

Spikelets lanceolate, 5 to 9-flowered, one-sixth to one-quarter inch in length, flowering glumes about one-seventh inch in length, obscurely 5-nerved; marginal teeth of palet continue to extreme apex. Wire grass seed is found with seed of Kentucky blue grass and other commercial grass seed.

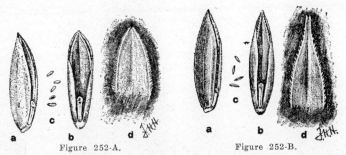

Figure 252-A.   Figure 252-B.

FIG. 252. A. Wire Grass (*Poa compressa*). a, b, two views of seed; c, natural size; d, upper portion of palet showing marginal spines. B. Kentucky Blue Grass (*Poa pratensis*). a, b, two views of seed; c, natural size; d, upper part of palet showing marginal spines.
(*Hillman, Bull. Mich. Agr. Exp. Sta.*)

Kentucky Blue Grass (*Poa pratensis* L.).

Spikelet 3 to 5-flowered, one-sixth inch long, on short scabrous pedicels; empty glumes slightly unequal, lower nearly lanceolate, 1-nerved, upper glume broader, 3-nerved; flowering glume ovate, scarious towards the apex, base cobwebby, rachilla slender; palet with marginal teeth disappearing short of the apex. This seed is found occasionally in fescue grass seed and in other commercial grass seed.

Meadow Fescue (*Festuca elatior* L.).

Spikelet lanceolate, 5 to 10-flowered; empty glume lanceolate, acute, one-quarter inch long, smooth, faintly striate; indistinctly 5-nerved; rachilla slender. This seed is occasionally found in brome grass and rye grass seeds.

Chess (*Bromus secalinus* L.).

Spikelets tinged, 6 to 12-flowered, pendulous in fruit, one-twelfth to two-fifths inch long; empty glume oblong-lanceolate; flowering glume ovate-oblong, obscurely 7-nerved, nearly awnless or short-awned from the back of apex; pubescent along margins and toward the apex; palet obtuse, strongly nerved; toothed or fringed with distant bristles; seed brownish. Found in oats and other small grain.

Soft Chess (*Bromus hordeaceus* L.).

Flowering spikelet 7 to 9 millimeters in length, obtuse and awned; awns 6 to 8 millimeters in length; roughened; glume with 3 nerves on each side; glume bearing numerous hairs upon the surface; caryopsis 5 millimeters long, 2 millimeters wide, light brown, scar at base, extending one-third length of seed.

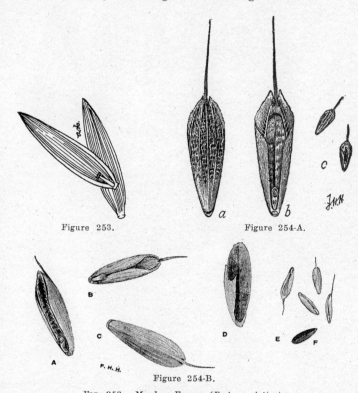

Figure 253.   Figure 254-A.

Figure 254-B.

FIG. 253.   Meadow Fescue *(Festuca elatior)*.
(*Drawing by Ada Hayden.*)

FIG. 254.   A.   Soft Chess *(Bromus hordeaceus)*. a, b, views of enlarged seed; c, natural size.

B.   Chess *(Bromus secalinus)*. a, b, c, d, views of seed, enlarged; e, natural size.
(*After Hillman.*)

Smooth Brome or Hungarian Brome Grass (*Bromus inermis* Leyss.).

Empty glumes unequal; flowering glumes awnless or short-awned, with broad scarious margin at obtuse or emarginate apex; veins of flowering glume conspicuous, roughened; veins of palet roughened; seed flattened, boat-shaped, one-third inch in length, one-twelfth inch in width.

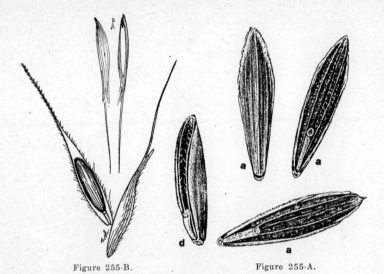

Figure 255-B.   Figure 255-A.

Fig. 255. A. Smooth Brome (*Bromus inermis*). B. a, Awned Brome (*Bromus tectorum*). d, Chess (*Bromus secalinus*).

(A, after Hillman; B, drawn by Ada Hayden.)

Awned Brome Grass (*Bromus tectorum* L.).

Spikelet with unequal, acuminate, pointed, hirsute empty glumes, and rough or hirsute flowering glumes 8 to 12 millimeters long; awn 12 to 16 millimeters long.

Perennial Rye Grass (*Lolium perenne* L.).

Spikelets about one-half inch in length, 5 to 12-flowered; empty glume much shorter than the spikelet; flowering glume obscurely nerved, obtuse, cuspidate, or very short awn-pointed, bearing callus at base; palet granulate; serrulate on margin.

Italian Rye Grass (*Lolium multiflorum* Lam.).

Spikelets two-fifths to three-fifths inch long, 6 to 15-flowered; flowering glume scabrous near the summit, awned; awn slender, about length of glume; margin of palet serrate.

Poison Darnel (*Lolium temulentum*).

Flowering glume about three-tenths inch long, awned or awnless, smooth, obscurely nerved; margins folded in over the palet; turgid; shorter than in *Lolium perenne*.

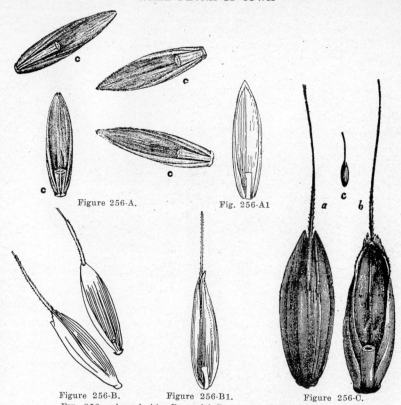

Figure 256-A.   Fig. 256-A1

Figure 256-B.   Figure 256-B1.   Figure 256-C.

FIG. 256.   A and A1.   Perennial Rye grass *(Lolium perenne)*.
    B and B1.   Italian Rye-grass *(Lolium multiflorum)*
C. Seed of Darnel *(Lolium temulentum)*. a, b, with awns enlarged; c, natural size.
    (A, after Hillman; B, drawn by C. M. King; C, after Winton.)

Western Wheat Grass *(Agropyron Smithii* Rydb.).

Fruit similar in shape and size to *A. repens*, but the broadest

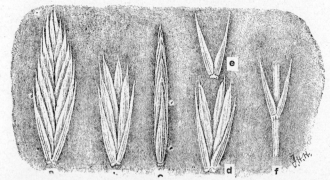

FIG. 257.   Western Wheat Grass *(Agropyron Smithii)*; a, large spikelet; b and d,
small spikelet; c, edge view of spikelet; e, empty glumes; f, empty glume attached
to axis of spikelet.

(After Hillman, Cir. U. S. Dept. Agr.)

portion nearer the tip, giving it more of the characteristic outline of brome grass; tip generally awned, surface finely pubescent; toothing on edge of palea seems finer than in *A. repens*.

Quack Grass (*Agropyron repens* (L.) Beauv.).

Spikelets 4 to 8-flowered; empty glumes 5 to 7-nerved, obtuse or notched, acute or acuminate; flowering glume awned near apex; two-fifths inch in length; 5 to 7-nerved above the middle, finely

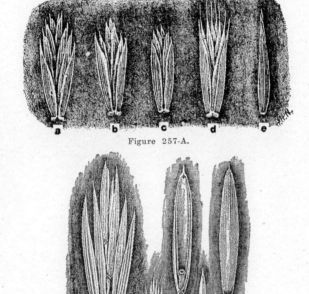

Figure 257-A.

Figure 257-B.
FIG. 257-A and B.   Quack Grass (*Agropyron repens*) showing various forms.

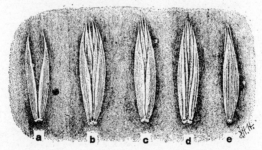

Figure 257-C.
C.   Slender Wheat Grass (*Agropyron tenerum*).
(*After Hillman; A and C, Circ. U. S. Dept. Agr.; B, Bull. Mich. Agr. Exp. Sta.*)

roughened, granular-serrate on margins, finely pubescent at apex; rachilla prominent, hairy, minutely roughened. This grass seed occasionally occurs in clovers.

Wild Barley (*Hordeum jubatum* L.).

Spikes narrow, 1 inch to 3 inches or more long; empty glumes rigid; the 4 internal ones of each group dilated above the base, those of central sublanceolate, all awn-pointed; outer glumes of lateral spikelets setaceous; flowering glume of central spikelet awned; florets of lateral spikelets awnless.

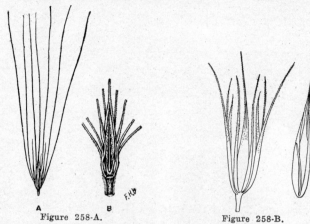

Figure 258-A.   Figure 258-B.

FIG. 258-A. Wild Barley (*Hordeum jubatum*). B. Little Barley (*Hordeum pusillum*). (*A, after Hillman, Bull. Mich. Agr. Ex. Sta.; B, drawn by Charlotte M. King.*)

Little Barley (*Hordeum pusillum* Nutt.).

Spikelet 1 to 3-flowered; empty glumes rigid, the 4 internal ones of each group dilated above the base, those of the central spikelet sublanceolate, all awn-pointed; outer glumes of the imperfect lateral spikelets setaceous; flowering glume of the central spikelet awned, awn equaling those of the empty glumes; florets of the lateral spikelets awnless, or nearly so.

CYPERACEAE, SEDGE FAMILY.

This group of plants furnishes several species, the "seeds" of which find their way into crop seeds. Among them the two following species are most important.

Spike Rush (*Eleocharis palustris* R. Br.).

Achenes slightly flattened, somewhat lenticular, with 2 or 3 obtuse angles one-twelfth to one-tenth inch long, brown, smooth, shining, minutely cross-striated; seed with persistent tubercle from tip; tubercle conical, triangular, constricted; bristles pale, longer than achene; the "seed" may appear with or without tubercle and bristles. This seed is occasionally found in seed of alsike and red clover from wet grounds.

Sedge (*Carex vulpinoidea* Michx.).

Achene enclosed in a utricle called perigynium, 3-angled, somewhat flattened, tipped by lanceolate 2-toothed beak, the persistent base of the flower-style; achene flask-shaped, about one-sixteenth of an inch in length, light brown; surface inconspicuously nerved; whitish projecting scar.

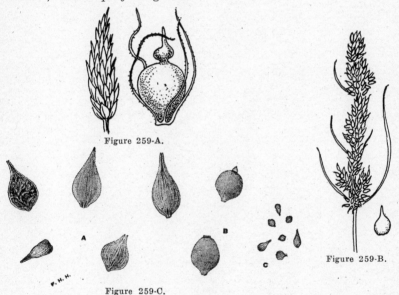

Figure 259-A.

Figure 259-B.

Figure 259-C.

FIG. 259   Forms of Sedges.   A, *Eleocharis palustris*; B, *Carex vulpinoidea*; C, Achenes, "seeds," of common forms of Sedges (*Carex*).
(A and B after Gray; C after Hillman, Bull. Nevada Agr. Exp. Sta.)

URTICACEAE, NETTLE FAMILY.

Hemp (*Cannabis sativa* L.).

Achene ovoid, brown with more or less light markings, 4 millimeters in diameter; surface smooth.

Nettle (*Urtica gracilis* Ait.).

The fruit enclosed in membranous calyx; seed pale straw-color, 1 millimeter long, flattened, ovate, slightly pointed towards the ends, smooth; point of attachment at broader end.

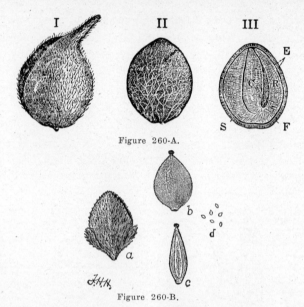

Figure 260-A.

Figure 260-B.

FIG. 260. A. Hemp *(Cannabis sativa)*. I. Seed in envelope. II. Seed without envelope. III. Cross section of seed. F. pericarp; S. testa; E. endosperm.
B. Nettle *(Urtica gracilis)*. a, seed in envelope; b, seed enlarged; d, natural size.
(A, after Winton; B, after Hillman, Bull. Mich. Agr. Exp. Sta.)

POLYGONACEAE, BUCKWHEAT FAMILY.

Curled Dock *(Rumex crispus* L.).

Perianth frequently persistent, consisting of thin veined lobes of the calyx, winged in fruit; wings cordate or notched at base;

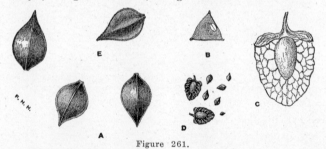

Figure 261.

FIG. 261. Curled Dock *(Rumex crispus)*. A, views of achenes. B, a cross-sectional view of the same. C, diagram of the calyx. D, achenes and calyces, natural size. E, a shrunken achene.
(After Hillman, Bull. Nev. Agr. Exp. Sta.)

margins entire, each with tubercle on the back; color brown; achene triangular, elliptical, with pointed apex; one-twelfth to one-eighth inch in length; color brown; surface smooth, shining; margins minutely roughened.

Tall Dock (*Rumex altissimus* Wood).

Usually but one wing of fruiting calyx bearing a tubercle; pedicel as long as wings; perianth segments veined; margins nearly entire; achene triangular, widened at the base; one-sixteenth to one-twelfth inch in length; scar prominent.

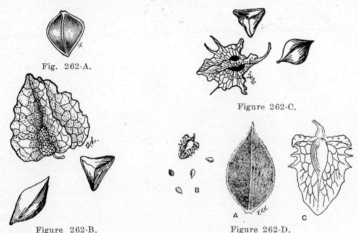

Fig. 262-A.

Figure 262-C.

Figure 262-B.

Figure 262-D.

FIG. 262. A and B, Tall Dock (*Rumex altissimus*). C and D, Broad-leaved Dock (*Rumex obtusifolius*). C, tubercle and calyx.
(*A, drawn by L. R. Collins; B and C, drawn by Ada Hayden; D, after Hillman, Bull. Nev. Agr. Exp. Sta.*)

Broad-leaved Dock (*Rumex obtusifolius* L.).

Wings of the fruit small, only 1-tubercled; margins of wings deeply toothed, backs rugose; fruit three-sixteenths inch long; achenes convex between angles, one-twelfth to one-eighth inch in length; conspicuous scar at base.

Sour Dock (*Rumex Acetosa* L.).

Inner sepals of calyx in fruit, with wings; achene convex between angles; one-twelfth inch in length, variable, smooth, shining; dark reddish brown. The seeds of this dock are likely to occur in European grown clover seed.

Sheep Sorrel (*Rumex Acetosella* L.).

Calyx usually persistent, not wing-margined in fruit, roughened, with prominent veins; closely fitting achene, elliptical or ovate with blunt angles, one-twenty-fourth to one-twentieth inch in length; color of fruit grayish to brownish. Common in red, white and alsike clover.

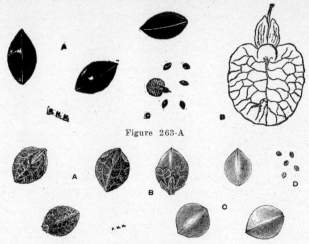

Figure 263-A

Figure 263-B.

FIG. 263.   A.   Sour Dock (*Rumex Acetosa*). A, various achenes. B, diagram of the calyx.   C, achenes and calyx, natural size.
B.   Sheep Sorrel (*Rumex Acetosella*). A, seeds bearing the calyx segments. B, one having the segments partly broken away.   C, achenes from which the calyx is removed.   D, seeds, natural size.
(After Hillman, Bull. Nev. Agr. Exp. Sta.)

Dooryard Knotweed (*Polygonum aviculare* L.).

Achenes 3-angled, ovoid, acute, sides deeply concave, one-eighth to one-seventh inch in length; color light to dark and reddish brown; surface finely granulated and striated lengthwise.

Figure 264-A.   Figure 264-B.   Figure 264-C.

FIG. 264.   A.   Water Smartweed (*Polygonum acre*).
B.   Dooryard Knotweed (*Polygonum aviculare*). A, group of seeds (achenes) snowing the usual forms; that at the right is one of the smooth, light colored specimens; B, a group showing the natural size; C, a cross section showing the relative positions of embryo and endosperm.
C.   Prince's Feather (*Polygonum orientale*).
(A and C, drawn by C. M. King; B, after Hillman.)

Water Smartweed (*Polygonum acre* HBK.).

Achenes oblong, thick, generally 3-angled, somewhat lenticular, one-tenth to one-eighth inch in length, smooth, finely reticulated; color dull; base of perianth adhering.

Prince's Feather (*Polygonum orientale* L.).

Achenes usually orbicular, flattened, with prominent remnant of style, one-ninth inch in length, finely reticulated; color dull brownish to black; base with large scar; remnant of colored calyx at base.

Water Pepper (*Polygonum Hydropiper* L.).

Achene lenticular, triangular; form broadly oblong or ovoid, slightly gibbous; one-tenth inch in length; dull, color light.

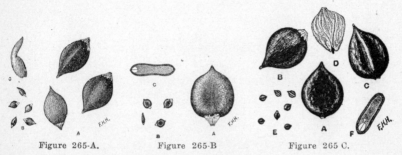

Figure 265-A.   Figure 265-B   Figure 265 C.

FIG. 265. A. Water Pepper *(Polygonum Hydropiper)*. Seeds enlarged and natural size; the embryo at C.
B. Slender Pink Smartweed *(Polygonum lapathifolium)*. A, a side view of an achene bearing a part of the perianth at the base, enlarged. B, a group showing the natural size, one shown edgewise. C, a cross section of an achene.
C. Lady's Thumb *(Polygonum Persicaria)*. A, B and C, side views of common forms of achenes; C, a three-angled specimen. D, one covered by the perianth (reduced from the size of A, B and C.) E, a group showing the natural size. F, a cross section of an achene.
(After Hillman, Bull. Nev. Agr. Exp. Sta.)

Slender Pink Smartweed (*Polygonum lapathifolium* L.).

Achenes ovoid-oblong, lenticular, edges slightly angled along the center, with a prominent remnant of the style at upper end, one-twelfth to one-tenth inch long; color light brown to dark brown, shining; base of achene with remnant of perianth adhering.

Lady's Thumb (*Polygonum Persicaria* L.).

Achenes broadly ovate, lenticular, often somewhat 3-angled at base, one-eleventh inch in length; surface smooth, shining; color dark; remnant of perianth present at base.

Heart's-ease, Pennsylvania Smartweed (*Polygonum pennsylvanicum* L.).

Achenes orbicular, usually broader than long, with edges as in *P. lapathifolium*, remnant of style short, one-seventh to one-sixth inch long; color blackish, dull, base of achene with perianth adhering.

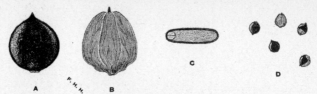

FIG. 266. Pennsylvania Smartweed (*Polygonum pennsylvanicum*). A, a side view of seed (achene). B, one surrounded by the calyx; the opposite side has two segments between those on the edges. C, a cross section of a seed. D, seeds, natural size.

(After Hillman, Bull. Nev. Agr. Exp. Sta.)

Bushy Knotweed (*Polygonum ramosissimum* Michx.).

Achenes sharply 3-angled, sides less deeply concave than in *P. aviculare,* one-eighth inch in length; color blackish, dull, calyx greenish, light straw-colored in dried specimens.

Mild Water Pepper (*Polygonum hydropiperoides* Michx.)

Achenes 3-angled, ovoid, angles between flattened, sides slightly concave, one-eighth to one-tenth inch in length; smooth, shining.

Black Bindweed (*Polygonum Convolvulus* L.).

Achenes large, prominently 3-angled, ovoid-pyramidal, one-eighth to one-sixteenth inch in length; surface dull, with minute striae; color blackish; perianth usually removed, when present straw-colored.

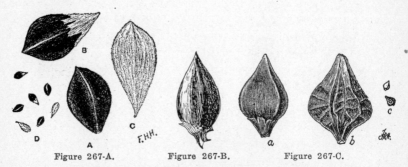

Figure 267-A.   Figure 267-B.   Figure 267-C.

FIG. 267. A. Black Bindweed (*Polygonum Convolvulus*). A and B, views of two seeds, the latter bearing a part of the perianth about the base. C, a view of an entire perianth covering a seed. D, a group showing the natural size. B. Bushy Knotweed (*Polygonum ramosissimum*). C. Erect Knotweed (*Polygonum erectum*).
(A and C, after Hillman, Bull. Mich. Agr. Exp. Sta.; B, drawn by L. R. Collins.)

Erect Knotweed (*Polygonum erectum* L.).

Achenes 3-angled, ovoid, less deeply concave between the angles than in preceding (*P. aviculare*); one-ninth to one-tenth inch in length; dull, minutely reticulated.

CHENOPODIACEAE, GOOSEFOOT FAMILY.

Cycloloma (*Cycloloma atriplicifolium* (Spreng.) Coult.).

Fruit enclosed by the calyx, lower surface prominently rayed, upper surface depressed, wing-margined, one-tenth to one-eighth inch in diameter; seed nearly spherical, somewhat flattened, one-twelfth inch in diameter, blackish; scar whitish; embryo slender, forming a ring about the endosperm.

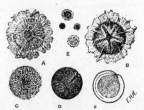

FIG. 268. Cycloloma (*Cycloloma atriplicifolium*). a, b, seed in envelope; c, d, enlarged views; e, seeds, natural size; f, cross section.
(*After Hillman, Bull. Mich. Agr. Exp. Sta.*)

Maple-leaved Goosefoot (*Chenopodium hybridum* L.).

Seeds dark grayish black, circular, 2.5 to 3 millimeters in diameter, flattened double-convex, with distinct margin, slightly indented by a notch; scar on middle of one face; seed shining, black, when envelope is entirely removed.

Lamb's Quarters (*Chenopodium album* L.).

Seeds one-twentieth inch in diameter, often surrounded by thin

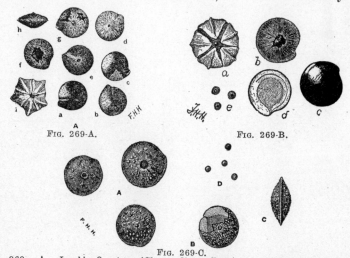

FIG. 269-A.   FIG. 269-B.

FIG. 269-C.

FIG. 269. A. Lamb's Quarters (*Chenopodium album*). a and b, different views of seed; d, g, f, seed with utricle; i, calyx attached.
B. Maple-leaved Goosefoot (*Chenopodium hybridum*). a, seed in envelope; b, c, general view of seed; d, cross section; e, natural size.
C. Western Lamb's Quarters (*Chenopodium murale*). A, B and C, views of seed; D, the natural size.
(*After Hillman. A and B, Bull. Mich. Agr. Exp. Sta.; C, Bull. Nev. Exp. Sta.*)

glandular utricle which varies from grayish to straw-color; seed dark brown, shining, firmly attached to pericarp, edge rounded, depressed, convex with a curved groove; seed somewhat irregular in shape; some seeds also surrounded by the pericarp and star-shaped calyx. In seed of small grains, clover and grasses.

Spinach (*Spinacia oleracea* L.).

Fruit broadly ovate, one-sixth inch in length, size variable; utricle unarmed, wrinkled, in some cases tuberculate, straw-colored; achene closely enveloped by utricle; scar elevated.

FIG. 270. Orach (*Atriplex patula* var. *hastata*). a, b, c, different views of seed in envelope; d, e, f, views of seeds.
(After Hillman, Bull. Mich. Agr. Exp. Sta.)

Orach (*Atriplex patula* var. *hastata* (L.) Gray).

Fruiting bracts ovate-triangular, entire toothed, often muricate on the back, united to near the middle; seed jet black, shining, nearly circular, edge bluntly rounded, bearing a notch; a groove leads from protuberance on the margin part way to center of face.

Russian Thistle (*Salsola Kali* var. *tenuifolia* G. F. W. Mey.).

Calyx persistent, 5-parted, membranaceous, enclosing the flattened utricle by a broad, flat, membranaceous wing; seed conical,

FIG. 271-A.   FIG. 271-B.
FIG. 271. A. Russian Thistle (*Salsola Kali* var. *tenuifolia*), a, seed in envelope; b, d, e, views of seed enlarged; c, natural size.
B. Kochia or Mexican Fireweed (*Kochia scoparia*).
(A, after Hillman, Bull. Mich. Agr. Exp. Sta.; B, drawing by C. M. King.)

upper end truncate, with a depression one-eighteenth inch in diameter, brownish; seed without endosperm, embryo coiled in a spiral; cotyledons slender.

AMARANTHACEAE, AMARANTH FAMILY.

Rough Pigweed (*Amaranthus retroflexus* L.).

Seeds from one-eighteenth to one-twentieth inch in length; oval, spherical or nearly spherical, both sides convex with a continuous ring on the margin; scar small; smooth, black, shining; seeds much like *A. blitoides* but somewhat smaller. In seeds of red clover, alsike and timothy.

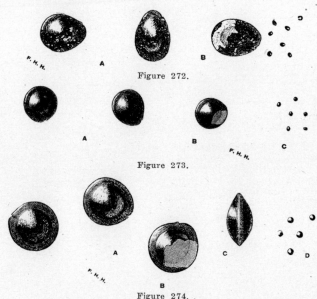

Figure 272.

Figure 273.

Figure 274.

FIG. 272. Rough Pigweed (*Amaranthus retroflexus*). A, seeds; B, one having the seed-coat broken; C, the natural size.
FIG. 273. Tumbleweed (*Amaranthus graecizans*). A, seeds. B, a broken one. C, the natural size.
FIG. 274. Spreading Amaranth (*Amaranthus blitoides*). A, seeds. B, a broken specimen. C, an edge view. D, the natural size.
(*After Hillman, Bull. Nev. Agr. Exp. Sta.*)

Tumbleweed (*Amaranthus graecizans* L.).

Seeds lenticular or roundish, one-twenty-fourth inch in diameter, glossy black, much like the preceding but smaller. In grasses and lawn mixtures.

Spreading Amaranth (*Amaranthus blitoides* Wats.).

Seeds lenticular or round to broadly egg-shaped, one-sixth inch in diameter, both sides convex with distinct margin, glossy, black; seeds borne in ovoid-oblong utricle, 2 to 3-beaked by the persistent style. Reported in western alfalfa seed.

Water Hemp (*Acnida tuberculata* Moq.).

Seeds erect, lens-shaped, one-fifteenth inch in diameter, smooth, shining, black, 2 to 5 remnants of stigmas, sometimes with the at-

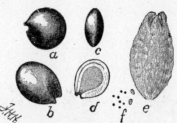

FIG. 275. Water Hemp (*Acnida tuberculata*). a, b, c, different views of seed; d, cross section; e, in seed envelope; f, natural size. (*After Hillman, Bull. Mich. Agr. Exp. Sta.*)

tached calyx and mucronate bracts; utricle longer than bracts; circumscissile, not angled. In seed of clover and alsike.

CARYOPHYLLACEAE, PINK FAMILY.

Chickweed (*Stellaria media* (L.) Cyrill.).

Kidney-shaped, broadly egg-shaped to wedge-shaped, one-twentieth inch in length, finely and closely tubercled; color grayish to

FIG. 276. Chickweed (*Stellaria media*). A, seeds, side view. B, one shown in edge view. C, a sectional view showing the embryo and endosperm. D, group showing the natural size. (*After Hillman, Bull. Nev. Agr. Exp. Sta.*)

light brown; scar marked by a longitudinal groove at basal end. Occasionally found in clover.

Corn Cockle (*Agrostemma Githago* L.).

Seeds large, angular, broadly wedge-shaped, one-eighth inch in length; tubercles prominent, lines of tubercles beginning at basal

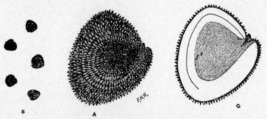

FIG. 277. Corn Cockle (*Agrostemma Githago*), a, seed enlarged; b, seed in cross section; c, natural size. (*After Hillman, Bull. Nev Agr. Exp. Sta.*)

end of seed; color brown to black; size of seed variable; according
to Dewey the larger ones hard to screen out. Most commonly
found in wheat; seed has poisonous properties. This weed is considered a pest in grain fields. The seed is found in wheat and in
chicken feed.

Evening Catchfly (*Lychnis alba* Mill.).

Seed smaller than that of *Silene noctiflora,* which resembles it,
one-fifteenth of an inch in length; ash-colored. Found in alfalfa
and clover seed.

Forked Catchfly (*Silene dichotoma* Ehrb.).

General shape of seed roundish triangular, somewhat flattened,
about 1.5 millimeters in breadth; color dull reddish brown; 5 to 7
rows of tubercles on each side in curved rows following the rounding outline of the shape of the seed; scar on the straight side of
seed.

Figure 278-A.   Figure 278-B.

FIG. 278. A. Forked Catchfly (*Silene dichotoma*). a, seed enlarged; b, natural size.
B. Night-flowering Catchfly (*Silene noctiflora*). A, side view of a seed; B, edge view
of the same, showing the scar-cavity. C, a longitudinal section of a seed, showing
the embryo curved about the endosperm. D, the natural size of the seeds.
(*After Hillman: A, Bull. Mich. Agr. Exp. Sta., B, Bull. Nev. Agr. Exp. Sta.*)

Night-flowering Catchfly (*Silene noctiflora* L.).

Seeds kidney-shaped, thick, with rounded edges, one-fifteenth to
one-tenth inch in length; surface roughened by peculiar tubercles;
on shorter side a black elevated scar; immature seeds red. Found
in clover and grass seed.

Figure 279-A.   Figure 279-B.
FIG. 279. A. Evening Catchfly (*Silene vespertina*).
B. Evening Catchfly (*Lychnis alba.*)
(*Drawings by L. R. Collins and Ada Hayden.*)

Bladder Campion (*Silene latifolia* (Mill.) Brit. & Rendle).

Seed kidney-shaped, more nearly spherical than in *Silene nocti-*

flora, one-fifteenth inch in length; shape of seed more nearly orbicular than in *S. noctiflora.* Found in some clovers.

FIG. 280. Bladder Campion (*Silene latifolia*). A, common form of seeds, side view.
B, edge view of a seed, showing the scar-cavity. C, the natural size of the seeds.
(*After Hillman, Bull. Nev. Agr. Exp. Sta.*)

Cowherb (*Saponaria Vaccaria* L.).

Seed nearly spherical, one-twelfth inch in length, minutely tubercled; color black; immature seeds reddish; scar whitish, in depression. Occurs in wheat and in red clover.

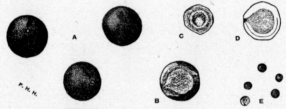

FIG. 281. Cowherb (*Saponaria Vaccaria*). A, different views of the seeds; the one
at the left and the lower one show the scar; the light spots show the minute
surface-projections. B and C, parts of a broken seed, B retaining a part of the
embryo. D, a sectional view of a seed. E, seeds, natural size.
(*After Hillman, Bull. Nev. Agr. Exp. Sta.*)

PORTULACACEAE, PURSLANE FAMILY.
Purslane (*Portulaca oleracea* L.).

Seeds broadly ovate, inclined to kidney-shaped, flattened, one-
thirtieth inch in length, roughened by minute tubercles in concen-
tric rows; small whitish scar at smaller end.

FIG. 282. Purslane (*Portulaca oleracea*). A, a side view of a seed, enlarged, showing
the whitish scar: B, a group, natural size: C, section of a seed, taken parallel
with the faces.
(*After Hillman, Bull. Nev. Agr. Exp. Sta.*)

RANUNCULACEAE, CROWFOOT FAMILY.
Small-flowered Crowfoot (*Ranunculus abortivus* L.).

Achene flattened-circular, with 2 convex faces, orange-brown in color, smooth and shining, very slightly impressed with wrinkles; remnant of style present as a short curved point on margin.

Figure 283-A.   Figure 283-B.

FIG. 283. A. Small-flowered Crowfoot *(Ranunculus abortivus)*. a, achenes enlarged; b, end view; c, achenes natural size.
B. Tall Buttercup *(Ranunculus acris)*. a, b, different views of seed; c, cross section; d, natural size.

(After Hillman, Bull. Mich. Agr. Exp. Sta.)

Tall Buttercup (*Ranunculus acris*).

Carpel 1-ovuled; achene flattened, tipped by remnant of curved style, one-tenth to one-eighth inch long; color greenish to brownish; surface apparently smooth, minutely pitted; scar minute, in a whitish depression at base of achene.

Meadow Rue (*Thalictrum dasycarpum* Fisch. and Lall.).

Fruit an achene, ovoid, one-fifth inch in length, with remnant of curved style, prominently ribbed, with from 6 to 8 wings, short-stalked, glabrous or pubescent; seed elongated, ovoid, one-tenth inch long, brownish, smooth, with prominent veins near base of seed. This seed is occasionally found in clover seed.

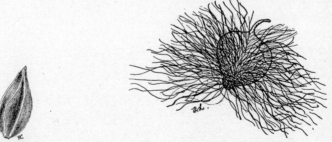

Figure 284-A.   Figure 284-B.

FIG. 284. A. Meadow Rue *(Thalictrum dasycarpum)*.
B. Long-fruited Anemone *(Anemone cylindrica)*.
(A, drawing by L. R. Collins; B, by Ada Hayden.)

Long-fruited Anemone (*Anemone cylindrica* Gray).

Achenes one-quarter inch in length and one-fifth inch in width, flat, compressed, 1-seeded, nearly orbicular, greenish, covered by dense pilose mass of whitish hairs.

Field Larkspur (*Delphinium Consolida* L.).

Seed angular, somewhat convex on back, one-twelfth inch long and equally wide, surface scabrous or scaly, with whitish margins; color blackish, brownish or grayish; seed with sharp bitter taste. This seed is reported as of frequent occurrence in Russian clover seed.

Prairie Larkspur (*Delphinium Penardi* Huth.).

Seeds somewhat flattened, upper end wider, nearly square, 4-angled or triangular, one-sixteenth to one-twelfth inch long, surface scabrous, becoming rougher on angles; color grayish.

Figure 285-A.    Figure 285-B. 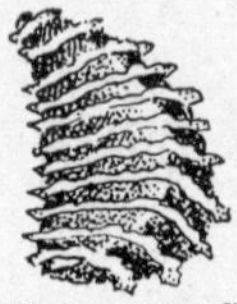   Figure 285-C.

FIG. 285. A. Prairie Larkspur *(Delphinium Penardi)*.
B. and C. Field Larkspur *(Delphinium Consolida)*.
(A, drawing by Ada Hayden; B, drawn by L. R. Collins; C, drawn by Charlotte M. King.)

PAPAVERACEAE, POPPY FAMILY.
Poppy (*Papaver somniferum* L.).

Seed about 1 millimeter in length, kidney-shaped, one end being slightly larger than the other; hilum and chalaza in a notch, connected by a short raphe; surface covered with fine, beautiful reticulations; embryo straight; considerable endosperm.

Figure 286-A. 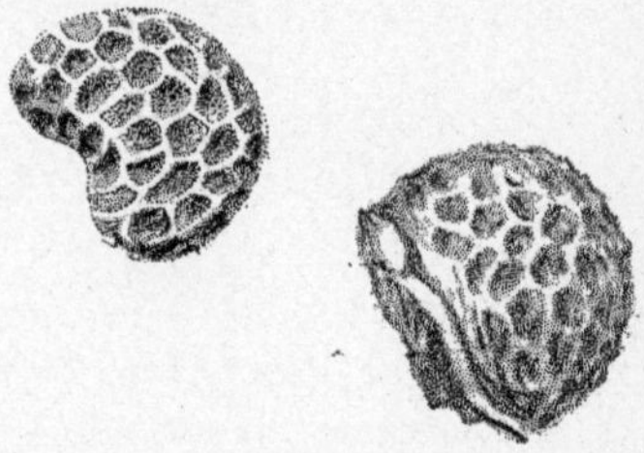   Figure 286-B.

FIG. 286. A. Poppy *(Papaver somniferum)*. To the left embryo of seed.
B. Prickly Poppy *(Argemone intermedia)*.
(A, after Winton. B, drawing, Charlotte M. King.)

Prickly Poppy (*Argemone intermedia* Sweet).

Pod ellipsoid, prickly; seeds spherical, crested, about 2 millimeters in diameter; dark brown, surface reticulate and deeply pitted.

CRUCIFERAE, MUSTARD FAMILY.
Pennycress (*Thlaspi arvense* L.).

Seed oblong, flattened, one-twelfth to one-tenth inch long; surface marked by curved ridges, simple or occasionally forked, which curve from base to apex in regular rows; color brownish to dark reddish brown; funicle sharp pointed. Found largely in wheat, barley and oats. This plant is reported as "a pest of grain (wheat) fields of Manitoba."

Figure 287-A.   Figure 287-B.

FIG. 287.   A.   Pennycress (*Thlaspi arvense*). A, side view of a seed; B, seeds, natural size; C, the embryo.
B, cress (*Lepidium sativum*).
(*After Hillman, Bull. Mich. Agr. Exp. Sta.*)

Large Peppergrass (*Lepidium virginicum* L.).

Seed elongated with prominent ridge on one side, one-twelfth inch in length; color light reddish brown; cotyledons incumbent;

FIG. 288.   Large Peppergrass (*Lepidium virginicum*).   A, three seeds shown in side view. The upper two show the narrow, curved groove of one face, the lower one shows the broader, shallow depression of the opposite face. The one immediately at the right of A shows the widened border and its light colored edge. B, entire pod. C, a seed showing the mucilage as it appears while wet. D is a cross sectional view of a seed, showing the flattened form of the cotyledons and the edgewise position of the caulicle. E, the embryo in side view. F, seeds, pod, and half-pod, natural size.
(*After Hillman, Bull. Nev. Agr. Exp. Sta.*)

seed coat becomes mucilaginous when wet. Generally found in small grains and commercial grass seed. This seed is frequent in timothy.

Small Peppergrass (*Lepidium apetalum* Willd.).

Seeds oblong, flattened, margin colorless, prominent ridge on one side, one-sixteenth to one-twelfth inch long, minutely roughened; cotyledons incumbent; seed coat becomes mucilaginous when wet; funicle prominent. This seed is very generally found in small grains and commercial grass seed.

Figure 289-A.   Figure 289-B.

FIG. 289. A. Small Peppergrass *(Lepidium apetalum)*. A, seeds shown in side view; B, a half-section of a pod; C, a seed in cross section, showing the three parts of the embryo, the caulicle being at the right; D, the embryo, the caulicle at the left; E, group of seeds, natural size.
B. *Lepidium apetalum*, with section of seed coat showing action of mucilaginous cells after moistening.
(A, after Hillman, Bull. Nev. Agr. Exp. Sta.; B, drawn by Charlotte M. King.;

Cress (*Lepidium sativum* L.).

Seed oval, one edge nearly straight, the other convex, one-tenth inch in length, apparently slightly marginate at basal end, basal portion bearing scar, also with white projecting tip, and end of funicle prominent, smooth, brownish.

Shepherd's purse (*Capsella Bursa-pastoris* (L.) Medic.).

Seed small, flattened, oblong, with 2 longitudinal grooves; one-

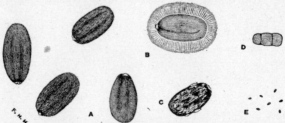

FIG. 290. Shepherd's Purse *(Capsella Bursa-pastoris)*. A, seeds showing various forms and degrees of color. B, showing the mucilage while wet. C, a seed showing the appearance of the dried mucilage. D, a seed in cross section. E, seeds, natural size.
(After Hillman, Bull. Nev. Agr. Exp. Sta.)

twenty-fourth to one-twentieth inch in length; color light brown; scar whitish, funicle prominent. This seed is found in alsike clover seed.

False Flax (*Camelina sativa* (L.) Crantz).

Seeds one-twelfth inch in length, light brown, minutely pitted; caulicle prominent, running lengthwise with conspicuous groove

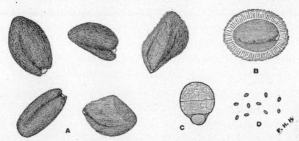

FIG. 291. False Flax (*Camelina sativa*). A, various forms of seeds. B, a seed showing the mucilage. C, a seed in cross section. D, seeds, natural size.
(After Hillman, Bull. Mich. Agr. Exp. Sta.)

between it and the cotyledons, which are incumbent. On addition of water the seeds become mucilaginous. This seed is occasionally found in seeds of clovers and grasses.

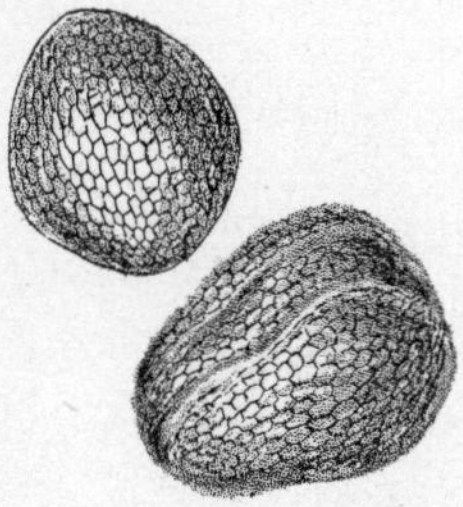

Radish (*Raphanus sativus* L.).

Seed spherical, ovate to oval, frequently angular, one-eighth to one-fifth inch in length, minutely pitted, brownish with glaucous or shining surface; scar inconspicuous, usually surrounded by small dark area; radicle near scar, prominent.

FIG. 292. Radish (*Raphanus sativus*), two different views.
(Drawn by Charlotte M. King.)

White Mustard (*Brassica alba* Boiss.).

Figure 293A.   Figure 293B.
FIG. 293. A. White Mustard (*Brassica alba*). B. Charlock (*Brassica arvensis*). a, tip of pod; b, seeds enlarged, and natural size; c, cross section.
(A, drawings by Ada Hayden and L. R. Collins; B, after Hillman, Bull. Mich. Agr. Exp. Sta.)

Seed nearly spherical, occasionally somewhat oblong, one-twelfth to one-ninth inch long, light colored, reticulations inconspicuous; scar whitish, projecting; seed coats mucilaginous when wet.

English Charlock (*Brassica arvensis* (L) Ktze.).

Seed nearly spherical, sometimes oblong, one-fourteenth to one-twelfth inch in diameter, marked with fine ridges, reticulated or honeycombed in appearance, light brown or grayish, with paler appearance; scar whitish, an elevated point at one end of the seed; embryo large; cotyledons conduplicate. With these seeds only a small amount of mucilage is produced in presence of water.

Indian Mustard (*Brassica juncea*).

Seed about the size of wild mustard seed; surface rather coarsely reticulated; color dark reddish brown.

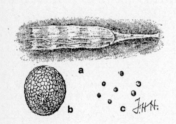
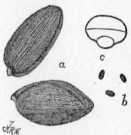

Figure 294-A.   Figure 294-B.

FIG. 294. A. Indian Mustard (*Brassica juncea*). B. Hare's-ear Mustard (*Conringia orientalis*). a, different views of seed; c, cross section; b, natural size.
(After Hillman, Bull. Mich. Agr. Exp. Sta.)

Black Mustard (*Brassica nigra* (L.) Koch.).

Seed nearly spherical, more generally broadly oblong, one-twentieth to one-fifteenth inch in diameter; surface marked with fine ridges; many seeds have whitish scar at one end; embryo as in *B. arvensis;* taste pungent. This seed is generally found in seed of clover and alfalfa.

Wild Turnip (*Brassica campestris* L.).

Seeds generally nearly spherical or oblong; the caulicle and radicle usually conspicuous along the middle, one-twentieth to one-twelfth inch in diameter, cultivated forms larger, roughened and more finely ridged than in *B. nigra* and *B. arvensis;* color grayish or brownish; scar at one end. This seed is sometimes found with clover and grass seed.

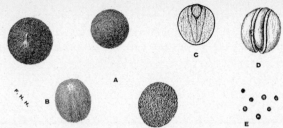

FIG. 295. Wild Turnip (*Brassica campestris*). A and B, various forms of seeds. C, a
seed in cross section showing cotyledons and caulicle. D, the embryo. E, seeds,
natural size.
(After Hillman, Bull. Mich. Agr. Exp. Sta.)

Rape (*Brassica Napus* L.).

Seed nearly spherical or sometimes oblong, one-fourteenth to
one-twelfth inch in length, prominently reticulated; closely resembles *B. arvensis*. Found in mustard and clover seed.

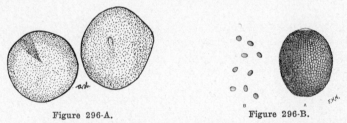

Figure 296-A.   Figure 296-B.

FIG. 296. A, Rape (*Brassica Napus*). B, Black Mustard (*Brassica nigra*). A, seed
enlarged, showing the surface network of dark lines. B, a group of seeds, natural
size.
(A, drawings by Ada Hayden; B, after Hillman, Bull. Mich. Agr. Exp. Sta.)

Hare's-ear Mustard (*Conringia orientalis* (L.) Dumort.).

Pod rigid, 4-angled; seeds brown, oblong narrowed to rounding
at the ends, 2 to 2.5 millimeters long; surface finely reticulated in
checks; scar at end of seed lighter in color; position of caulicle
indicated by two distinct, lengthwise grooves.

Hedge Mustard (*Sisymbrium officinale* (L.) Scop.).

Seed oblong, sometimes with upper end truncate, some almost
trapezoidal in outline, one-twenty-fourth to one-sixteenth inch
long; color yellowish or brownish, variable; caulicle evident from
prominent white scar; funicle in some cases present and pointed;
seed coat mucilaginous. Hedge mustard seeds are found in seed
of alsike and white clovers.

Tumbling Mustard (*Sisymbrium altissimum* L.).

Seed oblong, flattened, one-twenty-fifth inch in length; color reddish yellow; radicle prominent, variable in shape; form of embryo marked by deeper color, by lines; seed coat becomes mucilaginous when wet. This is a tumbling weed, with wide distribution. It is reported as a serious weed in commercial seeds of the northwest and Canada.

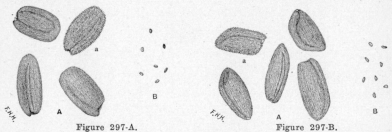

Figure 297-A.　　　　　　　Figure 297-B.

FIG. 297.　A.　Tumbling Mustard *(Sisymbrium altissimum)*.　B, Hedge Mustard *(Sisymbrium officinale)*.　A, a group of seeds indicating the usual forms; a, one showing the hairy appearance due to the mucilage, either when wet or after drying.　B, several seeds, natural size.

(After Hillman, Bull. Mich. Agr. Exp. Sta.)

Marsh Cress (*Radicula palustris* (L.) Moench.).

Pod ovoid; seed pale reddish brown, oval, finely reticulated, length about 0.62 millimeter to 3 millimeters; scar near one end, occupying a deep notch in the contour of the margin.

Winter Cress (*Barbarea vulgaris* R. Br.).

Seed oblong, flattened, one-sixteenth inch in length; surface finely reticulated; the scar a light-colored appendage at one end;

Figure 298.　　　　　　　　Figure 299.

FIG. 298.　Marsh Cress *(Radicula palustris)*.
(Drawing by Ada Hayden.)

FIG. 299.　Winter Cress *(Barbarea vulgaris)*.　A, various forms of seeds.　B, a seed in cross section.　C, seeds, natural size.
(After Hillman, Bull. Mich. Agr. Exp. Sta.)

position of caulicle marked by groove; color light brown; seed coats do not develop mucilage in water. The seeds are found occasionally with clover.

CAPPARIDACEAE, CAPER FAMILY.

Rocky Mountain Bee-plant (*Cleome serrulata* Pursh.).

FIG. 300. Rocky Mountain Bee-plant (*Cleome serrulata* Pursh.). (*Drawing by Ada Hayden.*)

Roughly wedge-shaped to triangular in outline, and wedge-shaped in cross section; mature seeds of a grayish brown color, immature seeds a creamy yellow; size 3 by 2.5 millimeters, basal scar extends from the edge of the wedge, well up on both flat faces; most of the surface of the seed roughly tubercled.

ROSACEAE, ROSE FAMILY.

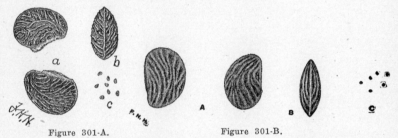

Figure 301-A.   Figure 301-B.

FIG. 301. A. Cinquefoil (*Potentilla canadensis*). B, Five-finger (*Potentilla monspeliensis*). A, two seeds (achenes), side view. B, a seed in edge view. C, group showing the natural size.
(*After Hillman; A, Bull. Mich. Agr. Exp. Sta.; B, Bull. Nev. Agr. Exp. Sta.*)

Five Finger (*Potentilla monspeliensis* L.).

Achenes small, ovate or kidney-shaped, one-twenty-fourth inch in length, prominently ridged; the ridges simple or branched, starting from base of seed; color light brown or straw-colored. This seed frequently occurs in alsike clover and timothy, as well as in red clover.

Cinquefoil (*Potentilla canadensis* L.).

Seed small, about 0.5 millimeter in length, short, obliquely egg-shaped; light brown.

Silver Weed (*Potentilla Anserina* L.).

Seed pointed, egg-shaped, unsymmetrical, about 1.6 millimeter in length; color yellowish to brown; surface furrowed throughout its length.

Avens (*Geum canadense* Jacq.).

Achene pale greenish brown, length 3 millimeters, width 1½ millimeters, general shape ovate, tapering to base, rounded at apex, which bears persistent hooked style 5 millimeters in length tipped with a hook; achene slightly flattened, with a narrow ring along each edge.

Prairie Rose (*Rosa pratincola* Greene).

Achenes dark to light brown, smooth, shining; length 3 to 5 millimeters, width 2 to 3 millimeters, general shape ovoid, modified by some flattening of portions at the surface, and corresponding angulation of the seed's form; scar at broader end, with dark line extending to the apex, which is tipped with a slight remnant of the style.

LEGUMINOSAE, PULSE FAMILY.
Rattlebox (*Crotalaria sagittalis* L.).

Pod blackish, cylindrical, inflated, many seeded; seed greenish brown, shining, smooth, somewhat flattened, circular-kidney-shaped,

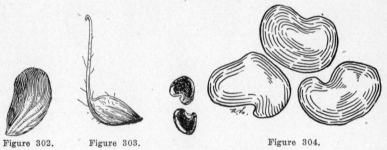

Figure 302.　　　　Figure 303.　　　　　　　　Figure 304.

Fig. 302.　Silver Weed (*Potentilla Anserina*).
(*After Burchard.*)
Fig. 303.　Avens (*Geum canadense*).
(*Drawing by C. M. King.*)
Fig. 304　Rattlebox (*Crotalaria sagittalis.*)
(*Drawing by Ada Hayden.*)

with one side interrupted by a deep rounded notch, bearing the conspicuous scar with dark center and light rim; width of seed 2.5 millimeters.

Red Clover (*Trifolium pratense* L.).

Seeds roughly triangular with angles rounded; no two sides equal length, sides somewhat convex with rounded edges, one-sixteenth to one-tenth inch long; color light yellow, purple or yellow and purple; old seeds brownish; scar near radicle, which is not so prominent as in other clovers; the seeds of mammoth clover resemble those of red clover but are usually larger.

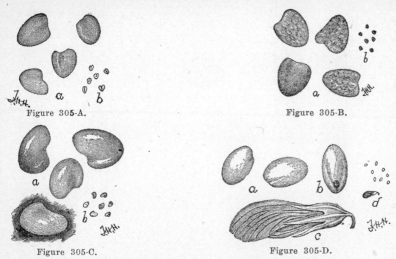

Figure 305-A.   Figure 305-B.

Figure 305-C.   Figure 305-D.

FIG. 305.   A.   White Clover (*Trifolium repens*).   a, enlarged; b, natural size.
B.   Alsike Clover (*Trifolium hybridum*).   a, enlarged; b, natural size.
C.   Red Clover (*Trifolium pratense*).   a, enlarged; b, natural size.
D.   Low Hop Clover (*Trifolium procumbens*).   a, enlarged; b, opposite face; c,
flower; d, seeds, natural size.
(*After Hillman, Bull. Nev. Agr. Exp. Sta.*)

White Clover (*Trifolium repens* L.).

Seeds varying from nearly square to triangular, margins rounded, flattened, often concave on one margin, one-twentieth to one-thirtieth inch long; smooth; color dull yellow to light reddish brown or slightly green; radicle slender club-shaped, about as long as the cotyledons.

Alsike Clover (*Trifolium hybridum* L.).

Seed more nearly oval than that of alfalfa or red clover; one-twentieth to one-sixteenth inch in length; color a peculiar yellowish green, often brown and mottled, individual seeds even yellow or brown; the projecting radicle gives the seed the appearance of having a nearly truncate top.

Low Hop Clover (*Trifolium procumbens* L.).

Seed light brown, shining, oval, length 1 millimeter to 1.3 millimeter, width 0.6 millimeter; scar in a notch a short distance from one end.

Sweet Clover, Bokhara Clover (*Melilotus alba* Desv.).

Seeds contained in an ovoid pod, one-twelfth to one-fifteenth inch long, reticulated, nearly smooth, elliptical, somewhat triangular, variable; color yellowish to greenish, scar brown in color;

micropilar processes near scar, not conspicuous. This seed is found in seeds of alfalfa and clover.

FIG. 306. White Sweet Clover (*Melilotus alba*). A, a group of seeds. B, the pods; the central one without the calyx. C, the embryo. D, a group of seeds and pods, natural size.
(After Hillman, Bull. Nev. Agr. Exp. Sta.)

Yellow Sweet Clover (*Melilotus officinalis* (L.) Lam.).

Pods one-seventh inch in length; rugose, more evenly transversely wrinkled than in *M. alba*; seeds subspherical or elliptical

FIG. 307. Yellow Sweet Clover (*Melilotus officinalis*). A, seeds. B, pods; the one at the right without the calyx, and showing the contracted base. C, a view of a seed in cross section, showing cotyledons and caulicle. D, a group of seeds and pods, natural size.
(After Hillman, Bull. Nev. Agr. Exp. Sta.)

to kidney-shaped, one-twelfth to one-tenth inch in length, smooth; yellowish or brownish to greenish; with small micropilar processes.

Bur Clover (*Medicago hispida* Gaertn.).

Seeds kidney-shaped, occasionally sausage-shaped, both sides

Fig. 308-A.   Fig. 308-B.

FIG. 308. Bur Clover (*Medicago hispida*).
(*A, after Hillman; B, drawn by Ada Hayden.*)

convex, one-sixth inch in length, larger than alfalfa, variable in size; color lighter than in alfalfa seed; scar about middle of seed, close to prominent micropilar processes; pods large, spirally twisted into several flat coils, covered by pointed projections; the prickles either straight or curved; each pod several-seeded; the seeds have general resemblance to alfalfa seed in form and color.

Yellow Trefoil (*Medicago lupulina* L.).

Seeds kidney to egg-shaped, much shorter than bur clover seed, one-twelfth to one-tenth inch long; about the size of alfalfa, which it closely resembles; color yellowish, reddish, or greenish; scar near

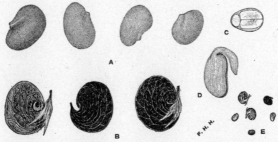

FIG. 309. Yellow Trefoil *(Medicago lupulina).* A, seeds showing the prevailing forms. B, pods; the central one with the calyx removed; the one at the left an immature, lighter colored specimen. C, a view of a seed in cross section, showing cotyledons and caulicle. D, the embryo. E, seeds and pods, natural size.
(After Hillman, Bull. Nev. Agr. Exp. Sta.)

one end; micropilar processes prominent; the pods clustered at the end of the peduncle, small, black, wrinkled, and coiled at tip, marked by prominent veins and hairs; each pod contains one seed.

Dalea (*Dalea alopecuroides* Willd.).

Seeds triangular to kidney-shaped, one-tenth inch in length; micropilar scar prominent, with whitish border and two micropilar processes; surface shining, slate-colored. Found in clover seed, from which it is separated with difficulty.

Figure 310-A.   Figure 310-B.   Figure 310-C.
FIG. 310. A. Dalea *(Dalea alopecuroides).* B, seed of Pink Dalea *(Dalea laxiflora).*
C, seed-pod of the same species.
(A, drawing by L. R. Collins; B and C, by C. M. King.)

Pink Dalea (*Dalea laxiflora* Pursh.).

Seeds one-tenth inch in length, triangular, kidney-shaped, one end projecting beyond sac, which is circular and has two micro-pilar processes on one side; yellowish or brownish in color; leaves have pellucid dots. This seed is occasionally found in clover seed.

Stemless Loco Weed (*Oxytropis Lamberti* Pursh.).

Pods coriaceous, silky pubescent, cylindrical; seed flattened, brown, about 2 millimeters broad and 2.5 millimeters long.

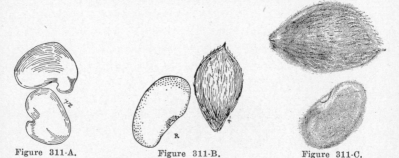

Figure 311-A.   Figure 311-B.   Figure 311-C.

FIG. 311.   A, Stemless Loco Weed (*Oxytropis Lamberti*). B and C, Bush Clover (*Lespedeza capitata*), pod and seed.
(*Drawings, A, by Ada Hayden; B and C, by Charlotte M. King.*)

Bush Clover (*Lespedeza capitata* Michx.).

Pod ovate-oblong, one-sixth inch in length, sessile, 1-ovuled, pubescent, brownish, reticulated, indehiscent, seed scarcely kidney-shaped, one-tenth inch in length, greenish to purplish.

Common Vetch (*Vicia sativa* L.).

Pod linear, several-seeded; seeds nearly spherical or compressed on the sides, variable, blackish to brownish.

Figure 312.   Figure 313.   Figure 314.

FIG. 312.   Common Vetch (*Vicia sativa*).
FIG. 313.   Hairy Vetch (*Vicia villosa*).
(*After Hillman, Circular U. S. Dept. Agr.*)
FIG. 314.   Wild Bean (*Strophostyles helvola*).
(*Drawing by L. R. Collins.*)

Hairy Vetch (*Vicia villosa* Roth.).

Seeds spherical to subspherical; one-tenth to one-sixth inch in diameter; blackish or brownish, surface smooth; scar elongated, represented by a narrow line slightly elevated, with depressed center, light in color, brownish to straw-colored.

Trailing Wild Bean (*Strophostyles helvola* (L.) Britton).

Pod terete, 5 to 7.5 centimeters long, nearly glabrous, 4 to 8 seeded, dark brown; seed cylindrical, rounded, truncate at both ends; length 6 millimeters, width 2.5 millimeters; color dull brown slightly mottled; narrow white scar along inner angle, nearly the entire length of the seed; seed strongly angled longitudinally on side opposite scar.

LINACEAE, FLAX FAMILY.
Common Flax (*Linum usitatissimum* L.).

Seeds ovate, flattened, one-fifth inch long, one-tenth inch wide, basal end curved on one side; color brown, margins with whitish

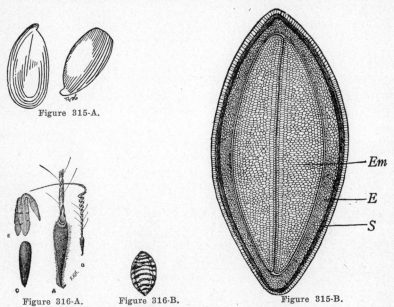

Figure 315-A.

Em

E

S

Figure 316-A.   Figure 316-B.   Figure 315-B.

Fig. 315.   Common Flax (*Linum usitatissimum*).   A, seed.   B, cross section of seed.
(*A, drawing by Ada Hayden; B, after Winton.*)
Fig. 316.   A, Storksbill or Alfilaria (*Erodium cicutarium*); A, a seed-vessel with a portion of its spirally coiled awn.   B, a seed-vessel and its awn, natural size. (In many the awn is smaller.)   C, a seed, magnified.   D, a line showing the length of the seed.   E, the embryo removed from the seed coats, the parts spread.
B.   Lady's Sorrel or Yellow Field Sorrel (*Oxalis corniculata.*)
(*A, after Hillman, Bull. Mich. Agr. Exp. Sta.; B, drawing by C. M. King.*)

luster, smooth, shining; scar on one side, near lower end, small, inconspicuous; embryo large, straight.

OXALIDACEAE, SORREL FAMILY.
Lady's Sorrel (*Oxalis corniculata* L.).

Pod prismatic, cylindrical, seeds 1 millimeter in length; shape and markings similar to preceding.

Oxalis (*Oxalis stricta* L.).

Pod angled, awl-shaped; seeds 1 millimeter in length, elliptical, pointed at one end; surface marked by broken transverse lines of white; seed longitudinally ribbed, slightly flattened.

GERANIACEAE, GERANIUM FAMILY.
Storksbill (*Erodium cicutarium* L'Her.).

Lobes of capsule 1-seeded, with elastic, dehiscent style, coiled at maturity, villous inside; hairs at base pointing obliquely upwardly; awn coiled for half its length; seed broadly club-shaped, one-fifth inch in length without awn; scar removed one-third length of seed from base; groove from scar to tip of seed.

EUPHORBIACEAE, SPURGE FAMILY.
Three-seeded Mercury (*Acalypha virginica* L.).

Seeds ovoid; one-twelfth to one-twentieth inch long; reddish, minutely striate, line running from apex to base; scar at smaller end. Found in clover seed.

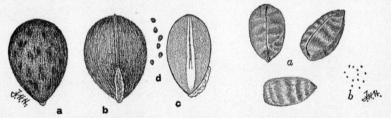

Figure 317-A.   Figure 317-B.

FIG. 317. A. Three-seeded Mercury (*Acalypha virginica*). a and b, different views of seed; c, sectional view showing embryo and endosperm; d, seed, natural size. B. Prostrate Spurge or Milk Spurge (*Euphorbia maculata*). A. Different views of seed. B. Seeds, natural size.
(*After Hillman, Bull. Agr. Exp. Sta.*)

Milk Spurge or Milk Purslane (*Euphorbia maculata* L.).

Seeds ovoid or oblong, obtusely angled, one-twentieth inch in length, minutely pitted and transversely wrinkled; grayish.

FIG. 318. Seeds of Spotted Spurge *(Euphorbia Preslii)*. A and B, different views of seed. D. Fruit. E. Seed, natural size.
(After Hillman, Bull. Mich. Agr. Exp. Sta.)

Spotted Spurge, Upright Spurge *(Euphorbia Preslii* Guss.).

Seeds lead-colored, obovoid-oblong, with 4 nearly equal sides; surface pitted and transversely wrinkled; a narrow dark raphe along one edge; length 1 millimeter to 1.3 millimeters.

Snow-on-the-mountain *(Euphorbia marginata* Pursh.).

Seed ovoid, slightly flattened at apical end, length 4 millimeters, width 3 millimeters; color light brown; surface roughly tuberculate; one side marked by a dark longitudinal line.

Flowering Spurge *(Euphorbia corollata* L.).

Seeds ovoid, one-tenth inch in length, smooth, grayish white, a line extending from apex to base on one side, with whitish bordered depression at base; apical point on larger end; seed coat mucilaginous.

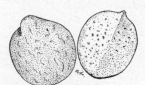

Figure 319-A.   Figure 319-B.

Fig. 319. A. Flowering Spurge *(Euphorbia corollata)*.
B. Snow-on-the-Mountain *(Euphorbia marginata)*.
(Drawings by Ada Hayden.)

MALVACEAE, MALLOW FAMILY.
Velvet-leaf, Butterprint *(Abutilon Theophrasti* Medic.).

Carpels 2-valved, beaked, each usually 2-seeded; seeds somewhat triangular, kidney-shaped, one-eighth inch in length, minutely granular and pubescent; color blackish gray; funicle extending to notch of seed. This seed may occur in small grain.

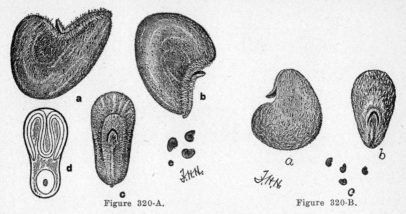

Figure 320-A. Figure 320-B.

FIG. 320.   A.   Indian Mallow or Butterprint *(Abutilon Theophrasti)*. a, b, c, different
views of seed; d, cross section showing embryo and caulicle; e, seeds, natural
size.
B.   Seeds of Bladder Ketmia. a and b, different views, c, natural size.
(After Hillman, Bull. Mich. Agr. Exp. Sta.)

Bladder Ketmia (*Hibiscus Trionum* L.).

Capsule 5-valved, globose-ovoid, hairy; seeds kidney-shaped,
one-fifteenth inch in length, blackened, roughened by short tuber-
cular processes, minutely granular; basal end of seed of much
smaller diameter; scar brownish; funicle extending to the notch.

Prickly Sida (*Sida spinosa* L.).

Seeds oval, one-sixteenth to one-twelfth inch long, one face convex, the other with a prominent ridge across its length; scar at
broad end; surface dull, smooth; color brownish. Reported in seed
of Missouri red clover.

FIG. 321.   Prickly Sida *(Sida spinosa)*. A, different views of seeds. B, a seed in
section taken midway between the two extremities showing embryo and caulicle. C,
seeds, natural size.
(After Hillman, Bull. Nev. Agr. Exp. Sta.)

Common Mallow (*Malva rotundifolia* L.).

Commonly called cheeses. Carpels arranged about a center, flat,
beakless, indehiscent; each carpel a single seed, kidney-shaped,
one-sixteenth to one-twelfth inch in diameter, flattened, with a

FIG. 322. Common Mallow *(Malva rotundifolia)*. A, two seeds in side viw. B, a seed retained by a carpel of the seed-vessel. C, a seed in cross section taken midway between the scar and the opposite edge. D, seeds, showing the natural size.
(After Hillman, Bull. Mich. Agr. Exp. Sta.)

prominent notch at base; seeds brownish or gray, minutely granular; scar small, frequently containing spongy tissue; embryo curved; small amount of endosperm. Reported in alfalfa and red clover seed.

ONAGRACEAE, EVENING PRIMROSE FAMILY.
Evening Primrose *(Oenothera biennis* L.).

Seeds prismatic, 4 or 5-sided, sometimes curved, variable, one-sixteenth inch in length, slightly wing-margined, rugose, brown, scar indistinct at one end, embryo straight.

UMBELLIFERAE, PARSLEY FAMILY.
Water Hemlock *(Cicuta maculata* L.).

Fruit ovate to oval, curved or nearly straight, one-eighth inch in length, smooth, with longitudinal brown and straw-colored lines; apex widened with 2 styles; ribs corky; oil-tubes solitary, in the intervals.

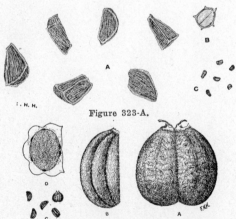

Figure 323-A.

Figure 323-B.

FIG. 323. A. Evening Primrose *(Oenothera biennis)*. A, different views of seed. B, cross section of seed. C, natural size.
B. Water Hemlock *(Cicuta maculata)*.
(After Hillman, Bull. Mich. Agr. Exp. Sta.)

Wild Parsnip *(Pastinaca sativa* L.).

"Seeds," carpels one-quarter inch in length, thin, circular or oblong; color light or dull yellowish brown; lighter conspicuous margin, ribs brownish or reddish; apex notched, with a conspicuous remnant of the style; oil tubes four, alternating with the ribs; inner face concave, with a central longitudinal ridge and one oil-tube on each side.

Wild Carrot (*Daucus Carota* L.).

Fruit one-eighth inch long, oblong, flattened dorsally; carpel with 5 slender, bristly, primary ribs bearing numerous spines, and 4 secondary wings; color whitish yellow; oil tubes one under each row of spines, and two between the ridges of the inner face; seeds commonly found with spines broken off. This seed occurs in alfalfa and clover seeds.

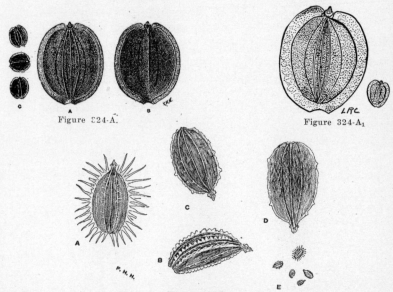

Figure 324-A.   Figure 324-A₁

Figure 324-B.

FIG. 324. A and A1. Wild Parsnip *(Pastinaca sativa)*. B. Wild Carrot *(Daucus Carota)*. A, the outer (at left) and inner (at right) faces of a seed (carpel). The spines occupy the margin and two rows along the outer face. The slender, hairy ridges alternate with the rows of spines. The inner face bears two, separated by a slender ridge or line which is not hairy. B, an oblique view of the outer face of a seed found with clover seed. C and D, views of the inner face of seeds similarly found. E, seeds, natural size.

(A and B, after Hillman, Bull. Nev. Agr. Exp. Sta.; A1, drawing by L. R. Collins)

ASCLEPIADACEAE, MILKWEED FAMILY.
Butterfly Weed (*Asclepias tuberosa* L.).

Seed ovate or elliptical, three-tenths inch in length; surface roughened by ridges on both back and inner faces; winged margin, lighter brown than middle part of seed; raphe marked by a distinct ridge; coma fine, silky, smooth.

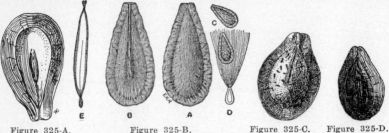

Figure 325-A.   Figure 325-B.   Figure 325-C.   Figure 325-D.

FIG. 325. A. Swamp Milkweed *(Asclepias incarnata)*. B. Common Milkweed *(Ascelpias syriaca)*. a, b, different views of seed; c, cross section; d, e, natural size. C. Butterfly Weed *(Asclepias tuberosa)*. D. Whorled Milkweed *(Asclepias verticillata)*.
(A, drawing by L. R. Collins: B, after Hillman: C, D, by O. M. King.)

Swamp Milkweed *(Asclepias incarnata* L.).

Seeds oval, wing-margined, three-tenths inch in length; surface less prominently veined than in *A. syriaca;* raphe marked by distinct ridge; coma attached to smaller end of fine silky hairs. This seed is probably never found in commercial seed.

Common Milkweed *(Asclepias syriaca)*.

Seeds flattened, oval or elliptical, apical end truncate, three-tenths inch in length, wing-margined; seed and wing distinctly veined; the raphe occurs in form of a distinct ridge on inner face of seed; coma a tuft of silky hairs attached to apical end, easily separated from seed. Seeds of common milkweed are not apt to be found in commercial seed.

Whorled Milkweed *(Asclepias verticillata* L.).

Seeds ovate, one-sixth inch in length, margin distinct, lighter in color than the rest of the reddish brown seed; surface veined, but not ridged or roughened; raphe a distinct ridge on inner face; coma soft, silky; very smooth.

CONVOLVULACEAE, CONVOLVULUS FAMILY.
Common Morning-glory *(Ipomoea purpurea* (L.) Roth.).

Seed dark brown, with one convex side opposite to 2 flattened faces meeting at an angle, length 5 millimeters, width 4 millimeters at the base of the seed; at lower end of the angle between the two flattened faces is the scar, also dark brown; surface dull, finely roughened.

Wild Blue Morning-glory *(Ipomoea hederacea* Jacq.).

Seed dark brown, one convex side opposite to two plane faces meeting at an angle. Length one-fourth inch, width one-fifth inch.

The surface covered closely with fine hairy processes, giving seed a granular appearance.

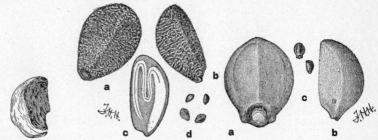

Figure 326-A.   Figure 326-B.   Figure 326-C.

FIG. 326. A. Common Morning-glory (*Ipomoea purpurea*). B. Small Bindweed (*Convolvulus arvensis*). a, b, different faces of seed, c, cross section, d, natural size. C. Wild Morning-glory (*Convolvulus sepium*). a, b, different faces of seed, c, natural size.

(*A, drawing by Charlotte M. King; B and C, after Hillman.*)

Wild Morning-glory (*Convolvulus sepium* L.).

The outer surface rounded; inner face with prominent ridge and a depression on each side; seed one-quarter inch long; smooth, brownish or blackish, with minute projections over the surface; hilum prominent, light brown, in semicircular depression.

Small Bindweed (*Convolvulus arvensis* L.).

Seeds large, oval, one side convex, the other side with a broad ridge, one-sixth inch long, a depression at one extremity representing the scar; surface of seed roughened, dark brown in color; embryo large, surrounded by the fleshy endosperm. This seed is occasionally found in cereal grains.

Clover Dodder (*Cuscuta Epithymum* Murr.).

Seed spherical or subspherical, one-thirtieth to one-twenty-fourth inch in diameter; surface roughened, with appearances of spongi-

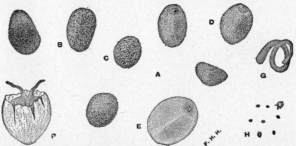

FIG. 327. Clover Dodder (*Cuscuta Epithymum*). A, a group showing various forms and views of seeds. B and C, seeds having the scurfy appearance. D and E show the angled, scar-bearing face, E, being one of the light-colored, sterile seeds. F, a torn, dried flower having the seed-vessel intact. G, the embryo. H, group of seeds showing the natural size.

(*After Hillman, Bull. Nev. Agr. Exp. Sta.*)

ness, dull, usually ashy, yellowish to light or dark brown, or purplish; embryo coiled, without cotyledons, consisting of slender
tapering body, with caulicle and radicle embedded in fleshy endosperm. Commonly distributed in seed of clovers and alfalfa.
Brown and Hillman state that this dodder is almost entirely confined to European grown seed, since the plant does not generally
produce seed in this country.

Chilean Dodder (*Cuscuta chilensis*).

Seeds spherical to subspherical or oval, inclined to be more angular than the preceding species, flattened on one side, one-seven-
teenth to one-fifteenth inch in diameter, about the size of large
field dodder seeds; dull brownish, minutely roughened; scar prominent, at end of flattened surface, lighter in color than rest of seed.
Chilean dodder seed is found in both clover and alfalfa seed, from
which it is screened with difficulty.

Field Dodder (*Cuscuta arvensis* Beyrich.).

Capsule globose, indehiscent; seed spherical to kidney-shaped or
ovate, occasionally with prominent angles; one-twenty-fourth to
one-sixteenth inch long; roughened but not pitted, dull yellowish,
grayish or light brown; scar at one extremity, frequently elevated
and prominent; Mr. Hillman finds field dodder seeds usually
lighter than those of Chilean dodder; in some samples the Chilean
dodder seeds are the lighter in color. Seeds of field dodders appear in clover seed, in many cases abundantly.

Figure 328.   Figure 329.
FIG. 328. Chilean Dodder (*Cuscuta chilensis.*)
(*Drawing after Burchard.*)
FIG. 329. Field Dodder (*Cuscuta arvensis*)
(*After Hillman, Bull. Nev. Agr. Exp. Sta.*)

BORAGINACEAE, BORAGE FAMILY.
Common Hound's Tongue (*Cynoglossum officinale* L.).

Ovary dividing into 4 achenes, each 5 to 7 millimeters in length, ovate to round, flattened; lower side bearing large ovate scar; surface covered with straight, stiff, barbed prickles.

Figure 330.   Figure 331.

FIG. 330.   Common Hound's Tongue *(Cynoglossum officinale)*. a, b, views of different faces of seed; c, natural size.
(After Hillman, Bull. Mich. Agr. Exp. Sta.)

FIG. 331.   Wild Comfrey *(Cynoglossum boreale)*.
(Drawing by Ada Hayden.)

Wild Comfrey (*Cynoglossum boreale* Fernald.).

Nutlets convex on the upper face, somewhat triangular, one-seventh inch in diameter, bearing short barbed prickles on convex surface; color brown.

Stickseed (*Lappula echinata* Gilibert).

Ovary separating into 4 achenes, 2.5 millimeters long, slightly flattened from ovate, under surface tuberculate, bearing straight ridge from point to middle; on the upper side, the margins bear a double row of slender barbed prickles.

Beggar's Lice (*Lappula virginiana* (L.) Greene).

Achenes 3 millimeters long, borne in clusters of 4, broadly ovate, flattened on outer side; the outer surface bearing short stiff barbed prickles, the inner side cone-shaped, free from hairs, and bearing a triangular scar.

American Gromwell (*Lithospermum latifolium* Michx.).

Nutlets ovoid to globose, one-sixth inch in diameter, white, shining; glabrous but prominently pitted; base oblique.

Corn Gromwell (*Lithospermum arvense* L.).

Ovoid nutlets 4 or fewer, convex on back, inner face with distinct ridge; one-sixteenth to one-twelfth inch in length; color from whitish to dark brown, surface glabrous, but wrinkled and pitted; base obliquely flattened, bearing the scar. This seed is reported as occurring with grain seed.

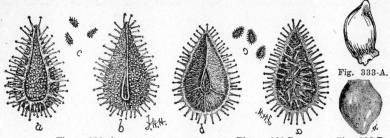

Figure 332 A.   Figure 332 B.   Fig. 333-B.

FIG. 332.   A.   Stickseed (*Lappula echinata*). a, b, views of different faces of seed;
c, natural size.
B.   Beggar's Lice (*Lappula virginiana*). a, b, views of different faces of seed; c,
natural size.
(After Hillman, Bull. Mich. Agr. Exp. Sta.)

FIG. 333.   A.   Narrow-leaved Puccoon (*Lithospermum angustifolium*).
B.   American Gromwell (*Lithospermum latifolium*).
(Drawings by L. R. Collins.)

Narrow-leaved Puccoon (*Lithospermum angustifolium* Michx.).

Nutlets ovoid, keeled on inner face, one-eighth inch long; surface smooth, shining, pitted; color white to yellowish white; base
irregular with projecting margin; bearing base with projecting
ridges.

Figure 334-A.   Figure 334-B.

FIG. 334.   A, Corn Gromwell (*Lithospermum arvense*).   A, different views of nutlets, B,
one bearing the flower-receptacle and portion of the stem, C, the natural size of
the larger nutlets.
B, Viper's Bugloss (*Echium vulgare*).
(A, after Hillman, Bull. Mich. Agr. Exp. Sta.; B, drawn by L. R. Collins.)

Viper's Bugloss (*Echium vulgare* L.).

Nutlets erect, ovoid, one-eleventh inch in length, back distinctly
convex; seed straight or curved; outer face with distinct ridge;
surface rugose; color white, base flattened.

VERBENACEAE, VERVAIN FAMILY.
White Vervain (*Verbena urticaefolia* L.).

Nutlets cylindrical, convex on back, 2-faced on inner side, with
prominent central line; one-tenth to one-eighth inch in length;
back somewhat rugose, with 2 or 3 prominent lines extending from

base to apex and some cross lines; inner face somewhat granular; scar a whitish elevated point. This seed is found in seeds of clovers.

Blue Vervain (*Verbena hastata* L.).

Nutlets 3-sided, with a distinct line of separation, back convex, rugose, inner face 2-sided; one-fifteenth to one-thirteenth inch long; color light brown; scar slightly elevated, whitish, at base of nutlet. This seed is often found in seed of clover.

Hoary Vervain (*Verbena stricta* Vent.).

Nutlets cylindrical, 3-sided, one-eighth inch in length, outer face convex, back with 4 prominent veins, upper portion slightly pitted; color dark brown; whitish scar at base. Seed found in clover seed.

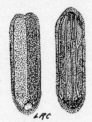 

Figure 335-A. Figure 335-B.
FIG. 335. A. Hoary Vervain (*Verbena stricta*). B. White Vervain (*Verbena urticaefolia*).
(A, drawing by L. R. Collins: B, after Hillman, Bull. Mich. Agr. Exp. Sta.)

Large-bracted Vervain (*Verbena bracteosa* Mx.).

Nutlets cylindrical, 3-sided, outer face convex, one-tenth inch in length, outer face rugose at upper end, lower end marked by lines, inner face pitted, scar somewhat elevated, whitish. In seeds of clovers and grasses.

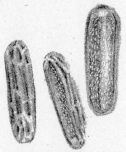 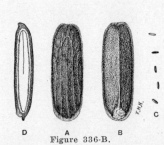

Figure 336-A. Figure 336-B.
FIG. 336. A. Large-bracted Vervain (*Verbena bracteosa*).
B. Blue Vervain (*Verbena hastata*). A, the outer face, and B, the inner face of a nutlet; the latter shows the whitish, spongy scar at the base. C, a group showing the natural size. D, a section of a nutlet, taken lengthwise.
(A, drawing by C. M. King; B, after Hillman, Bull. Nev. Agr. Exp. Sta.)

LABIATAE, MINT FAMILY.
Catnip (*Nepeta Cataria* L.).

Oval, dark brown seeds, about 1.5 millimeters in length, slightly flattened, surface smooth; one face bears at the base two white characteristic spots, which are a part of the scar.

American Germander (*Teucrium canadense* L.).

Nutlets obovoid, one-tenth inch in length, outer surface convex; color brown; surface prominently rugose, reticulated except the scar at the lower end. This seed is common in commercial seed.

Figure 337-A.   Figure 337-B.

FIG. 337.   A.   Catnip (*Nepeta Cataria*).   A, views of various seeds (nutlets), three showing the scar-marking.   B, one having the nutlet wall partly broken away, exposing the seed proper.   C, a nutlet in longitudinal section, showing the embryo.   D, group showing the natural size.
B.   American Germander (*Teucrium canadense*).
(*A, after Hillman, Bull. Nev. Agr. Exp. Sta.; B, drawn by L. R. Collins.*)

Horehound (*Marrubium vulgare* L.).

Seed ovate, one side convex, flattened side divided into 2 faces by strong central ridge; one-twelfth of an inch in length; brown-

Figure 338-A.   Figure 338-B.
FIG. 338.   A.   Giant Hyssop (*Agastache scrophulariaefolia*).
B.   Common Horehound (*Marrubium vulgare*); a, angled face; b, convex face; c, longitudinal section; d, tranverse section; e, natural size of seed.
(*A, drawing by L. R. Collins; B, after Hillman, Mich. Agr. Exp. Sta.*)

ish or blackish, with straw-colored markings; scar inconspicuous, in a slight depression somewhat paler in color than seed.

Giant Hyssop (*Agastache scrophulariaefolia* (Willd) Ktze.).

Light brown seed one-sixteenth of an inch long; the length 3 times the width. Back convex; inner side 2 plane faces meeting at the longitudinal ridge. Hairs borne at the apex. Seed now and then found in clover seed.

Self-heal (*Prunella vulgaris* L.).

Nutlets ovoid, faces convex, marked by longitudinal grooves; one-twelfth of an inch in length; smooth, shining; color brown; small bud marked by white scar appendage. Seeds of self-heal are found in red clover.

Motherwort (*Leonurus Cardiaca* L.).

Nutlets 3-sided, occasionally flattened, 1.10 inches long, smooth except at upper end, which is papillose; minutely roughened; straw-colored to brownish. These seeds are found in cultivated grass seed.

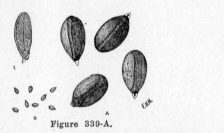
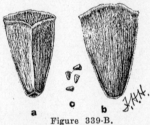

Figure 339-A.   Figure 339-B.

Fig. 339. A. Self heal (*Prunella vulgaris*). A, a group of seeds, enlarged, the lower left-hand one with the scar appendage broken away; the upper left-hand figure showing the outer face. B, a group showing the natural size; C, a longitudinal section of a seed showing the embryo.
B. Motherwort (*Leonurus Cardiaca*). a and b, different views of seed; c, seed, natural size.
(*After Hillman, A, Bull. Nev. Agr. Exp. Sta.; B, Bull. Mich. Agr. Exp. Sta.*)

SOLANACEAE, NIGHTSHADE FAMILY.

Black Nightshade (*Solanum nigrum* L.).

Berries black, globular, smooth; seed asymmetrically ovate, flattened, pale yellowish brown, finely granular; diameter about 1.5 millimeters.

Horse Nettle (*Solanum carolinense* L.).

Berry orange-yellow, 1.6 to 2 centimeters in diameter; seeds pale dull yellow, much flattened, obovate, 2 to 3 millimeters in length; finely granular, or indented over whole surface.

Buffalo Bur (*Solanum rostratum* Dunal.).

Black berry enclosed in spiny yellow calyx; seeds nearly circular, bearing a dent on one side of the margin; flattened, pitted on the surface; both sides irregularly indented with depressions; color, dull dark brown; seed about 2.5 millimeters broad.

Jimson Weed (*Datura Stramonium* L.).

Seed one-eighth inch in length, brownish or blackish, kidney-shaped, elliptical or nearly spherical, with numerous large depressions and smaller pits; hilum with a small depression.

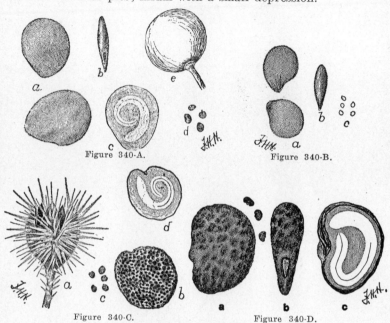

Figure 340-A. Figure 340-B. Figure 340-C. Figure 340-D.

FIG. 340. A. Horse Nettle *(Solanum carolinense)*. a, b, c, and d, different views of seed; e, fruit.
B. Black Nightshade *(Solanum nigrum)*. a, two seeds, side view, enlarged; b, group showing the natural size; c, a section of a seed, parallel with the faces, showing the spirally curved embryo imbedded in the endosperm.
C. Buffalo Bur *(Solanum rostratum)*. a, prickly calyx; b, seeds with pits; c, seed, natural size; d, cross section of seed with embryo.
D. Jimson Weed *(Datura Stramonium)*. a and b, seeds from different views; between a and b, seeds, natural size; c, cross section of seed showing embryo.
(After Hillman, A, C, D, Mich. Agr. Exp. Sta. Bull.; B, Bull. Nev. Agr. Exp Sta.)

SCROPHULARIACEAE, FIGWORT FAMILY.
Mullein (*Verbascum Thapsus* L.).

Seeds columnar, 4 to 6-sided, top usually truncate, base nearly so; one-thirtieth inch in length; faces deeply transversely pitted; surface dull; color brown; scar in middle of flattened base. Mullein seeds are reported as frequently found in seeds of timothy and other grasses.

Moth Mullein (*Verbascum Blattaria* L.).

Seeds light to dark brown, 0.5 to 1 millimeter in length, prismatic, 6-sided, base truncate, broader than the rounded apex; each side face pitted in longitudinal rows.

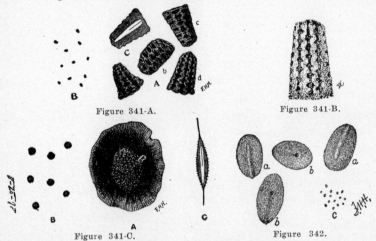

Figure 341-A.

Figure 341-B.

Figure 341-C.

Figure 342.

FIG. 341. A. Moth Mullein (*Verbascum Blattaria*). A, a group of seeds, enlarged, showing different forms and kinds of surface markings. a, b and c were reproduced from seeds of *V. Blattaria*, and d from *V. Thapsus*. B represents a group natural size. C, a section taken lengthwise through the center of a seed, showing the embryo and surrounding endosperm.
  B. Common Mullein (*Verbascum Thapsus*).
C. Toad Flax (*Linaria vulgaris*). A, a side view of a seed much enlarged, the scar within the notch on the upper right-hand margin. B, a group showing the natural size. C, a section through the center of a seed showing the embryo.
(*A and C, after Hillman, Bull. Mich. Agr. Exp. Sta.; B, drawing by L. R. Collins.*)

FIG. 342. Speedwell (*Veronica peregrina*). a, b, d, different views of seeds; c, seeds, natural size.
(*After Hillman, Mich. Agr. Exp. Sta.*)

Toad-flax (*Linaria vulgaris* Hill.).

Seeds flattened, wing-margined, orbicular in outline, wing wavy, notched at one end; one-twelfth inch in diameter; surface rugose; wings one-thirtieth to one-twenty-fifth inch wide; embryo slender, curved. This seed occasionally occurs in grass seed and occasionally in clover.

Speedwell (*Veronica peregrina* L.).

Seeds oblong to egg-shaped, flattened, one-thirty-second to one-thirtieth inch long, slightly curved, the outer face with a central ridge; embryo straight, surrounded by the endosperm; raphe on the inner face; scar projecting.

PLANTAGINACEAE, PLANTAIN FAMILY.
Dooryard Plantain (*Plantago major* L.).

Seeds oblong to trapezoidal in shape, usually 4-sided, some of them 3-sided, one-twenty-second to one-sixteenth inch long; brownish to black; surface bearing 5 ridges radiating from scar; scar on middle of inner face, often with white markings.

Rugel's Plantain (*Plantago Rugelii* Dcne.).

Seeds oblong, rhomboidal, generally trapezoidal with flattened edges, one-eighteenth to one-twelfth inch in length; color brownish to black; surface minutely roughened, ridgelike markings absent; scar circular, whitish.

Ribgrass, Buckhorn (*Plantago lanceolata* L.).

Seeds oblong, convex on back, one-twelfth to one-seventh inch in length, edges folded inwardly to deep central longitudinal

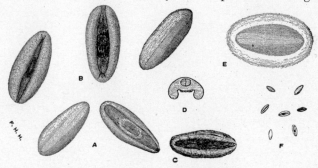

FIG. 343. Buckhorn *(Plantago lanceolata)*. A and B, group of seeds showing both the convex and grooved faces. C, a sterile seed. D, a seed in cross section. E, seed showing the mucilage. F, the natural size.
(After Hillman, Bull. Nev. Agr. Exp. Sta.)

groove on inner face; brown, smooth, shining; scar at center of groove frequently of dark color.

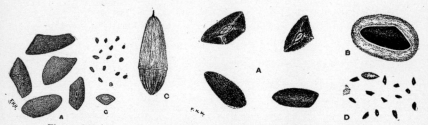

Figure 344-A. Figure 344-B.

FIG. 344. A. Common Plantain *(Plantago major)*. a, a group of seeds enlarged, showing the relative form and size, also the surface ridges as dark lines; b, a group showing the natural size; c, a cross section of a seed.
B. *Plantago Rugelii*. A, seeds, the upper two showing the scar. B, seed showing the mucilage. C, a seed-vessel. D, seeds, natural size.
(After Hillman, Bull. Nev. Agr. Exp. Sta.)

Bracted Plantain (*Plantago aristata* Michx.).

Seeds oval or oblong, back of seed convex with transverse ring across the middle or nearly so, one-twelfth to one-eighth inch long;

inner face with white marginal ring, in center of inner face 2 pit-like markings each surrounded by whitish area, giving appearance of 2 rings, or 2 links of a chain.

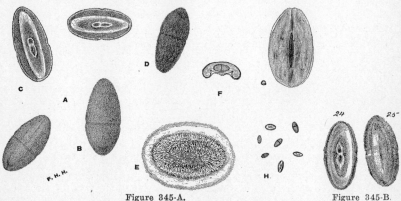

Figure 345-A.   Figure 345-B.

FIG. 345. Bracted Plantain (*Plantago aristata*). A, group of seeds. B, the convex face. (A, after *Hillman, Bull. Nev. Agr. Exp. Sta.*; B, drawing by *Charlotte M. King*.)

Pursh's Plantain (*Plantago Purshii* R. & S.).
Seeds boat-shaped, oval.

White Dwarf Plantain (*Plantago virginica* L.).
Seeds flat, oval.

RUBIACEAE, MADDER FAMILY.
Cleavers (*Galium Aparine* L.).
Fruit indehiscent, spherical, one-tenth to one-eighth inch in diameter, roughened with prickles, tuberculate when prickles are

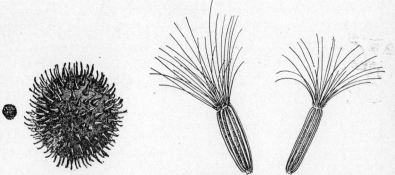

Figure 346.   Figure 347-A.   Figure 347-B.
FIG. 346.   Cleavers, or Bedstraw (*Galium Aparine*).
(After *Winton*.)

FIG. 347. Ironweed seeds. A. *Vernonia fasciculata*. B. *Vernonia Baldwini*. Achenes with pappus.
(Drawings by *Charlotte M. King*.)

rubbed off; color blackish; embryo curved; endosperm horny; fruit covered with hooked trichomes.

COMPOSITAE, COMPOSITE FAMILY.
Ironweed (*Vernonia fasciculata* Michx.).

Achenes 3 to 3.5 millimeters long, and 1 millimeter broad; general form slender, cylindrical, often slightly curved; strongly 9 to 10-ribbed, ribs of same color as achene, pale brown; tuft of purplish brown pappus bristles attached at larger end; length of pappus hairs 6 millimeters.

Baldwin's Ironweed (*Vernonia Baldwini* Torr.).

Achenes practically indistinguishable from those of the preceding species.

White Snakeroot (*Eupatorium urticaefolium* Reichard).

Achene long, 5-angled, prominently grooved between the angles one-twelfth to one-tenth inch; generally blackish except at the base where it is yellowish; the scar at base with a small circular opening, and whitish border; smoothish (see figure), pappus of fine white capillary bristles; the upper part of beak expanded into candelabra form, bearing the somewhat fragile pappus.

Joe-Pye Weed (*Eupatorium purpureum* L.).

Achenes smooth, prominently ribbed; 5-angled, truncate; about one-eighth of an inch long; base white; pappus with numerous tawny-colored capillary bristles. Miss Mary Nichols, who studied the achenial hairs of *E. villosum*, finds that they are short with lateral canals. The achenial hairs of *E. purpureum*, according to Mr. Fracker, are simple, in *E. villosum* duplex.

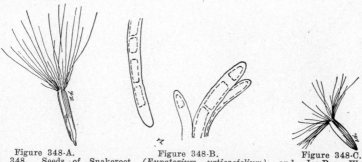

Figure 348-A.   Figure 348-B.   Figure 348-C.
FIG. 348. Seeds of Snakeroot (*Eupatorium urticaefolium*) and Joe-Pye Weed (*Eupatorium purpureum*). A. *Eupatorium purpureum*. B. Achenial hairs of same. C. *Eupatorium urticaefolium*.
(*A and C, drawings by Ada Hayden; B, drawing by S. B. Fracker.*)

Figure 349-1.   Figure 349-2.

FIG. 349.   1.   Hairs from achenium of *Eupatorium villosum*.   2.   Surface of achenium
of *Eupatorium urticaefolium*.
(Drawings by S. B. Fracker.)

False Boneset (*Kuhnia eupatorioides* L.).

Achenes oblong, columnar, 10 to 15-ribbed; blackish or reddish,
base with prominent disklike area marked by circular, somewhat
bulging ring; from one-eighth to one-tenth inch in length; pappus
of fine tawny-colored capillary, somewhat brittle, bristles.   The
achenial hairs of *Kuhnia eupatorioides,* according to Miss Mary A.
Nichols, are mostly simple and short; a few duplex hairs also occur.

Blazing-star (*Liatris punctata* Hook.).

Achenes 10-ribbed; slender, tapering to the base; one-quarter
to one-third inch long; grayish, pubescent, almost pilose; apex
brownish; scar at base indistinct; pappus or numerous plumose
bristles.   The achenial hairs of *Liatris gracilis,* according to Miss
Nichols, are duplex with an indistinct wall arising from the base.
The hairs of *L. punctata,* according to Mr. Fracker, are duplex
and simple.

The achenes of other species of *Liatris* are similar to those of *L.
punctata.*

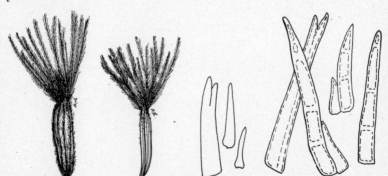

Figure 350-A.   Figure 350-B.   Figure 351-A.   Figure 351-B.
FIG. 350   Seeds (achenes) of: A.   Blazing Star *(Liatris punctata)*.   B.   False Boneset
(Kuhnia eupatorioides).
(Drawings by Ada Hayden.)

FIG. 351.   Achenial hairs of: A. *Kuhnia eupatorioides*.   B. *Liatris punctata*.
(Drawings by Fracker.)

Broad-leaved Gum-plant (*Grindelia squarrosa* Dunal).

Achenes short, thickened, faintly 4-angled, with veins between the angles; curved; one-twelfth to one-eighth of an inch in length; straw-colored; apex truncate; base with light scar. The related *Bigelovia nudata,* according to Mr. Fracker, has duplex hairs.

Canadian Goldenrod (*Solidago canadensis* L.).

Achenes minute, nearly terete, obovate, many-ribbed; brownish or greenish, somewhat pubescent; pappus of numerous fine capillary equal bristles.

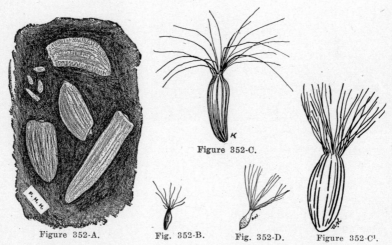

Figure 352-C.

Figure 352-A.   Fig. 352-B.   Fig. 352-D.   Figure 352-C¹.

FIG. 352. Seeds (achenes) of: A. Gum Weed (*Grindelia squarrosa*), enlarged and natural size. The one at the top shows the wrinkled appearance of the corky-thickened angles. B, Canadian Goldenrod (*Solidago canadensis*). C, Stiff Goldenrod (*Solidago rigida*). D, Late Goldenrod (*Solidago serotina*). (A, *after Hillman, Bull. Nev. Agr. Sta.; C, drawing by Charlotte M. King; B, C¹ and D, drawings by Ada Hayden.*)

Stiff Goldenrod (*Solidago rigida* L.).

Achenes ribbed, somewhat 4-angled, with minute ribs between the angles; scar at base small, whitish, one-sixth to one-twelfth inch long, pale straw-colored; pappus of minute capillary bristles of nearly equal size, spreading.

Late Goldenrod (*Solidago serotina* Ait.).

Achenes minute, somewhat teretish, many-ribbed, minutely pubescent, straw-colored, one-twentieth inch in length; small obovoid scar at base, whitish; pappus spreading, of fine white capillary bristles.

Daisy Fleabane (*Erigeron annuus* (L.) Pers.).

Achenes pale straw color, smooth, shining, flattened, obovate; length 0.7 to 0.9 millimeter; the apex bears a row of small straw-colored bristles.

Horseweed (*Erigeron canadensis* L.).

Achenes one-twenty-fourth to one-twentieth inch long, white or whitish, oblong lance-shaped, much flattened, one side often more convex than the other; scar of seed with small, whitish, raised

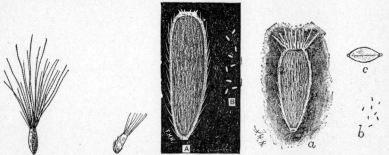

Fig. 353-A.   Fig. 353-B.   Fig. 353-C.   Fig. 353-D.

FIG. 353.   Seeds of Aster, Whiteweed and Horseweed. A, *Aster salicifolius*. B. Daisy Fleabane or Whiteweed (*Erigeron annuus*). C, Horseweed (*Erigeron canadensis*). D, Whiteweed (*Erigeron ramosus*).
(A and B, drawings by Charlotte M. King; C and D, after Hillman; C, Bull. Nev. Agr. Exp. Sta.; D, Bull. Mich. Exp. Sta.)

border, pubescent; pappus small, of numerous, fragile, capillary bristles, usually breaking away.   These seeds occur with grass seeds and lawn mixtures.

Willow-leaved Aster (*Aster salicifolius* Ait.).

Achene slender, pale brown, about 1.5 millimeters long and 0.25

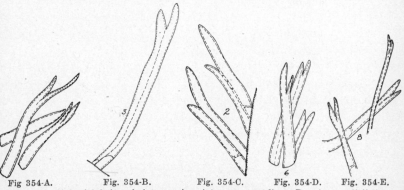

Fig 354-A.   Fig. 354-B.   Fig. 354-C.   Fig. 354-D.   Fig. 354-E.

FIG. 354.   Achenial hairs of Asters. A. *Aster novae-angliae*. B. *Aster salicifolius*. C. *Aster Tradescanti*. D. *Aster oblongifolius*. E. *Aster multiflorus*.
(Drawings by Mary A. Nichols and S. B. Fracker.)

millimeter broad; 5 longitudinal ribs at angles of seed; pappus straw-colored, hairs or bristles 6 millimeters in length. The achenial trichomes are long, the duplex character very pronounced, according to Mr. Fracker. He found much variation in the trichomes of the genus. The hairs of *A. Drummondii* are shorter. The trichomes of *A. Tradescanti* and *A. macrophyllus* are longer and more slender than in *A. Drummondii*. The duplex hairs of *Aster laevis, A. oblongifolius, A. novae-angliae* and *A. multiflorus* are slender.

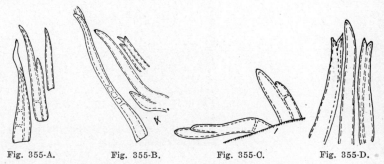

Fig. 355-A.   Fig. 355-B.   Fig. 355-C.   Fig. 355-D.

FIG. 355. Achenial hairs of Asters and Bigelovia. A. *Aster laevis.* B. *Aster macrophyllus.* C. *Aster Drummondii.* D. *Bigelovia nudata.*
(*Drawings by Mary A. Nichols and S. B. Fracker.*)

Cup Plant (*Silphium perfoliatum* L.).

Achenes large, two-fifths inch in length, dorsally flattened, 2-winged, notched at apex, grayish or bronze-colored, margins thin.

Marsh Elder (*Iva xanthiifolia* Nutt.).

Achenes obovoid, brown to black, with somewhat flattened longitudinal faces 1.5 to 2 millimeters in length, longitudinally striate with fine markings.

Lance-leaved Ragweed (*Ambrosia bidentata* Michx.).

Involucre top-shaped (turbinate), closed, yellowish or brownish; length, exclusive of the spine, one-tenth to one-eighth inch; 1 very prominent lobe and 6 or more prominent tubercles; surface of involucre rough and hispid, pubescent.

Large Ragweed (*Ambrosia trifida* L.).

Achene one-fifth to three-tenths inch in length, one-sixth inch across at widest part near upper end, containing seed one-fifth to

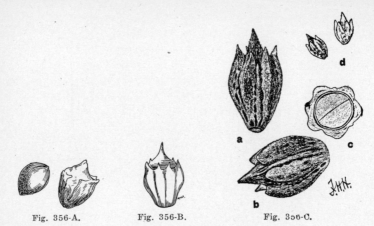

Fig. 356-A.   Fig. 356-B.   Fig. 356-C.

FIG. 356. Seeds of some Ragweeds. A. *Ambrosia bidentata.* B. *Ambrosia psilostachya.* C. *Ambrosia trifida.*

(Drawings, A. Charlotte M. King; B. Ada Hayden; C, after Hillman, Bull. Mich. Exp. Sta.)

three-tenths inch long, or in extreme cases nearly one-half inch; width at upper end 1.6 inch, involucre obovate, narrow below, gradually widening toward top, tipped by tapering beak; fruit prom-

Fig. 357-A   Fig. 357-B.

FIG. 357. Seeds of Small Ragweed and Cup Plant. A. Single achene of Cup Plant *(Silphium perfoliatum).*
B. Achenes, various views of Small Ragweed *(Ambrosia artemisiifolia);* A, five specimens having the outer covering, and showing the crown of teeth, or spines; B, one having the covering partly broken away, exposing the achene; C, achene, the covering persisting only at the base; D, a sectional view of a fruit; E, a group showing the natural size.

(A, drawing by Ada Hayden; B, after Hillman, Bull. Nev. Agr. Exp. Sta.)

inently ridged, forming rather long projecting tubercles, 4 to 10 in number, near upper end; involucre pitted or marked by cross ridges; color grayish or brownish; pubescent or nearly smooth; encloses a single achene, commonly called seed; outer parts of achene blackish or brownish; embryo with large thick cotyledons;

seed oily, caulicle thick, short. This seed is sometimes found in un-
cleaned clover seed.

Small Ragweed (*Ambrosia artemisiifolia* L.).

Involucre containing a single achene one-twelfth to one-sixth
inch long, obovoid or globular, tipped by a tapering beak one-
quarter length of involucre; ridges several (4 to 10), prominent,
with projecting tubercles, short, acute; color grayish or brownish,
pubescent; involucre reticulated, somewhat brittle, achene with
thick, rather hard wall; cotyledons 5, large, thick, fleshy, oily;
caulicle short. These seeds are found in clovers and alfalfa.

Western Ragweed (*Ambrosia psilostachya* DC.).

Bur teretish, one-eighth to one-fifth inch long, obovoid, with
beak less prominent than in preceding species; tubercles when
present, short; ridges 4 to 5; color grayish; pubescent; involucre
pitted, readily removed leaving brown achenium, with short beak;
cotyledons large, fleshy, oily. This seed occurs in clover seed.

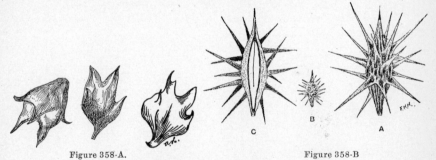

Figure 358-A.   Figure 358-B

Fig. 358.   A.   White-leaved Franseria *(Franseria discolor)*.   B.   *Franseria Hookeriana*.
A, bur enlarged; B, natural size; C, bur cut lengthwise.

*(A, drawings by Ada Hayden and Charlotte M. King; B, after Hillman, Bull. Nev.
Agr. Exp. Sta.)*

White-leaved Franseria (*Franseria discolor* Nutt.).

Involucre with burs from a little less than one-quarter inch to
slightly more in length, with 2 achenes, each in a separate cell,
oblong, with 2 pointed spines usually incurved at apex and tapering base; several prominent ridges; 3 or more tubercles, furrowed;
light straw color, surface pubescent; achene slightly reticulated.

Hooker's Franseria (*Franseria Hookeriana* Nutt.).

Involucre lanceolate or oval, two-fifths inch in length, with a
prominent conical spine and numerous straight or recurved rigid

spines, variable in number, as long as the width of the bur; surface wrinkled; involucre with one elongated achene; color yellowish, slightly pubescent.

Cocklebur (*Xanthium spinosum* Kearney).

Involucre one-third to one-half inch long, cylindrical, obtuse, armed with short prickles, inconspicuous, 2-beaked, or pointless, occasionally a single straight spine; bur oblong or somewhat flattened; surface sparingly covered with slender hooked prickles one-twelfth inch long; color dull; smooth or covered with yellowish hairs; achenes 2 in each bur.

Cocklebur (*Xanthium canadense* Mill.).

Involucre containing 2 achenes, three-fourths to an inch or more long, each in a separate cell, the lower placed farther down in the bur than the upper; bur hard, woody, thick-walled, bearing numerous hispid recurved spines, the 2 spines at the end thicker, heavier, and incurved; surface of achene blackish in color, thin-walled; and embryo slender with 2 long cotyledons and a thick caulicle; each seed cavity connects with a channel, frequently may also show styles connecting with this channel. This seed has a strong odor.

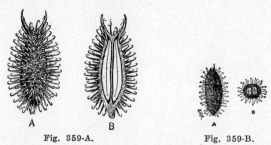

Fig. 359-A.　　　　　　　Fig. 359-B.

FIG. 359. Burs of Cockleburs. A. Common Cocklebur *(Xanthium canadense)*, with view of entire bur, and of cross section showing the pair of seeds in place. B. Spiny Clotbur or Cocklebur *(Xanthium spinosum)*.
(After Hillman, Bull. Mich. Agr. Exp. Sta.)

Cocklebur (*Xanthium echinatum* Murr.).

Involucre one inch long; brownish in color; prominently bristly spines curved; achenes 2 in each bur. This bur closely resembles that of *X. canadense.*

Rough-Ox-eye (*Heliopsis scabra* Dunal).

Achenes thick, obtusely 3 to 4-angled, with truncate summit;

one-eighth to one-seventh inch long; margins pubescent; blackish; apex somewhat depressed; scar at base light or straw-colored; pappus none.

Fig. 360-A.   Fig. 360-A1.   Fig. 360-B.   Fig. 360-C.

Fig. 360. Seeds of Heliopsis and Rudbeckia. A, A1, Ox-eye (*Heliopsis scabra*). B. Black-eyed Susan or Nigger-head (*Rudbeckia hirta*); a, two views of achenes, b, achenes, natural size. C. Coneflower (*Rudbeckia laciniata*). (A, C, drawings by L. Collins; A1, Charlotte M. King; B, after Hillman, Bull. Mich. Agr. Exp. St.)

Black-eyed Susan, Nigger-head (*Rudbeckia hirta* L.).

Achene purplish black, 1.5 to 1.8 millimeters long, tapering slightly from base to apex; a distinct ridge at each of the 4 angles of the achene; each side with fine longitudinal strips; pappus absent.

Cone-flower (*Rudbeckia laciniata* L.).

Achenes 4-angled, brownish, truncate, one-fifth inch long; minutely roughened; upper end with projecting truncate point; apex with an inconspicuous scar.

Gray-headed Cone-flower (*Lepachys pinnata* Torr. and Gray).

Achene short, flattened or angular, one-tenth of an inch long, 2 slightly marginal wings, and 2 intermediate ones, or only 1, convex; apex whitish, depressed with slight projecting scar; base with inconspicuous scar of nearly the same color as the rest of the achene.

Sunflower (*Helianthus annuus* L.).

Achenes obovate, oblong, somewhat flattened, one-fifth to one-quarter of an inch long; with appressed pubescence especially at upper end, grayish and mottled with brown; marked by longitudinal lines; more prominent ridge in center; lower end of achene notched, containing the scar; the apical scar with a slightly elevated circular margin; cotyledons large and fleshy. The achenial hairs, according to Mr. Fracker, are long, slender, and duplex; *H. tuberosus* has simple and several-celled trichomes but none duplex. *H. occidentalis* has short, thick, duplex hairs.

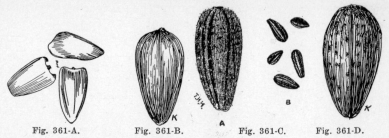

Fig. 361-A.   Fig. 361-B.   Fig. 361-C.   Fig. 361-D.

FIG. 361. Seeds of Cone-flower and Sunflower. A. Cone-flower (*Lepachys pinnata*).
B and C. Common Sunflower (*Helianthus annuus*). D. Meadow Sunflower
(*Helianthus grosse-serratus*).
(*A, drawing by Ada Hayden; B and D, drawings by C. M. King; C, after Hillman,
Bull. Mich. Exp. Sta.*)

Saw-toothed Sunflower (*Helianthus grosse-serratus* Martens).

Achenes oblong, narrowed at base and broad at apex, flattened,
with 2 edges, and 1 prominent ridge, sometimes 2 on each side;
one-sixth to one-fifth inch long; pappus of 2 lanceolate awns;
smooth or slightly hairy; brownish or lighter color, mottled with
brown; the scar at the end is in the form of a small notch; the
remnant of a corolla tube at the apex; cotyledons fleshy.

Prairie Sunflower (*Helianthus petiolaris* Nutt.).

Achenes obovate-oblong, but slightly flattened, villous pubescent,
a prominent longitudinal ridge and several lines on each side;
grayish, mottled with brown; scar in notch at the lower end; scar
on upper end circular; cotyledons 2, large and fleshy. According
to Mr. Fracker, the achenial hairs are long and slender and duplex.

Fig. 362-A.   Fig. 362-B.

FIG. 362. Seeds of Sunflowers. A. Prairie Sunflower (*Helianthus petiolaris*). B.
Wood Sunflower (*Helianthus strumosus*).
(*Drawings by L. R. Collins.*)

Wild Sunflower (*Helianthus strumosus* L.).

Achenes obovate, flattened, several fine lines and a longitudinal
ridge on each side, one-sixth to one-fifth inch long, nearly glabrous; yellowish or light brown, finely mottled except near apex
and base, which are lighter in color; lower end marked by small

distinct scar, occurring in a notch; upper end bearing large circular scar; the two cotyledons large, fleshy.

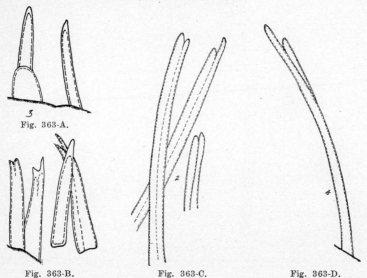

Fig. 363-A.

Fig. 363-B.   Fig. 363-C.   Fig. 363-D.

FIG. 363. Achenial hairs of Sunflower seeds. A. Artichoke (*Helianthus tuberosus*). B. Prairie Sunflower (*Helianthus occidentalis*). C. Common Sunflower (*Helianthus annuus*). D. Prairie Sunflower (*Helianthus petiolaris*).
(*Drawings by S. B. Fracker.*)

Small Stick-tight (*Bidens discoidea* (T. and G.) Britton).

Achenes small, flat, narrowly acuminate, upwardly strigose; pappus of upwardly hispid, rarely downwardly barbed awns.

Beggar-ticks (*Bidens frondosa* L.).

Achenes flattened, oval or obovate, three-tenths to two-fifths inch exclusive of the awns; slightly ciliate on the margins; awns generally diverging, downwardly barbed; corolla tube whitish, with small opening in the center; basal portion of achene with a prominent depression with a light border. The achenial hairs, according to Miss Mary A. Nichols and Mr. Fracker, are duplex. In *B. cernua* they are simple. The related species (*B. aristosa*) formerly called Coreopsis has duplex hairs, although some hairs are simple.

Spanish Needles (*Bidens bipinnata* L.).

Achenes exclusive of awns one-half to three-fifths inch long, linear, 4-angled, slightly pubescent; pappus consisting of usually

4 divergent downwardly barbed awns, lighter in color than the achene; base of seed having a pale ringed border around a small depression.

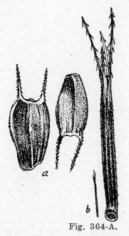

Fig. 364-A.   Fig. 364-B.

FIG. 364. A. Seeds of Spanish Needles, Pitchforks, or Bootjacks. a, Spanish Needle
                  (*Bidens frondosa*), b, *Bidens bipinnata*.
B. *Bidens discoidea*.
                        (*Drawings by Charlotte M. King*.)

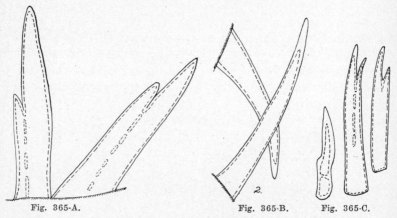

Fig. 365-A.   Fig. 365-B.   Fig. 365-C.

FIG. 365. Achenial hairs of Beggar-ticks. A. *Bidens frondosa*. B. *Bidens cernua*.
                  C. *Bidens aristosa*.
                  (*Drawings by Mary A. Nichols*.)

Sneezeweed (*Helenium autumnale* L.).

Achenes straw-colored, with several longitudinal ribs, length 1 millimeter, breadth 0.3 millimeter at apex, toward which the achene widens; surface bears scattered appressed hairs; pappus several chaffy points on margin of truncate apex.

Fetid Marigold (*Dyssodia papposa* (Vent.) Hitchc.).

Achene slender, 4-angled; length 3 millimeters, width at trun-cate apex 0.75 millimeter; black, with numerous scattered, ap-pressed black hairs; pappus a row of chaffy scales, dividing into numerous rough, bristly hairs. According to Mr. Fracker the achenial hairs are simple and duplex, the tip in duplex hairs being deeply cleft.

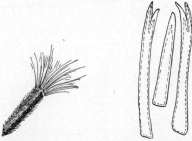

Fig. 366-A.   Fig. 366-B.   Fig. 366-C.

FIG. 366. Seeds and achenial hairs of Sneezeweed and Fetid Marigold. A Sneeze-weed (*Helenium autumnale*). B. Fetid Marigold (*Dyssodia papposa*). C. Achenial hairs of Fetid Marigold.
(*A and B, drawings by Charlotte M. King; C, from drawing by Mary A. Nichols.*)

Yarrow (*Achillea Millefolium* L.).

Achenes one-twelfth to one-tenth inch long, oblong to obovate, somewhat compressed; light on the margin, the remainder some-what brownish; sometimes slightly curved, base with prominent scar with slightly raised border; apex larger with a notch in the center and a projecting knob; surface of the achene marked with fine lines; pappus absent.

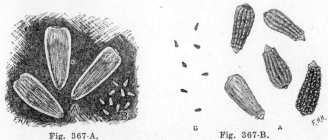

Fig. 367-A.   Fig. 367-B.

FIG. 367. Seeds of Yarrow and Mayweed. A, Yarrow (*Achillea Millefolium*); a, seeds (achenes) in side view, the two at the left showing the minute, circular scar; b, group showing the natural size.
B. Mayweed (*Anthemis Cotula*); a, a group of seeds showing the prevailing forms; b, a group showing the natural size.
(*After Hillman, Bull. Nev. Agr. Exp. Sta.*)

Mayweed (*Anthemis Cotula* L.).

Achenes one-twentieth to one-sixteenth inch long, oblong with prominent tubercled ribs, or occasionally smoothish curved, the base tipped with smooth nipple-like projections; pappus absent; straw-colored to light brown; bearing a projection scar; base with round, light-colored scar. This seed is frequently found in clover and grass seeds.

Ox-eye Daisy (*Chrysanthemum Leucanthemum* L.).

Achenes flattened, club-shaped, straight or slightly curved, one-twentieth to one-tenth inch long, oblong; angles white, with brown interstices; 5 to 10-ribbed; small scar at basal end; pappus wanting.

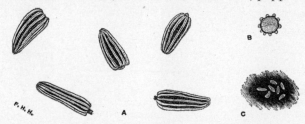

FIG. 368. Seeds of Ox-eye Daisy (*Chrysanthemum Leucanthemum*). A, prevailing forms of seeds (achenes); B, one in cross section; C, a group showing the natural size.

(After Hillman, Bull. Nev. Agr. Exp. Sta.)

Wormwood (*Artemisia biennis* Willd.).

Achenes brown, smooth, 3 to 4 flattened faces, angled between longitudinally; length 0.8 millimeter, width 0.3 millimeter, broader at apex than at base.

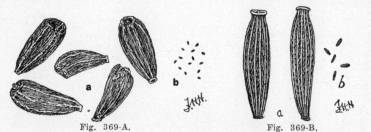

Fig. 369-A.   Fig. 369-B.

FIG. 369. Seeds of Wormwood and Fireweed. A. Wormwood (*Artemisia biennis*); a, achenes, b, natural size. B. Fireweed (*Erechtites hieracifolia*); a, achenes, b, natural size.

(After Hillman, Bull. Nev. Agr. Exp. Sta.)

Fireweed (*Erechtites hieracifolia* (L.) Raf.)

Achene linear-oblong, straight or curved, prominently striate, pubescent, beakless, one-sixth inch in length; upper end with a white ring, within the ring a slight depression; scar at the lower end with whitish ring, and a small depressed opening; pappus of numerous white, soft, capillary bristles.

Indian Plantain (*Cacalia tuberosa* Nutt.).

Achenes oblong, straight, or slightly curved, one-fifth inch in length; brown; prominently ribbed, the ribs minutely roughened; the apex of the seed with a slightly projecting rim or border to which the pappus is attached; the base with a circular ring; pappus with numerous fine, white, capillary bristles.

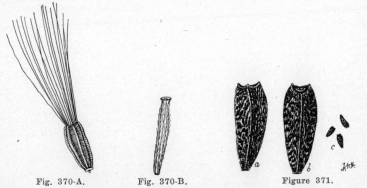

Fig. 370-A. Fig. 370-B. Figure 371.

FIG. 370. Seeds of Indian Plantain and Groundsel. A. Indian Plantain (*Cacalia tuberosa*). B. Groundsel (*Senecio vulgaris*).
(*Drawings by Charlotte M. King.*)
FIG. 371. Seeds of Burdock (*Arctium Lappa*). a, a side view of one of the inner achenes of a bur; b, showing the inner surface of a curved, outer achene, and exhibiting the character of the apex, both enlarged; c, a group showing natural size.
(*After Hillman, Bull. Nev. Agr. Exp. Sta.*)

Groundsel (*Senecio vulgaris* L.).

Achenes teretish or those of marginal flowers compressed, narrow, cylindrical; 5 or 10-ribbed, pubescent; one-half inch long; upper part expanded, extending beyond narrow portion of upper part of achene; lower part with a depression; color reddish; pappus of fine, white, capillary bristles.

Burdock (*Arctium Lappa* L.).

Achenes 3 to 5-ridged, upper portion truncate, one-fifth to one-fourth inch long, compressed or oblong, nearly straight to slightly curved, 3-angled; surface mottled in appearance, due to the small serrulate scales with projecting tips of ridges beyond the border; scar surrounded by a circular lighter colored area; scar at base lighter in color; pappus of numerous short scales. This seed may occasionally be found in commercial seeds.

Bull Thistle (*Cirsium lanceolatum* (L.) Hill).

Achene lanceolate, curved, tapering, in many cases somewhat angular, one-eighth to one-sixth inch long; brownish, not darkly striated, marked with definite grooves, upper part lighter, ringed, also showing at center of concave apex; apex with projecting point. This seed is found in red clover and in alfalfa seed.

Wavy-leaved Thistle (*Cirsium undulatum* (Nutt.) Spreng.).

Achene in general outline lanceolate, tapering from base, inner edge slightly convex, several prominent ridges, light brown, not pigmented; upper part yellowish; apex with prominent rim and prominent remnant of corolla tube; achene slightly thicker than that of *C. discolor*. This seed is found in seeds of red clover and alfalfa.

Field Thistle (*Cirsium discolor* (Muhl.) Spreng.).

Achenes obovate, inner edge nearly straight, outer curved, convex; one-seventh to one-sixth inch long, tapering from narrowed base to apex, upper part longitudinally striated, slightly pig-

Fig. 372. Seeds of Thistle. 3. *Cirsium altissimum*. 4. *Cirsium discolor*. 5. *Cirsium undulatum*. 6. *Cirsium ioense*. (Drawing by Charlotte M. King.)

mented; grayish, upper part yellowish for one-third length of the achene. Found in seed of alfalfa and red clover.

Tall Thistle (*Cirsium altissimum* Willd.).

Achenes lanceolate-obovate, tapering toward lower end, and somewhat narrowed toward the apex, wider in the middle, one-

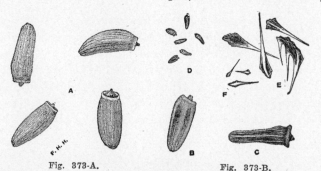

Fig. 373-A.   Fig. 373-B.

Fig. 373. Seeds of Thistles. A. Different views of Canada Thistle (*Cirsium arvense*). B. Bull Thistle (*cirsium lancoelatum*). (After Hillman, Bull. Mich. Agr. Exp. Sta.)

eighth inch in length; width one-twelfth inch; dull brown or grayish excepting light colored ring at upper end; numerous fine ridges; apex concave, with the remnant of corolla tube projecting from the center; color uniform, not marked by light and dark areas as is the case with the bull thistle.

Iowa Thistle (*Cirsium ioense* (Pammel) Fernald).

Achenes obovate, lanceolate, one side of seed straight, outer side slightly convex, one-fifth to one-fourth inch long, one-twelfth to one-sixteenth inch in width, gradually tapering from lower end toward upper end, prominently widened just below the apex, marked by longitudinal striations and dark areas, upper part yellowish, prominent rim glossy; apex concave, with the prominent projecting remnant of flower center.

Canada Thistle (*Cirsium arvense* (L.) Scop.).

Achene lanceolate, narrowed at lower end, tapering from somewhat thickened top, one-twelfth to one-eighth inch long; the cup-shaped top with a projecting conical portion, straight or slightly curved; marked with longitudinal dark lines or furrows; apex with a light colored border, giving appearance of a ring. The seeds of this thistle are quite commonly found in seed of small grains, clovers and grasses.

Barnaby's Thistle (*Centaurea solstitialis* L.).

Involucre ovoid, 1.5 centimeters in diameter, with stout straw-colored spines, widely spreading; achene cream or pale brown often mottled; length 2 millimeters, scar of attachment in a notch above rounded base; apex truncate, bearing tubercle in the center.

Corn-flower (*Centaurea cyanus* L.).

Achene oblong or obovoid, compressed, one-sixth to one-fifth inch long; smooth, shining; with inconspicuous veins or nerves; lower part of achene oblique; ivory-white; the elliptical or somewhat circular scar at base with whitish rimmed border, depressed, made up of soft tissue; pappus of several series of scaly bristles; brownish in color. The achenial trichomes, according to Mr. Fracker, are long and simple.

Chicory (*Cichorium Intybus* L.).

Achenes oblong, ribbed, 5-angled, spotted, grayish or straw-colored, with darker spots, one-twelfth to one-eighth inch in length.

apex with the base of the pappus scales extending beyónd the scar; minutely, transversely roughened; base of seed lighter in color, with

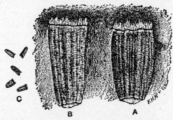

FIG. 374.　Chicory (Cichorium Intybus).　A, B, two views of seeds; C, seeds, natural size.
(After Hillman, Bull. Mich. Agr. Exp. Sta.)

small depressed scar; achenes from the inner part of the flower more slender and straight than from outer part. This seed is found with various commercial seeds.

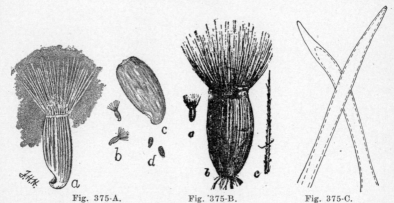

Fig. 375-A.　　　　　Fig. 375-B.　　　　　Fig. 375-C.

FIG. 375.　Seeds of Corn-flower and Knapweed.　A. Barnaby's Thistle or Knapweed (Centaurea solstitialis); a, achene with pappus, c, pappus removed, b and d, achenes, natural size.
B. Corn-flower (Centaurea cyanus).　C. Achenial hairs of Corn-flower.
(A, after Hillman, Bull. Nev. Agr. Exp. Sta.; B, after Nobbe; C, drawing by S. B. Fracker.)

Bristly Ox-tongue (*Picris echioides* L.).

Achene elliptical, narrowed at base, with projection at tip; one-tenth inch in length; light brownish red; wrinkled transversely, especially toward apical end. This seed is occasionally found in seed of alfalfa and clover.

Oyster Plant, Salsify (*Tragopogon porrifolius* L.).

Achenes linear, terete, beaked or long, covered with scalelike tubercles on the ribs, or merely roughened, light straw-colored or darker pappus of numerous plumose bristles; small scar at apex, whitish with a depression scar at base with an oval depression. This plant has been reported as a weed of alfalfa meadows.

Meadow Salsify (*Tragopogon pratensis* L.).

Achenes linear, terete, one-half inch or little more long, exclusive of beak; scar at base, whitish, with an oval depression; beak one-third inch long; scar at end of beak whitish, with a depression, striate, smooth or slightly roughened, light straw-colored or darker; pappus of numerous soft, brownish, plumose bristles.

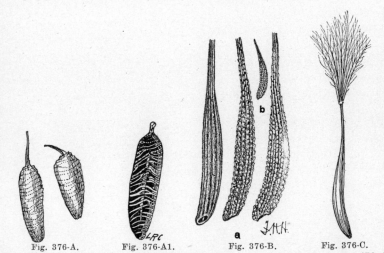

Fig. 376-A.   Fig. 376-A1.   Fig. 376-B.   Fig. 376-C.

FIG. 376.   Seeds of *Picris* and *Tragopogon*.   A and A1.   Bristly Ox-tongue (*Picris echioides*).
B.   Oyster Plant (*Tragopogon porrifolius*); a, achenes enlarged, b, achenes natural size.
C.   Meadow Salsify (*Tragopogon pratensis.*)
(A, drawings by L. R. Collins; B, after Hillman, Bull. Mich. Agr. Exp. Sta.; C, drawing by C. M. King.)

Dandelion (*Taraxacum officinale* Weber).

Achenes two-fifths inch long including persistent beak, fusiform in shape, prominent ribs, and projecting teeth at ribs, especially at upper end; beak four-fifths to one inch in length; achenes light gray in color, otherwise like preceding; pappus capillary, whitish, fragile.   Dandelion seeds occur with grass seeds.

Dark-seeded Dandelion (*Taraxacum erythrospermum* Andrz.).

Achenes one-sixth to one-fifth inch long; lance-shaped, or spindle-shaped, 5 longitudinal ridges, upper end with rough tubercles, persistent long beak about two-fifths inch long, brownish, somewhat pointed, prominently ribbed; pappus of numerous capillary, fragile, white bristles; color reddish; toothed at apex; beak and pappus both shorter; achenes more prominently tubercled than in *T officinale*.

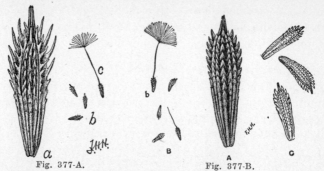

Fig. 377-A.   Fig. 377-B.

FIG. 377. Dandelion seeds. A. Red Seeded Dandelion *(Taraxacum erythrospermum)*;
    a, seed enlarged, b and c, seed, natural size, c, with pappus.
B. Common Dandelion *(Taraxacum officinale)*. A, an enlarged view of one of the
    two similar faces of an achene, in which no attempt is made to show the minute
    surface-scales which are not evident under the ordinary lens. B, a group of
    seeds, natural size. b, one bearing the beak and pappus. C, a group showing
    common variation in the form of the achenes.
    (After Hillman: A, Bull. Mich. Agr. Exp. Sta.; B, Bull. Nev. Agr. Exp. Sta.)

Field Sow Thistle (*Sonchus arvensis* L.).

Achenes dark reddish brown, dull, ends slightly truncate, length
2.5 to 3 millimeters, width 0.8 millimeter, somewhat flattened, with
4 strong ribs or angles, between which lie smaller ridges; numerous
transverse ridges on the ribs.

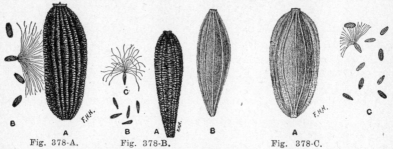

Fig. 378-A.   Fig. 378-B.   Fig. 378-C.

FIG. 378.   Seeds of Sow Thistles. A.   Field or Perennial Sow Thistle *(Sonchus
      arvensis)*; B, natural size, showing pappus on one achene.
B. *Sonchus oleraceus*, different views of achenes.
C. *Sonchus asper*, A and B, different views of achenes, C, achenes, natural size.
      (After Hillman, Bull. Mich. Agr. Exp. Sta.)

Sow Thistle (*Sonchus oleraceus* L.).

Achenes light brown, flattened, ribbed, the prominent ribs roughened; one-eighth inch long; pappus of white capillary bristles,
much like the preceding. "Apt to occur among grass seeds."

Spiny Sow Thistle (*Sonchus asper* Vill.).

Achenes broadly oblong or lance-shaped, similar faces, many-
ribbed, one-tenth inch long, slightly pubescent, prominent ridges

minutely roughened; base with a minute scar, brownish; the apex
with projecting point and fine, capillary, white bristles. This seed
is found with grass seeds.

Prickly Lettuce (*Lactuca scariola* var. *integrata* Gren. and Godr.).

Achenes brownish, margin somewhat lighter, surface roughened,
one-ninth to one-sixth inch long; beak one-tenth to one-eighth inch
long, lance-shaped, straight or slightly curved, upper end tapering

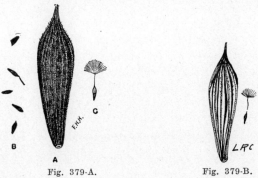

Fig. 379-A.   Fig. 379-B.

FIG. 379. Lettuce Seeds. A. *Lactuca scariola*; A, side view of an achene, enlarged.
  B, a group of the same, natural size. C, an achene bearing its beak and fragile
  pappus.
B. Prickly Lettuce (*Lactuca scariola* var. *integrata*).
  (A, after Hillman, Bull. Nev. Agr. Exp. Sta.; B, drawing by L. R. Collins.)

toward the beak, somewhat flattened, on one side margined, faces
convex, with 5 to 7 longitudinal nerves; scar circular, with a small
depression.

Wild Lettuce (*Lactuca canadensis* L.).

Achene three-twentieths inch in length, straight or curved, sides

Fig. 380-A.   Fig. 380-B.

FIG. 380. Seeds of Lettuce. A. *Lactuca canadensis*; a, enlarged achene, b, natural
  size. B. *Lactuca floridana*.
  (A, after Hillman, Bull. Mich. Agr. Exp. Sta.; B, drawing by Charlotte M. King.)

somewhat unequal, transversely wrinkled, blackish brown, beak one-twentieth inch long, shorter than in *L. floridana;* one faint rib on each side of prominent midrib; decidedly convex on each side of midrib to the flattened margin; scar with whitish ring and small depression; pappus white, capillary. Much like *L. floridana,* beak smaller and shorter. This seed may occur with commercial seed.

False Lettuce (*Lactuca floridana* (L.) Gaertn.).

Achene brown, transversely wrinkled, three-twentieths to seven-fortieths inch in length, straight or slightly curved; beak light brown, about one-fifth inch long, generally persistent, convex; ribs rather faint, one on each side of prominent midrib, strongly convex on each side of midrib, margin flattened; pappus white, capillary.

Rattlesnake Root (*Prenanthes alba* L.).

Achene oblong or columnar, truncate, somewhat flattened, 4 to 5 angled, brownish; upper part with a projecting ring to which the bristles of pappus are attached; scar at the base whitish, not prominent; one-eighth inch in length; pappus tawny.

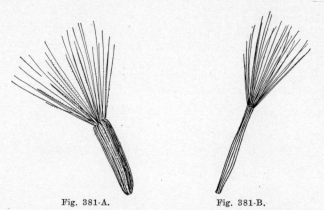

Fig. 381-A.   Fig. 381-B.

Fig. 381.   Seeds of Rattlesnake Weed and False Calais.   A.   Rattlesnake Weed (*Prenanthes alba*).   B.   False Calais (*Agoseris cuspidata*).
(*Drawings by Charlotte M. King.*)

False Calais (*Agoseris cuspidata* (Pursh.) Steud.).

Achenes fusiform, slightly contracted at the apex, with 10 prominent ribs; one-half inch long, or little longer; pappus of soft, white, capillary bristles; scar at base, whitish, with a small opening.

Orange Hawkweed (*Hieracium aurantiacum* L.).

Achene oblong, columnar, one-tenth inch long; blackish or dark brown, marked with prominent longitudinal ridges, minutely roughened; base of achene with small circular raised border, lighter than remainder of achene; pappus of numerous somewhat brownish bristles, frequently breaking away near the top of the achene, then showing short bristles.

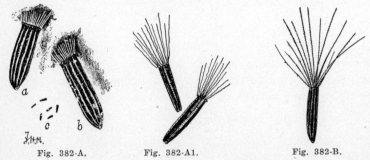

Fig. 382-A.   Fig. 382-A1.   Fig. 382-B.

FIG. 382. Seeds of Hawkweeds. A and A1, Orange Hawkweed (*Hieracium aurantiacum*). B. Hawkweed (*Hieracium canadense*). (*A, after Hillman, Bull. Mich. Agr. Exp. Sta.; A1, drawing by L. R. Collins; B, drawing by Charlotte M. King.*)

Hawkweed (*Hieracium canadense* Mx.).

Achenes one-tenth to one-eighth inch long, oblong, columnar, 10 to 15-ribbed; blackish or reddish; base with prominent disklike area marked by circular ring; apex with somewhat fine tawny-colored capillary bristles; below point of attachment is an area bulging outward; the capillary bristles have tendency to break.

CHAPTER III.

MORPHOLOGY OF LEAVES AND FLOWERS OF WEEDS
J. N. MARTIN.

ROOTS AND ROOT-STOCKS OF WEEDS
J. C. CUNNINGHAM.

LEAVES.

INTRODUCTORY STATEMENT.

Leaves are distinguishable into primary and secondary. The primary leaves arise directly from the first cells produced by the division of the fertilized egg and in seed plants are called cotyledons. They are usually transient, and not rarely are so distorted by acting as storage places for reserve food that they do not function as foliage leaves at all. The secondary leaves arise upon the sides of the stem and are the ordinary foliage leaves of the plant. They are very important organs in connection with the work of nutrition.

PARTS OF A LEAF.

In the typical foliage leaf there are three parts—the expanded portion which is called blade or lamina, the leaf stalk (petiole), and a pair of appendages at the base of the petiole known as stipules.

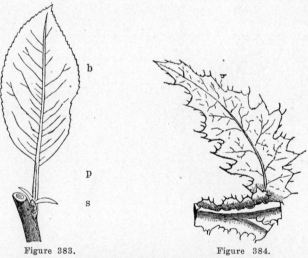

Figure 383.   Figure 384.

FIG. 383.   Apple leaf; b, blade; p, petiole; s, stipules.
(After Thome.)
FIG. 384.   Sessile leaf of Thistle.
(After Thome.)

In some cases, as in the Hare's-ear mustard, (*Conringia orientalis*) and in the upper leaves of Canada thistle (*Cirsium arvense*) the petiole is absent and the blade is directly attached to the stem. Such leaves are designated as sessile.

The stipules are small leaf-like structures which appear at the place where the leaf is attached to the stem. They are very often absent but are conspicuous in the cinquefoils, vetches and other members of the rose and pulse families.

<h3 style="text-align:center">VEINING.</h3>

The blade of the leaf is traversed by a framework of fibrovascular bundles known as veins. In the leaves of grasses, sedges and rushes, the veins run more or less parallel from the base to the tip of the leaf. These leaves are the *parallel-veined* type. In the leaves of most of our common weeds, the veins are branched so as to form a network. These are the *netted veined* type.

Palmate and pinnate veining.—Netted-veined leaves are palmately veined when the primary ribs radiate from the base of the petiole as in the great ragweed. If there is only one midrib from which smaller ribs extend both ways, as in dandelion, dock, goldenrod, etc., the veining is said to be pinnate (meaning featherlike).

<h3 style="text-align:center">LEAF ARRANGEMENT.</h3>

In some instances, as in dandelion and evening primrose, the stem does not appear above ground or is late in appearing and the leaves at the surface of the ground are called *radical* leaves in distinction to the stem or *cauline* leaves.

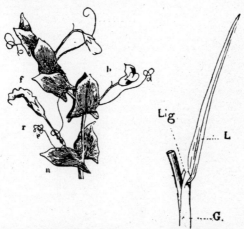

Fig. 385-I. Fig. 385-II.

FIG. 385. I. Vetch. (*Lathyrus aphaca*), showing opposite leaves; r, tendril; b, flower; f, fruit. Stipules performing the function of leaves.
II. Grass type of leaf; L, leaf blade; G, leaf sheath; Lig., ligule.
(*After Thome.*)

Leaves are usually arranged so as to secure the best exposure to the light. In the milkweed there is a pair of leaves at each node and the two leaves are on opposite sides of the stem. Here the leaves are said to be *opposite*.

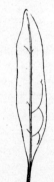

Figure 386.　　　　　　　　Figure 387.

FIG. 386. The clinging stem of the Bindweed, showing the alternate leaves.
FIG. 387. Leaf of the Privet plant showing entire margin.
(After Thome.)

In the asters, ironweed, goldenrods, lamb's quarter, etc., there is only one leaf at each node, and they are spoken of as *alternate*. In some cases several leaves appear at each node in a whorl. Such examples of *whorled* or verticillate leaves are found in the bed-straw and Joe-Pye weed.

BRANCHING.

The outline of a blade is extremely various. When the general

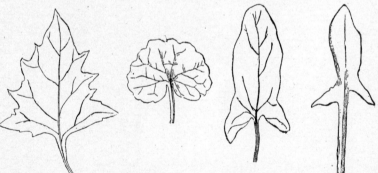

Fig. 388-I.　　　Fig. 388-II.　　　Fig. 388-III.　　　Fig. 388-IV.

FIG. 388. I. Triangular, lobed leaf of the Notch-weed. II. The reniform or kidney shaped leaf of Ground Ivy, illustrating wavy margin. III. Arrow-shaped leaf of Bindweed. IV. Spear-shaped leaf of Sorrel.
(After Thome.)

outline is completely filled out and the margin represents an even line, the leaf is said to be *entire*. Examples of such leaves are found in water pepper (*Polygonum Hydropiper*), mild water pepper (*P. hydropiperoides*), Pennsylvania smartweed (*P. pennsylvanicum*), etc.

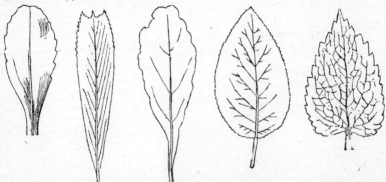

Fig. 389-I.   Fig. 389-II.   Fig. 389-III.   Fig. 389-IV.   Fig. 389-V.

FIG. 389.   I.   Leaf of Daisy, spatulate in shape with a serrate margin.   II.   Spiny-pointed, serrulate leaflet of Alfalfa.   III.   Wavy-margined leaf of Pigweed (*Amaranthus*).   IV.   Ovate, dentate leaf of Snowball.   V.   Serrate leaf of Henbit.
(*After Thome.*)

To designate the amount and character of the branching, the following terms are used:

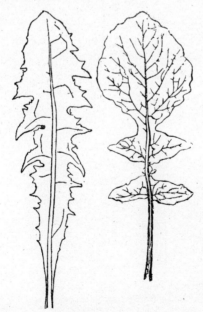

FIG. 390.   Cleft and pinnatifid leaves of Wild Lettuce.
(*After Thome.*)

Wavy margin, when the margin forms a wavy line bending slightly inward and outward in succession, as in the bitter dock (*Rumex obtusifolius*).

Toothed or dentate, when the margin is cut into sharp teeth and the teeth point out, as in the lower leaves of the daisy fleabane (*Erigeron annuus*).

Serrate, when the teeth point forward, as in the common sunflower (*Helianthus annuus*).

Serrulate, when the margin is finely serrate as in milk purslane (*Euphorbia maculata*).

Crenate, when the teeth are broad and rounded as in the common mallow (*Malva rotundifolia*).

Lobed, when the leaf is deeply cut, as in the great ragweed. The

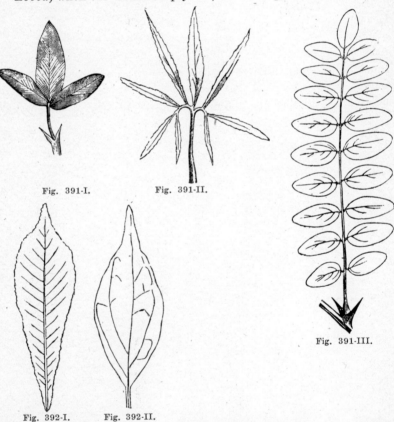

Fig. 391-I.   Fig. 391-II.

Fig. 391-III.

Fig. 392-I.   Fig. 392-II.

Fig. 391. Compound leaves. I. Leaf of Clover with three leaflets. II. Pedately divided leaf of Dragon Root. III. Pinnate leaf of Locust with 19 leaflets.
Fig. 392. I. Wedge-shaped leaflet of Horse Chestnut. II. Pointed leaf of the Wall Pellitory.
(*After Thome.*)

projecting portions are then called lobes. When the incisions are sharp the term *cleft* is often used; the leaf is *pinnatifid* when the incision extends almost to the midrib, as in the prickly lettuce (*Lactuca scariola*); it is *pinnate* when the incisions have extended to the midrib and each separated portion takes the character of a leaf. Each of the smaller portions is a leaflet, and the leaf is now considered compound. The spotted cowbane (*Cicuta maculata*), spring vetch (*Vicia sativa*) and cinquefoil (*Potentilla monspeliensis*) are good examples.

All of the above marginal characters may characterize the lobes of a simple leaf or the leaflets of a compound leaf.

LEAF STRUCTURE.

Before considering the work of the leaf it will be necessary to become acquainted with its structure.

The leaf is covered with an epidermis which is composed of compact layers of cells, so modified as to protect the more delicate inner parts. The epidermis may be peeled off as a delicate transparent skin. A microscope shows that this transparent skin is made up of many cells, so closely fitted together as to make a con-

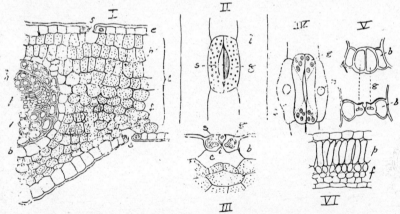

FIG. 393. I. A cross section of a leaf of Peppergrass (*Lepidium*) showing the upper epidermis (e), the lower epidermis (è), stoma (s), the chlorenchyma (c), consisting of closely placed palisade cells (p) and more loosely placed spongy tissue (f), and a vascular or conductive tract (v), with bundle sheath (b), hadrome or xylem (h), and leptome or phloem (l).
II. Surface view of stoma from Easter Lily; g, the kidney-shaped guard cells enclosing the stomatal aperture (s); b, the subsidiary cells.
III. Cross section of stoma; g, guard cell; s, central slit; o, outer slit; i, inner vestibule; c, stomatal cavity; b, subsidiary cell.
IV. Surface view of a grass stoma (*Poa pratensis*) showing the guard cells (g), with their dumb-bell-shaped lumina; b, subsidiary cells with prominent nuclei (n).
V. Median cross section and cross section through end of stoma of *Poa annua*; g, guard cell lumina; b, lumina of subsidiary cells.
VI. A cross section of a leaf of blue violet (*Viola cucullata*) showing a single row of elongated palisade cells (p), and the loose spongy tissue (f).
(*Drawings after Cowles modified by Charlotte M. King.*)

tinuous sheet or covering. Many slitlike openings between two crescent-shaped cells (*guard cells*) appear quite evenly distributed in the epidermis. The opening and guard cells constitute the stoma (plural stomata) which really means mouth. These numerous openings are passageways into the interior of the leaf and permit interchange of gases between outside air and the air in the leaf interior. The guard cells can change their shape and so vary the size of the opening. In horizontal leaves the stomata are chiefly and sometimes exclusively on the lower surface, a fair average number being about 62,500 to the square inch.

A cross section of a leaf will show the interior filled with a mass of thin walled cells containing green bodies (*chloroplasts*). This inner mass of thin walled cells is called the *mesophyll* and is the food-making tissue of the leaf. In the leaves of most weeds the cells just under the upper epidermis are much elongated and stand at right angles to the epidermis. These elongated cells are known as the *palisade-cells*. Between the palisade-cells and lower epi-

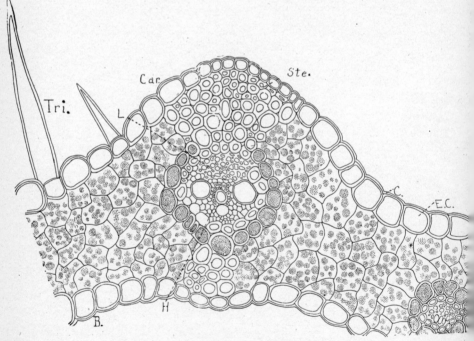

FIG. 394. Section of leaf of *Bromus mollis*. Car. mid-nerve; L, leptome; H. hadrome; B, bulliform cells; Ste, stereome; CB, chlorophyll-bearing parenchyma; EC, epidermal cells; Tri, trichome.
(*Sirrine and King.*)

dermis is the *spongy tissue* made up of irregularly shaped cells, so loosely joined as to form a system of intercellular spaces which permit the circulation of gases through the interior of the leaf. In the lower epidermis are seen the stomata with the air chambers beneath. Scattered through the mesophyll are the cross sections of veins and veinlets which form the framework of the leaf and conduct materials to and from the green working cells.

FUNCTION OF LEAVES.

Photosynthesis.—This is the process by which sugar and starch are produced for the plant. It is really a process of food manufacture by which raw materials are made into plant food and is an exceedingly important one, for upon it depend the lives of all plants and animals.

If an active leaf be submerged in water in the sunlight, bubbles will be seen continuously forming on the leaf surface and rising through the water. If light is excluded, the action will cease, and by increasing and decreasing the amount of light, it will be found that the process varies with the amount of light. An examination of this gas will show that it is oxygen. It has also been found that at the same time the oxygen is given off by the leaf, carbon dioxide (CO_2) is taken in, and that the outgo of oxygen and intake of carbon dioxide have a close relation.

The formula for sugar shows that it is composed of three elements, carbon, hydrogen, and oxygen. These elements are furnished by the carbon dioxide (CO_2) which is taken in from the air, and the water (H_2O) which is taken from the ground by the roots and conducted to the leaf tissue by the vascular bundles of the plant. Although CO_2 and H_2O furnish the necessary elements for sugar and starch, these are only the raw materials and some agent or factory is needed to cause these elements to combine and to combine in the right proportions. These factories are the chloroplasts, which give the green color to the entire leaf. The green pigment (chlorophyll) is the active agent of the chloroplast in the manufacture of sugar. The process by which these raw materials are combined is not well understood, and it seems that several simpler products are formed before sugar is produced. We know that CO_2 plus H_2O forms carbonic acid ($OH.COOH$). The carbonic acid is probably reduced to formaldehyde ($H.COH$). If six molecules of formaldehyde were properly combined we would have one of the simple sugars ($H_6C_6O_6H_6$) or better written

($C_6H_{12}O_6$). Two molecules of the simpler sugars combined with one molecule of water eliminated will give cane sugar—$C_6H_{12}O_6 +$ $C_6H_{12}O_6$=cane sugar, $C_{12}H_{22}O_{11}$ plus H_2O. By a further synthesis starch is produced.

When formaldehyde is produced as described above, oxygen is eliminated and this forms the escaping bubbles from the submerged leaf.

In this process of photosynthesis, the chloroplasts constitute the factory, carbon dioxide and water furnish the raw materials, sugar and starch are the products, and sunlight is the necessary condition without which the machinery will not run.

Respiration.—Plant cells as well as animals cells have much work to do and in order to perform work, energy is needed. Plant cells transform material into cell walls, increase and repair protoplasm, divide and do many other things which require energy. This work never ceases as long as the plant lives. The external indication of it is the absorption of oxygen and the giving out of carbon dioxide. This exchange is spoken of as respiration. It will be noted at once that this is exactly the reverse of what takes place in photosynthesis. During the day both carbon dioxide and oxygen are being both absorbed and eliminated. Photosynthesis and respiration are independent processes and must not be confused.

Transpiration.—We are familiar with the fact that the air is continually taking up water in the form of vapor. A dish filled with water and exposed to the air in the laboratory or out of doors will soon become dry. We hang wet clothes upon the line so that the air will take up the water which they contain. When we look into the physics of this process, we find that the water is really the active agent, and that it is continually changing into vapor and passing into the air. This process of changing into vapor we call evaporation, and its rate depends upon temperature, the amount of moisture already present in the air and atmospheric pressure. This same process of evaporation goes on in the leaf, for the air surrounds the leaf and fills the intercellular spaces within. This continuous loss of moisture from the leaves is called *transpiration*.

As seen in photosynthesis, water must be present in the leaf cells in sufficient quantity or the process of food making will be hindered. Water is further needed for dissolving and transporting food materials. It is evident that transpiration is continually diminishing this quantity of water which is so necessary and if the supply, which is furnished from the ground through the roots and stems, does not equal the loss, disaster will come to the plant. So far transpiration seems to be only a detriment to the plant. It is thought to be of use in that it increases the flow of the water from the soil and through the plant and thus increases the amount and better distributes the salts secured from the soil.

It is remarkable how well most weeds can thrive, when economic

Fig. 395-I.   Fig. 395-II.

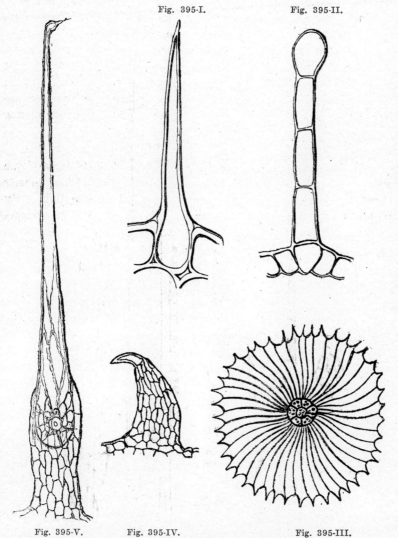

Fig. 395-V.   Fig. 395-IV.   Fig. 395-III.

FIG. 395. Some protective structures of leaves and stems. I. One-celled hair of the Pelargonium. II. Multicellular hair of Geranium. III. Scale of Oleaster (Elaeagnus). IV. Prickle from common Hop. V. Stinging hair of Nettle. (After Thomé.)

plants are suffering severely from transpiration. This may be due to protective modifications which cut down transpiration or to the ability to supply the loss through a more efficient root system.

One of the harmful effects of weeds is the taking from the soil of the water which economic plants need. According to careful estimates a sunflower (*Helianthus annuus*) six feet high transpires on the average about 1 quart per day. A grass plant has been found to give off its own weight of water every twenty-four hours in hot, dry summer weather. This would make about 6½ tons per acre or more than one thousand gallons every twenty-four hours for ordinary grass fields, or rather about 200 gallons for a plot about the size of a city lot. From the above figures we can form some notion of the immense loss of water from the soil through weeds, and see how weeds can retard the growth of economic plants.

LEAF PROTECTION.

Such an important organ as the leaf, with its delicate active tissue well displayed, is exposed to numerous dangers. Chief among these dangers are excessive transpiration and intense light. By regulating the opening in the stomata, which are the chief passage-

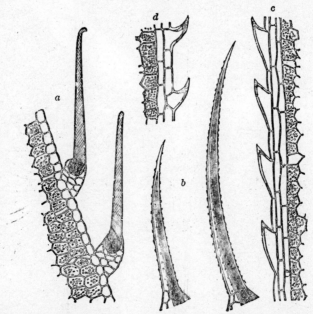

FIG. 396. Urticating hairs and cutting leaves. a, urticating hair of Nettle; b, bristle of Bugloss; c, barbed margin of a leaf of Sedge; d, barbed margin of a leaf of Grass.

ways for the escaping moisture, the leaf is able to check transpiration. The various epidermal modifications which are quite
common among the weeds afford protection. In some cases this
consists of a waxy layer on the outside of the epidermis as in some
milkweeds and some species of wild lettuce. This layer of wax
prevents the escape of moisture, and protects the chlorophyll-
bearing tissue of the leaf from the intense light rays.

Another very common protective structure upon the leaves is
to be found in the great variety of hairs developed by the
epidermis. In the mullein the hairs are so prominent that they
form a felt-like covering. Among the cinquefoils and thistles, the
hairs are usually not branched as in the mullein and the covering
is not so dense.

All stages from those in which the hairs are very small, giving
the leaf a downy appearance, up to the extreme case in the mullein,
can be found among the weeds.

FLOWERS.

A satisfactory definition of a flower has not yet been agreed
upon by botanists. For this reason it seems better to describe a
flower rather than attempt to define it.

A complete flower consists of four cycles or sets of organs—
sepals, petals, stamens and pistils. The sepals taken together constitute the calyx; the petals taken together constitute the corolla.

Since the cells of the stem most active in forming new organs lie
in the tip, it seems most natural that the organs appearing last,

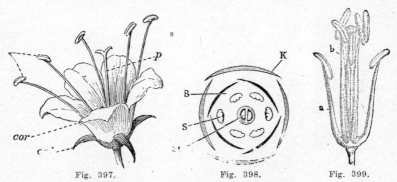

Fig. 397.   Fig. 398.   Fig. 399.

FIG. 397. Complete flower; cal, calyx; cor. corolla; p, pistil, and s, stamens.
(After Thome.)
FIG. 398. Diagrammatic cross section of a perfect flower. St, ovary showing two
cells; S, stamens; B, corolla; K, calyx.
(After Thome.)
FIG. 399. Essential organs of the flower of the Black Mustard. a, two short stamens;
b, four long stamens. Pistil is enclosed by the stamens; the filiform body is the
filament of the stamen; the enlarged portion of the stamen is called the anther.
(After Thome.)

would be at the stem tip and that the age of organs would increase
as their distance from the stem tip.   According to this scheme, the
succession of floral sets would be sepals, petals, stamens and pistils.
This is probably the order of succession in many flowers, but many
exceptions have been found.   In shepherd's purse (*Capsella*) the
petals are last to appear, while in the dandelion and other composites the sepals are last to appear.

FIG. 400.   Irregular flower of a leguminous plant, dissected so as to show the difference in shape and size of petals.
(After Thome.)

Since the work of the flower is to produce seeds, and seed forming
is due to the co-operation of the stamens and pistils, these are
known as the essential organs of the flower.   A flower is a perfect

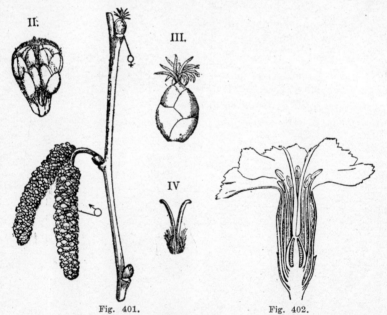

Fig. 401.   Fig. 402.

FIG. 401.   II.   Staminate flower of the Hazel showing the stamens and bracts.   III.
Pistillate flower showing pistils and enclosing bracts.   IV.   Style and two stigmas.
Catkin at middle of stem containing the staminate flowers; female flower at top
of stem.   The Hazel is a monoecious plant.
(After Thome.)
FIG. 402.   Longitudinal section through the hypogynous flower of the Pink, showing the
attachment of floral parts.
(After Thome.)

flower if it contains both of the essential organs. The simplest flower would have one stamen or one pistil and no corolla or calyx. Imperfect flowers are designated as staminate when they contain stamens, but no pistils; pistillate when they contain pistils but no stamens. The term "bisexual" is applied to the flower which contains both stamens and pistils. This is the most common type of flower.

Plants such as ragweed and corn, which have pistillate and staminate flowers (i. e., pistils and stamens in separate flowers but both kinds of flowers on the same plant) are monoecious (one household). Such plants as the red campion (*Lychnis dioica*), mulberry, willows and poplars, which bear the pistillate flowers on one plant and staminate on another are dioecious (two households). A plant which bears some perfect flowers and some staminate or pistillate only, is polygamous.

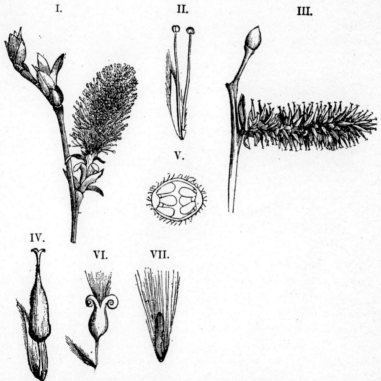

FIG. 403. I and III. Staminate and pistillate catkins of the Willow. II and IV Staminate and pistillate flowers. V. Cross section of ovary showing the one cell, two placentae and ovules. VI and VII show opening of pod and character of the seed. Since the male and female catkins are borne on different trees, this plant is dioecious.

(After Thome.)

Fig. 404-I.　　　　　Fig. 404-II.　　　　　Fig. 404-III.　　　　　Fig. 404-IV.

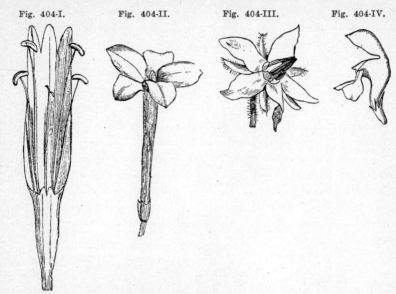

FIG. 404.　Flowers with petals joined (gamopetalous).　I.　Globularia.　II.　Jasmine.
III.　Borage.　IV.　Ground Ivy.
(*After Thome.*)

FLORAL ENVELOPES AND THEIR CHARACTERS.

The sepals and petals constitute the two floral envelopes. The envelopes, taken together, are sometimes called the perianth. This is especially true in the lily family where the two envelopes do not differ much in shape and color. Floral envelopes are not essential and one or both may be absent. If only one is absent, it is the corolla, and the flower is apetalous. In the grasses and sedges there is no true perianth but the essential organs are enclosed by chaff-like bracts and glumes.

Stamens.—The stamens surround the pistils and their number is various. They may be opposite the petals or alternate with them. In the mustards and buttercups the stamens are inserted on the receptacle. When they are inserted on the corolla, as in the morning-glory, they are epipetalous. Stamens are usually distinct or free from each other. When they are united by their filaments into one set, as in the mallow family, lupines and lobelia, they are monadelphous (one brotherhood). If united into two sets as in clover, they are diadelphous (two brotherhoods). More sets would be designated by tri-, tetra-, etc.

Relation of the attachment of floral envelopes and stamens to the pistil.—An examination of the floral sets in shepherd's purse (*Cap-*

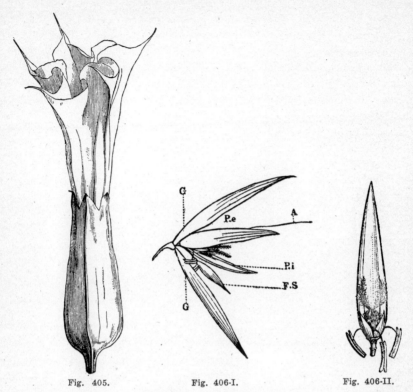

Fig. 405.   Fig. 406-I.   Fig. 406-II.

FIG. 405. Gamosepalous and gamopetalous flower of Jamestown or Jimson Weed.
(After Thome.)

FIG. 406. I. Flower of oats showing the grass type of floral envelopes. G. empty
glume; Pe, lemma bearing an awn A; Pi, palea; F. S., sterile flower. **Between**
lemma and palea are pistil and stamens.

II. Flower with lemma removed, showing palea and the small bracts (lodicules) **at the**
base of the pistil and stamens.
(After Thome.)

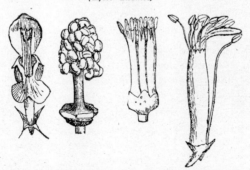

Fig. 407-I.   Fig. 407-II.   Fig. 407-III.   Fig. 407-IV.

FIG. 407. I. Flower of Ground Ivy with stamens differing in length. II. Mallow
with monadelphous stamens. III. Orange with polydelphous stamens. IV.
Clover with diadelphous stamens.
(After Thome.)

sella) or mustard (*Brassica alba*) will show that sepals, petals and stamens are inserted on the receptacle below the ovary. This flower is hypogynous (i. e., parts under the pistil). When the petals and stamens are joined to the calyx, the flower is perigynous (i. e., parts around the pistil). In such flowers as the evening primrose and those of the composites, the calyx is adherent to the ovary and the corolla seems to arise from the top of the ovary. Such a flower is said to be epigynous (parts on the pistil).

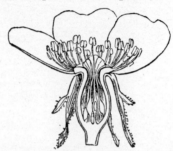

FIG. 408.   Perigynous flower of the Rose.
(After Thome.)

Arrangement of flowers (*inflorescence*). —Flower arrangement is of three classes; namely, indeterminate, when the flowers arise laterally and successively as the floral axis elongates; determinate,

Fig. 409.   Fig. 410.

FIG. 409.   Strap-shaped and tubular flowers from the head of Squaw Weed (*Senecio*).
The corolla and calyx appear to arise from the top of the ovary. Such a flower
is epigynous and the free portion of the calyx is called pappus.
(After Thome.)
FIG. 410.   Solitary funnel-shaped flower of field Bindweed.
(After Thome.)

when the flowers arise from the terminal buds and thus check the elongation of the floral axis; and mixed, when these two are combined.

Flowers may arise singly, as in silverweed (*Potentilla Anserina*), and are then designated as solitary. If in the axils of ordinary leaves, they are axillary and solitary.

A raceme is that indeterminate inflorescence in which the flowers are stalked and arranged along the sides of a floral axis. The shepherd's purse has the raceme type of inflorescence. New flowers are continuously arising at the top as the floral axis elongates.

If the inflorescence is of the raceme type with the exception that the flowers have no stalks, as in the plantain, we have the spike.

If the lowest pedicels or flower stalks are elongated (or the upper ones remain short) so that the cluster is convex or nearly flat on top, we have the corymb type of inflorescence.

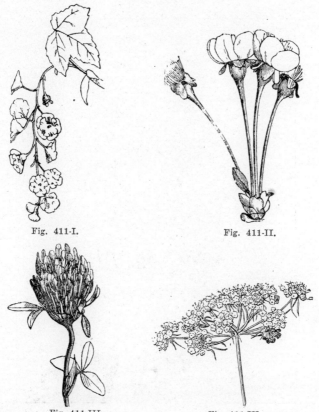

Fig. 411-I.

Fig. 411-II.

Fig. 411-III.

Fig. 411-IV.

FIG. 411. Types of inflorescence. I. Raceme of Currant. II. Umbel-like inflorescence of Cherry. III. Head of Clover. IV. Umbel of Parsley.

In the wild carrot, common yarrow, and parsley family in general, the axis of the corymb is so much shortened that all pedicels

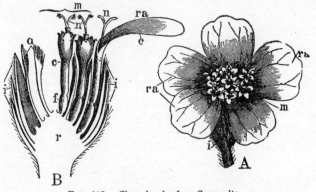

FIG. 412.   Close head of a Composite.
(After Thome.)

FIG. 413.   Milkweed with flowers in umbels.

seem to start from the same point and resemble the rays of an inverted umbrella. This is the umbel.

In the clover (*Trifolium procumbens*) the flower axis is short and the pedicels of the flowers are either short or absent. This causes the flowers to be crowded into a roundish cluster which is called a head.

The flower axis is so much shortened in the dandelion, sunflower and composites in general, that it may be a concave, flat, or conical surface. The flowers are crowded upon this surface, and the entire group is surrounded by one or more rows of leaf-like bracts which form the involucre. This is the close head or composite type of inflorescence.

In many cases, as in field sorrel and in five-finger (*Potentilla norvegica*), the oldest flower of the floral axis is terminal and all later flowers must arise from axils below. This is the determinate type of inflorescence and this type of flower cluster is called a cyme.

FIG. 414. Close head of the Dandelion
(After Thome.)

Fig. 415-I.   Fig. 415-II.   Fig. 415-III.

FIG. 415. Flower of Milkweed, showing the peculiar hooded and horned stamens. I. Flower. II. Stamen. III. Pistil with adhering pollen masses. IV. Pollen masses or pollinia.
(After Thome.)

THE DEVELOPMENT OF A STAMEN AND ITS FUNCTION IN SEED PRODUCTION.

Every one knows that the pollen produced by the stamens has an important part to play in seed production. It is for this reason that the stamen is considered one of the essential organs of the flower.

There is so little variation in the general development of stamens in the higher seed plants that the history of a stamen from any weed will suffice for all.

A mature stamen consists of a stalklike portion, the filament, and the pollen-bearing portion, the anther, which is borne on top of the filament. The filament may be variously modified or even wanting.

An anther appears distinctly four lobed. If a cross section of a young anther be made, four distinct regions will be found, one in each lobe or a pair on each side of the axis. These four distinct regions are conspicuous because the cells contained are larger and have a denser content. Each of these cells will produce four pollen grains and for this reason are called pollen mother cells.

Surrounding each group of pollen mother cells is usually one layer of cells whose content is quite dense. These are sacrificed as food material for the pollen mother cells and are designated as tapetal cells.

After the pollen grains are formed, they lie loose in these cavities. Each cavity is considered as a case or angium and since a pollen grain is a spore, this case is called a sporangium.

The partition between each pair of sporangia usually breaks down, and two spore-containing cavities are formed. These are generally called pollen sacs. The pollen sacs are now ready to open or dehisce as the process is called. This is due to especially modified cells, which produce such strains through the variation of moisture, that usually longitudinal slits or terminal pores are produced.

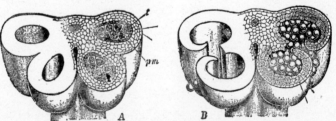

FIG. 416.　Cross section of anther showing pollen sacs. A. pm, pollen mother cells; t, food cells. B. Pollen grains mature and being shed.
(From Coulter, after Baillon & Luerssen.)

The pollen is now either by wind, insects, or water carried to the stigma of the pistil where it begins the performance of its important function. This process of pollen transference is pollination. An examination of a pollen grain at the time of pollination will usually show that it has two nuclei; one of these has to do with the production of a tube which traverses the tissues of the pistil and furnishes a passage way to the embryo sac which contains the cells to be fertilized. The other nucleus of the pollen grain produces two small nuclei which are called sperms. These sperms pass down the pollen tube to the embryo sac and fertilize the egg and endosperm nucleus.

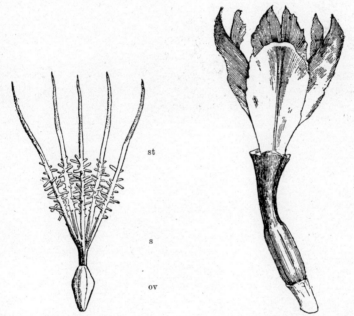

st

s

ov

FIG. 417.   Thrift, ov, ovary; s, style; st,   FIG. 418.   Iris with petal-like stigmas.
papillary stigmas.   (After Thome.)
(After Thome.)

THE PISTIL AND ITS FUNCTION IN SEED PRODUCTION.

A flower may have one or more pistils, which occupy the center of the flower. They are the last to appear, since the order of development is usually sepals, petals, stamens, and pistil.

A complete pistil consists of three parts—the expanded base, which bears the seed and is called ovary (or "egg-case"); the expanded portion at the top, or the stigma; the portion that connects the ovary and stigma, the style.

The style is not an essential part of the pistil and may be absent without disturbing the function of the pistil.

The stigma has on its surface many minute papillae which retain the pollen and excrete usually a sticky fluid which serves as a nourishment and stimulant for the pollen grain.

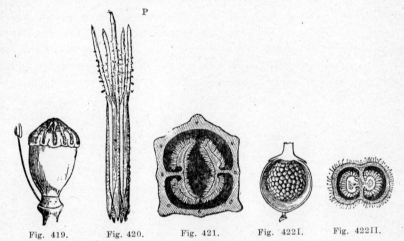

Fig. 419.   Fig. 420.   Fig. 421.   Fig. 422I.   Fig. 422II.

FIG. 419.   Corn-poppy with a shield-shaped stigma capping the ovary.
FIG. 420.   P.   Pistil of Thistle.
FIG. 421.   Cross section of the ovary of Gesneria showing one cell and two parietal placentae.
FIG. 422.   I.   Cross section of the compound pistil of Snapdragon, showing the two cells and the axillary placentae.   II.   Longitudinal section of an ovary with a free central placenta.

(After Thome.)

If we cut a cross section of the ovary of the May-apple, we find within a cavity bearing on one side a projection to which are attached the small, somewhat globular bodies or ovules. This cavity within the ovary is usually called a cell by manuals, but a better term is loculus, since the term "cell" is universally used to designate the unit of tissues. The thickened portion to which the ovules are attached is the placenta.

The pistil of the May-apple is a simple pistil and according to the older views concerning the pistil, it is a carpel. The older view was that the carpel is a modified leaf. If one will imagine a leaf folded and the margins joined so as to enclose a loculus and then the outer part modified so as to form a style and stigma, the conception of a carpel will be clear. An examination of the pistil of oxalis will reveal five styles and stigmas, and one ovary with five loculi. This indicates that the pistil of oxalis consists of five carpels whose ovaries have united to form one with five loculi.

This uniting may even extend to the styles and stigmas. A pistil that is made up of more than one carpel is compound.

Ovule.—The ovule is the most essential part of the pistil because it is the forerunner of the seed. The ovule consists of a central portion, the nucellus, which is enclosed by one or two jackets which are called the integuments. The integuments do not entirely close at the outer end of the nucellus and this small opening left is the micropyle through which the pollen tube usually passes. In the interior of the nucellus is a region which resembles a large cavity since it contains no cell walls. This is the embryo sac. At about the time the flower opens the embryo sac contains seven cells. The two which have an important future history are the egg and endosperm cells.

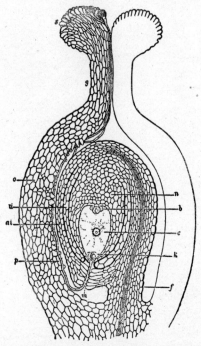

Fig. 423. Diagrammatic representation of the lengthwise section through a pistil, showing ovule, ovary wall, style, stigma, and pollen tube. o, ovary wall; g, style; s, stigma with two pollen grains; p, pollen tube; m, micropyle; k, egg; e, primary endosperm nucleus; b, antipodal cells; f, stalk; n, the nucellus; and ai the outer integument, and ii the inner integument of the ovule.
(After Luerssen.)

The egg is in the end of the sac nearest the micropyle, in the most convenient position for the entering pollen tube. The endosperm cell is near the center of the embryo sac. The embryo sac is now mature and awaits the entrance of the pollen tube.

Fertilization.—The pollen tube traverses the tissues of the stigma and style and finds its way to the micropyle. It passes through the micropyle, penetrates the tissues of the nucellus, and pierces the membrane of the embryo sac. The two sperms, which have had a rather long journey through the pollen tube, now enter the embryo sac. One finds its way to the egg and soon fuses with the egg nucleus. The other fuses with the nucleus of the endosperm cell. This process in which the sperms or male nuclei fuse with the nuclei of the egg and endosperm cell is fertilization, and both fusions are designated as double fertilization.

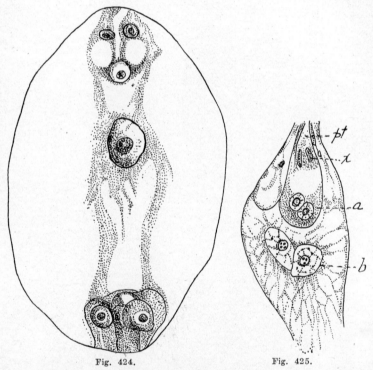

Fig. 424.   Fig. 425.

FIG. 424. Embryo sac of Buttercup (*Ranunculus multifidus*). Near the center is the large endosperm nucleus. The egg is the inner one of the three cells at the upper end of the sac and lies between the inner ends of the two synergids. The three antipodals are shown closely crowded at the lower end of sac.
(After Coulter.)

FIG. 425. Fertilization in the Fleabane (*Erigeron*); pt, pollen tube with two densely staining bodies (x); a, male cell fusing with egg; b, male cell fusing with endosperm nucleus.
(After Land.)

THE DEVELOPMENT OF THE EMBRYO AND SEED.

When the fertilized egg germinates, a filament of cells, the sus-

pensor, is usually found. At the end of the suspensor the embryo
is developed which, when mature, is more or less surrounded by
nourishing endosperm which has resulted from the growth and
division of the endosperm nuclei.

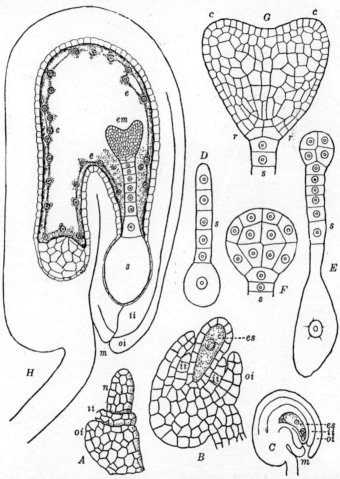

FIG. 426. Development of the ovule and embryo of the Shepherd's Purse (*Capsella*).
A, young ovule, showing origin of two integuments at base of nucellus, n. B,
outer integument growing beyond the inner, and the ovule beginning to bend
over; es, embryo sac. C, diagram of a later stage with mature embryo sac. D,
development of the suspensor s. E, early division of the terminal cell (embryo
cell). F, later stage, showing the differentiation of an outer cell layer in the embryo, which is to become the epidermis. G, the two cotyledons c and the root
region r now clearly defined. H, lengthwise section of an ovule, showing the
position of an embryo in an embryo sac; em, embryo; s, suspensor; e, endosperm;
ii, inner integument; oi, outer integument; m, micropyle.
(*A, B, C, adapted after Campbell, Ginn & Co.*)

The two groups of higher seed plants, or Angiosperms, differ
widely in the structure of the embryo. In the group including the

grasses, rushes, sedges and such plants as wild onion (*Allium canadense*) the globular embryo soon develops into an axis with the root tip at one end and one cotyledon at the other. The stem tip arises from the side of the axis as a lateral member. This group of plants is designated as Monocotyledons (one cotyledon).

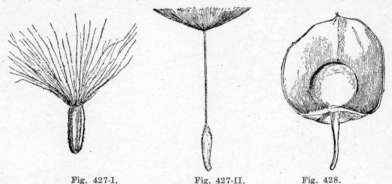

Fig. 427-I.   Fig. 427-II.   Fig. 428.

FIG. 427.   Fruit of Squaw Weed (*Senecio*). II. Fruit of Dandelion. Each is crowned with pappus which aids in distribution.
FIG. 428.   The fruit of the Winter Cherry (*Physalis*) with a portion of the inflated calyx removed to show the enclosed berry.
(*After Thome.*)

In the other group, to which a large number of the weeds belong, the axis of the embryo develops a root tip at one end, a stem tip at the other, and a pair of cotyledons, one on each side of the stem tip. Since two is the prevailing number of cotyledons, the term Dicotyledons is applied to this group.

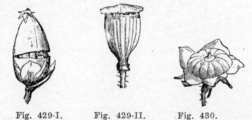

Fig. 429-I.   Fig. 429-II.   Fig. 430.

FIG. 429.   I. Fruit (pod) of Plantain with upper portion of pod breaking and falling off to allow seeds to escape. II. Pod of Poppy opening by a lid.
FIG. 430.   Fruit of Mallow which separates into as many one-seeded carpels as there are styles.
(*After Thome.*)

Seed.—The seed is the matured ovule. It contains the young plant or embryo, which is the essential part of the seed since it is through the later development of this young plant that new individuals are produced. Accompanying this maturing of the ovule, various other changes take place which give distinguishing features to different seeds. Frequently the endosperm grows so extensively as to absorb and replace the cells of the nucellus and thus comes to occupy all the space within the coats of the integuments, as in the morning-glory, onion, etc. The embryo may remain comparatively small as in the morning-glory or onion, or it may in turn absorb and replace all the cells of the endosperm and so come to occupy the space within the integuments, as in the bean and clover. Sometimes some of the nucellus and endosperm remain. The integuments also undergo various changes during the formation of the seed, often becoming hard or papery or provided with hairs, hooks or spines, or becoming smooth or pitted.

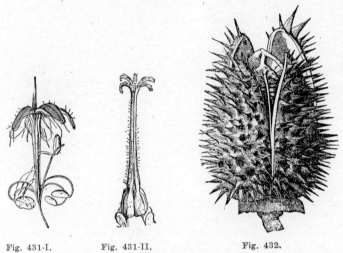

Fig. 431-I.   Fig. 431-II.   Fig. 432.

FIG. 431.   I.   Immature pistils of Geranium.   II.   Mature pistil and carpels with their long styles are separating from the elongated axis.

FIG. 432.   Burry fruit of Jamestown or Jimson Weed *(Datura)* showing method of dehiscing.

(After Thome.)

Fruit.—A fruit is a ripened ovary alone or a ripened ovary plus closely related parts such as calyx, involucre, and receptacle. In the beggar-ticks *(Bidens)* the ovary becomes tough and invests the seed, while the awns which represent the calyx become barbed and aid in distribution. In the buttercups the ovary invests the seed while the style forms a hook. The involucre in the clotbur and ragweed remains around the pistils and becomes more or less spiny. In the nightshade *(Solanum nigrum)* the ovary becomes fleshy and the fruit is called a berry.

ROOTS AND ROOT-STOCKS.
BY J. C. CUNNINGHAM

The study of root systems is accompanied with more or less difficulty and expense, and this, no doubt, accounts for the small amount of work done along this line.

Two methods have been employed to obtain the complete root system of growing plants. That used by Ten Eyck is perhaps the most satisfactory, although tedious and expensive. It consists of excavating about a plant and enclosing the whole mass of earth containing the roots in a cage of wire netting. Steel rods are thrust through the cage horizontally to prevent the roots from breaking. The soil is then carefully washed away, leaving the roots very nearly in their natural position.

The other method, employed by a Russian investigator, Rotmistrov, has given quite satisfactory results. The plants are grown in soil made up of top- and subsoil. This is placed, the subsoil below and the topsoil above, in boxes 1 inch wide, 20 to 40 inches deep and 20 to 40 inches long. These boxes are placed in the ground level with the surface. The plants are then grown in these boxes and removed when desired, the soil carefully washed away and the entire plant transferred to paper.

The pictures shown here are of plant roots obtained by the first method, the wire cages being omitted.

The roots of weedy plants vary widely in form, structure, and in longevity. Their function is three- and sometimes fourfold: First, to absorb water and dissolved mineral matter; second, to

FIG. 433. Root-stocks or rhizomes of Quack Grass *(Agropyron repens)*. These root-stocks are in some cases more than four feet long.
(Photograph by Stevens.)

anchor the plant in the soil; third, to act as a storehouse for reserve food, and fourth, they may serve to propagate the plant.

Fig. 434.   Roots of White Sweet Clover *(Melilotus alba)*.   Plants with several strong
branching roots.
(Photograph by Stevens.)

ROOT FORMS.

Root forms may be divided into four general types: First, primary; in this case a single, usually enlarged central root is developed. From it grow the smaller lateral roots. The burdock *(Arctium Lappa)*, is of this class. Second, multiple primary, in which the embryonic root almost immediately breaks up into many usually enlarged and fleshy roots. Sweet clover *(Melilotus alba)*, Fig. 434, offers a good example of this type. Third, tuberous or those that develop an enlarged portion at the end of a somewhat smaller one. Fourth, fibrous in which a mass of small roots develop usually just below the stem as in most of the grasses and in the plantains.

Besides the forms already mentioned we find various types of aerial roots, or those that develop on the plant above ground. The aerial roots of the ivy become finger-like and cling to objects to assist the plant in climbing; those of the mistletoe and the dodder become parasitic by pushing their aerial roots into the tissues of the host plant and drawing nourishment from it.

In performing the four functions mentioned above the roots of a single plant may occupy considerable area. Doctor Pammel has prepared the following table showing the depth and spread of the root system of a number of our noxious weeds.

Weed	Depth	Spread
Buckhorn	2– 8 in.	24 sq. in.
Plantain	3–13 "	30 " "
Wild hemp	1– 6 "	10 " "
Evening primrose	3– 5 "	30 " "
Beggar-ticks	3–- 5 "	40 " "
Dog fennel	2– 3 "	4 " "
Nigger-head	3– 6 "	20 " "
Goldenrod	5 "	70 " "
White vervain	2– 4 "	36 " "
Canadian lettuce	5– 7 "	144 " "
Field thistle	8 "	50 " "
Burdock	40 "	150 " "
Black nightshade	1– 4 "	88 " "
Pennsylvania smartweed	1– 4 "	45 " "
Lady's thumb	1– 4 "	90 " "
Yellow oxalis	1– 2 "	24 " "
Prickly lettuce	½– 2½ "	6 " "
Cocklebur	4–10 "	425 " "
Greater ragweed	4 "	48 in. long
Rough pigweed	7–14 "	144 sq. in.
Horseweed	7–14 "	144 " "
Tumble-weed	2– 8 "	60 " "
Small ragweed	8– 9 "	60 " "
Spanish dagger	5– 8 "	42 " "

The amount of reserve food stored within weed roots depends to a considerable extent upon the length of time they continue to live.

Roots may be classified according to their length of life, and this is, perhaps, the most practical knowledge to possess concerning weeds. Without this knowledge no intelligent nor successful method of eradication can be adopted.

First we have the annuals or those which complete their growth and mature their seed in one year. These plants produce an enormous amount of seed, sometimes as high as 50,000 to a single plant.

The root system is simple, although it may extend to a considerable distance horizontally. Such plants are easily destroyed by culti-

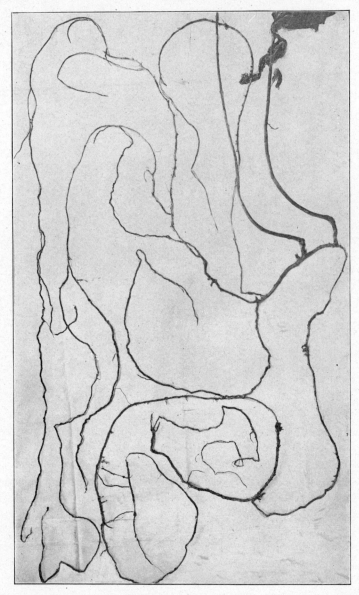

FIG. 435. Roots of Common Milkweed *(Asclepias syriaca)*. Some of these roots are more than 14 feet long. Buds are numerously produced on the root. More than 100 were found on the roots of this plant.

(Photograph by Colburn.)

vation unless they root from the joint as in the case of the crab grass (*Digitaria sanguinalis*).

FIG. 436.　Roots of Curled Dock (*Rumex crispus*).
(*Photograph by Stevens.*)

Second are the winter annuals. These plants may begin their growth in the spring, in which case they become annuals. Many of the seeds, however, germinate in the fall and throw up a rosette of leaves and thus pass the winter stage. In the spring stems are thrown up from these leaves and seed is produced. Our common shepherd's purse (*Capsella Bursa-pastoris*) is an example of the winter annual.

The third class is the biennials or those which expend their energy the first season in forming a root system, usually fleshy, and the second season in maturing seed. We have numerous examples among the garden crops, such as the beet, turnip, carrot, etc., while among the weedy plants we have the burdock (*Arctium Lappa*), the sweet clover, figure 434, the wild parsnip and others. If these plants are prevented from forming seed the second year they perish.

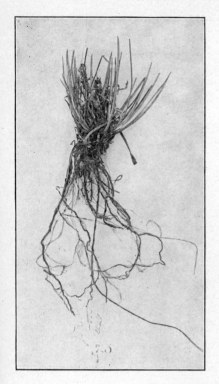 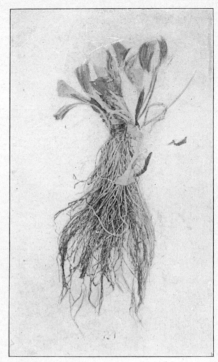

FIG. 437. Roots of Buckhorn *(Plantago lanceolata)*. This perennial weed is easily destroyed by cultivation.
(Photograph by Colburn.)
FIG. 438. Fibrous roots of Buckhorn.
(Photograph by Gardner.)

In the fourth class belong the perennials which live year after year and for this reason become our most noxious weeds. When the roots once become well established it is very difficult to eradicate them, as is shown by the lawns, fields and pastures which are infested with such weeds as dandelions, quack grass, Canada thistle, docks and wild morning-glory. These plants do not, as a rule, produce large quantities of seed but depend upon roots or stems as a means of propagation. Thus if a field infested with quack grass or morning-glory is plowed or disked the roots or rhizomes are broken up and each piece may produce a new plant.

Some roots which do not spread extensively through the soil but form new plants from offshoots from the crown, such as the docks and wild gourds, form heavier roots from year to year for the following reason: Root growth is most active at the apex of the main roots. This resumption of growth starves many of the older roots, as we find few laterals on these older portions, and it thus extends the root system.

In the annuals there is little need for a large amount of reserve food within the roots for the elaborated food is used up largely as it is manufactured. The life of the plant ceases when seed is produced. In the biennials, however, large quantities of reserve food

FIG. 439. Biennial root of young Bull Thistle *(Cirsium lanceolatum)* after one year's growth.
(Photograph by Charlotte M. King.)

are stored in the roots. The same is true of the perennials although to a less marked degree than of the biennials.

By studying the plant in the late fall we may determine roughly whether the weed is an annual, a biennial or a perennial. That is to say, dead small fibrous or primary roots and seed production indicate an annual; large fleshy roots and no seed production a biennial; reserve food within the roots besides seed production a perennial.

PROPAGATION OF WEEDS BY ROOTS AND STEMS.

Professor Hitchcock says that weeds may be propagated by seed and buds or by vegetative sprouts. The layman is inclined to call

all parts of the plant below ground root. It may be, however, a stem called a root-stock or rhizome. Microscopical examination is often necessary to determine which is root and which is stem.

Roots.

Adventitious buds are produced at indefinite points along the roots and from them stems and plants develop. A number of our noxious weeds are propagated by these running or creeping roots,

Fig. 440. Roots and rhizomes of: I, *Lycopus rubellus;* II and III, *Cirsium arvense;* IV, *Convolvulus arvensis;* V, *Convolvulus sepium;* VI, *Cirsium canescens.* Drawn by C. M. King.

such as: milkweed (*Asclepias syriaca*), bindweed (*Convolvulus arvensis*), sheep sorrel (*Rumex Acetosella*), Indian hemp (*Apocynum cannabinum*), perennial ragweed (*Ambrosia psilostachya*), wavy-leaved thistle (*Cirsium undulatum*).

The weeds mentioned above are comparatively shallow rooted. A few weeds are propagated by buds which come from deep vertical roots. Among them we find the following: horse nettle

FIG. 441.   Roots of Sour Dock (*Rumex crispus*).
(*Photograph by Stevens.*)

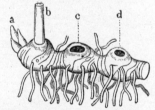

FIG. 442.   Rhizome of Solomon's Seal; a, Leaf bud; b, old stem; c, d, old stem scars.
(*After Thome.*)

(*Solanum carolinense*), ground cherry (*Physalis* sp.), Canada thistle (*Cirsium arvense*).

FIELD BINDWEED
(Convolvulus arvensis L.)

Fig. 443.   European Morning-glory or Bindweed (*Convolvulus arvensis*).   In gardens
and fields.

(After Clark and Fletcher.)

UNDERGROUND STEMS OR RHIZOMES.

These underground stems are usually found at a short distance beneath the surface. Along these stems are found nodes with leaf scales at definite intervals. From these nodes develop roots which penetrate the soil and leafy stems which develop above ground. Some of the weeds so propagated are as follows: quack grass (*Agropyron repens*), morning-glory (*Convolvulus sepium*), smartweed (*Polygonum Muhlenbergii*), poison ivy (*Rhus Toxicodendron*), nettle (*Urtica gracilis*), wild rose (*Rosa pratincola*).

CROWNS OR SHORT OFFSHOOTS.

A long list of weeds produce heavy crowns near the surface of the soil. Stems spring from these crowns year after year. Parts of the crown may become separated from the parent plant and thus form an independent plant. Among the weeds so propagated we find the dandelion (*Taraxacum officinale*), white vervain (*Verbena urticaefolia*), plantain (*Plantago lanceolata*), catnip (*Nepeta Cataria*), curled or sour dock (*Rumex crispus*), smooth dock (*Rumex altissimus*), rib grass (*Plantago lanceolata*), ox-eye daisy (*Chrysanthemum Leucanthemum*).

CHAPTER IV.

SEASONAL SUCCESSION OF WEEDS.
CHARLOTTE M. KING.

Several species of weedy plants bloom very early in the spring, responding to a comparatively limited amount of light and warmth; others come to bloom after the growing season is more advanced; while a number blossom throughout the season, or from spring until fall.

The time of bloom is, in each species, related to its definite physiological constant of warmth, sunshine and moisture. Warm, sunshiny weather in the early part of the season will hasten the time of bloom, as cold, cloudy weather will retard it. There is a difference of about two weeks between the blooming date of plants of northern and southern parts of Iowa.

The season of a plant's activity is related in part to its hardiness, and to the climatic conditions of the geographical region selected by it as most favorable to its existence.

It is indicated by the accompanying table, as known also by common experience, that the rain, warmth and sunshine received by the arrival of midsummer produce greatest bloom of weedy plants in both number and kinds of any time during the growing season, and since weeds usually mature quickly it is apparent that the harvest of weed seeds steadily increases from that time until fall.

Crucifers are among our earlier blooming weeds, such as the winter annuals, shepherd's purse and peppergrass; the legumes and umbellifers are at their full growth about midsummer; the plantains begin in May, the polygonums in June; whilst composites are usually blooming throughout the latter part of the season.

Grasses distribute their blossoming-time throughout the summer from May until October; vanilla grass and blue grass appear in May, orchard grass, quack grass, needle grass and timothy in June, crab grass, fescue grass, and rye grasses about July, Bouteloua in August, blue-stem and drop-seed grasses in September.

Many weedy plants, either annual or perennial, have a prolonged period of bloom and seeding, thus maintaining a vigorous hold. In favorable seasons, many plants will produce a second or third crop of seeds.

Common cosmopolitan weeds, belonging to various orders, have often remarkable continuance, as in case of the dandelion, shepherd's purse and chickweed; these weeds begin to bloom in earliest spring and are also more resistant to frost than are other weeds.

The period of time required after bloom for maturing fruit varies in different species; a comparatively short time is needed in case of most weeds, especially the late blooming ones.

The dormant period required by a seed before germination will take place differs with species and with individual seeds of the same species. In seeds requiring a period of rest, this delay may be a matter of days, weeks, or years; therefore there is a distribution for seeds through time as well as through space. Many seeds germinate immediately if conditions are favorable. Many young plants must be lost by this autumnal vegetating, in case of seedlings overtaken by frost before they can bear seeds or establish roots; but the hardy nature of the winter annual, the biennial and perennial protects for the most part such young plants after fall germination.

Quack grass has a crop of seedlings of the same season as the ripening of seed; this is true also of wild carrot, burdock, thistles, horse nettle and rib grass, all of which being biennial or perennial persist throughout the winter.

The freezing and thawing of winter facilitates germination of weed seeds in the spring; and very early one may note, in the location of the parent of last season, as soon as the soil grows warm enough, many flourishing young colonies of seedlings, such as spurge, oxalis, pigweed and smartweed, crowding each other for foothold. The culturist is greatly influenced by considerations of blooming-time, seed-time and time of seed-germination in his efforts to control and to exterminate weeds.

Blooming Period of Common Weeds.[a]

	Mar.	Apr.	May	June	July	Aug.	Sept.	Oct.	Nov.
Capsella Bursa-pastoris, A., Shepherd's purse	+	+	+	+	+	+	+	+	+
Medicago lupulina, A., Yellow trefoil	+	+	+	+	+	+	+	+	+
Oxalis corniculata, A. & P., Lady's sorrel	+	+	+	+	+	+	+	+	+
Stellaria media, A., Chickweed	+	+	+	+	+	+	+	+	+
Taraxacum officinale, P., Dandelion	+	+	+	+	+	+	+	+	+
Barbarea vulgaris, B., Yellow rocket		+	+	+					
Cynoglossum boreale, B., Hound's tongue		+	+						
Nepeta hederacea, P., Ground ivy		+	+						
Plantago lanceolata, P., Buckhorn		+	+	+	+	+	+	+	+
Ranunculus abortivus, B., Small-flowered buttercup		+	+	+					
Ranunculus septentrionalis, P., Buttercup		+	+	+	+				
Rumex altissimus, P., Smooth dock		+	+	+					
Taraxacum erythrospermum, P., Small-flowered dandelion		+	+	+					
Allium canadense, A. & P., Wild garlic			+	+					
Asclepias speciosa, P., Showy milkweed			+	+	+				
Brassica arvensis, A., Wild mustard			+	+	+	+	+	+	+
Bromus tectorum, A., Downy brome grass			+	+					
Carum Carvi, B., Caraway			+	+	+				
Cerastium viscosum, A. & P., Mouse-ear chickweed			+	+	+	+	+		
Convolvulus arvensis, P., European morning-glory			+	+	+	+	+		
Convolvulus sepium, P., Wild morning-glory			+	+	+	+	+		
Datura Tatula, A., Purple thorn-apple			+	+	+	+	+		
Euphorbia marginata, A., Snow-on-the-mountain			+	+	+	+	+	+	
Euphorbia Preslii, A., Spurge			+	+	+	+	+	+	
Glycyrrhiza lepidota, P., Wild liquorice			+	+	+	+			
Hierochloe odorata, P., Vanilla grass			+	+	+				
Hordeum pusillum, A., Small squirrel-tail grass			+	+					
Lepidium apetalum, A., Apetalous peppergrass			+	+	+	+			
Lepidium virginicum, A., Wild peppergrass			+	+	+	+	+	+	+
Lithospermum arvense, A., Corn gromwell			+	+	+	+			
Lolium multiflorum, B. or P., Italian rye grass			+	+	+				
Malva rotundifolia, P., Common mallow			+	+	+	+	+	+	+
Oxybaphus nyctagineus, P., Wild four-o'clock			+	+	+	+			
Plantago major, P., Dooryard plantain			+	+	+	+	+		
Plantago Purshii, A., Pursh's plantain			+	+	+	+	+		
Potentilla Anserina, P., Silverweed			+	+	+	+	+		
Radicula palustris, A. or B., Marsh cress			+	+	+				
Rhus Toxicodendron, P., Poison ivy			+	+					
Rudbeckia hirta, B., Black-eyed Susan			+	+	+	+	+		
Rumex Acetosella, P., Sheep sorrel			+	+	+	+			
Sisymbrium officinale, A., Hedge mustard			+	+	+	+	+	+	+
Solanum carolinense, P., Horse nettle			+	+	+	+			
Solanum rostratum, A., Buffalo bur			+	+	+	+			
Sonchus oleraceus, A., Sow thistle			+			+	+	+	+
Trifolium procumbens, A., Hop clover			+				+		
Verbena bracteosa, P., Bracted verbena			+						
Veronica peregrina, A., Speedwell			+				+	+	
Vicia sativa, A., Vetch			+						
Achillea Millefolium, P., Yarrow						+	+	+	+
Acalypha virginica, A., Three-seeded mercury					+	+	+	+	
Amaranthus graecizans, A., Tumble weed				+	+	+	+		
Amaranthus blitoides, A., Spreading pigweed				+	+	+	+		

Blooming Period of Common Weeds—Continued.

	Mar.	Apr.	May	June	July	Aug.	Sept.	Oct.	Nov.
Anthemis Cotula, A., May-weed				+	+	+	+	+	+
Apocynum cannabinum, P., Indian hemp				+	+	+			
Asclepias syriaca, P., Milkweed				+	+	+			
Berteroa incana, A. or P., Hoary alyssum				+	+	+	+		
Brassica nigra, A., Black mustard				+	+	+	+	+	+
Bromus secalinus, A., Cheat				+	+	+			
Camelina sativa, A., False flax				+	+				
Carex vulpinoidea, P., Sedge				+	+	+			
Chenopodium album, A., Lamb's quarter				+	+	+	+		
Cicuta maculata, P., Cowbane				+	+	+			
Cirsium arvense, P., Canada thistle				+	+	+	+		
Cirsium undulatum, B., Wavy-leaved thistle				+	+	+	+		
Crotalaria sagittalis, A., Rattle-box				+	+	+	+		
Cycloloma atriplicifolium, A., Winged pigweed				+	+	+	+		
Datura Stramonium, A., Jimson weed				+	+	+	+		
Daucus Carota, B., Wild carrot				+	+	+	+		
Erigeron annuus, A., Fleabane				+	+	+	+	+	
Erigeron canadensis, A., Horse-weed				+	+	+	+	+	+
Erigeron ramosus, A., Branched fleabane				+	+	+	+	+	
Euphorbia maculata, A., Spotted-leaved spurge				+	+	+	+	+	+
Geum canadense, P., Avens				+	+	+			
Helianthus petiolaris, A., Petiolate sunflower				+	+	+	+		
Hordeum jubatum, A. or B., Squirrel-tail				+	+	+			
Hypericum perforatum, P., St. John's-wort				+	+	+	+		
Lactuca canadensis, A. or B., Wild lettuce				+	+	+	+	+	+
Lactuca pulchella, P., Blue lettuce				+	+	+	+		
Lappula virginiana, A., Beggar's lice				+	+	+	+		
Leonurus Cardiaca, P., Mother-wort				+	+	+	+		
Lygodesmia juncea, P., Lygodesmia				+	+	+	+		
Melanthium virginicum, P., Bunch flower				+	+	+			
Melilotus alba, B., White sweet clover				+	+	+	+	+	+
Oenothera biennis, B., Evening primrose				+	+	+	+	+	
Parietaria pennsylvanica, A., Pellitory				+	+	+			
Pastinaca sativa, P., Parsnip				+	+	+			
Plantago Rugelii, P., Rugel's plantain				+	+	+			
Polanisia trachysperma, A., Polanisia				+	+	+			
Polygonum aviculare, A., Dooryard knotgrass				+	+	+	+	+	
Polygonum hydropiperoides, P., Mild water pepper				+	+	+	+		
Polygonum lapathifolium, A., Slender smartweed				+	+	+	+		
Eleusine indica, A., Goose grass				+	+	+	+		
Eragrostis megastachya, A., Candy grass				+	+	+	+		
Linaria vulgaris, P., Toadflax				+	+	+	+	+	
Silene antirrhina, A., Sleepy catchfly				+	+	+	+		
Thlaspi arvense, A., Pennycress				+	+	+			
Urtica gracilis, P., Nettle				+	+	+	+	+	
Conringia orientalis, A., Hare's-ear mustard				+	+	+	+	+	
Polygonum Persicaria, A., Lady's thumb				+	+	+	+	+	
Portulaca oleracea, A., Purslane				+	+	+			
Radicula Armoracia, P., Horseradish				+	+	+			
Raphanus sativus, A. or B., Radish				+	+	+		+	+
Rumex crispus, P., Curled dock				+	+	+			
Rumex obtusifolius, P., Bitter dock				+	+	+			
Saponaria Vaccaria, A., Cow-herb				+	+	+			
Sida spinosa, A., Prickly sida				+	+	+			

Blooming Period of Common Weeds—Continued.

	Mar.	Apr.	May	June	July	Aug.	Sept.	Oct.	Nov.
Sisymbrium altissimum, A. or B., Tumbling mustard				+	+	+			
Stachys palustris, P., Woundwort				+	+	+	+		
Teucrium canadense, P., Germander				+	+	+	+		
Tribulus terrestris, A., Caltrop				+	+	+	+		
Verbascum Thapsus, B., Mullein				+	+	+	+		
Verbena hastata, P., Blue vervain				+	+	+	+		
Bromus hordeaceus, A., Soft chess				+	+	+			
Agrostemma Githago, A., Corn cockle				+	+	+	+		
Verbena stricta, P., Hoary vervain			+	+	+	+			
Atriplex patula, A., Orach				+	+				
Acnida tuberculata, A., Water hemp				+	+	+	+	+	
Avena fatua, A., Wild oats				+	+	+			
Ambrosia artemisiifolia, A., Small ragweed				+	+	+	+	+	
Ambrosia trifida, A., Large ragweed				+	+	+	+	+	
Arctium Lappa, B., Burdock				+	+	+	+		
Bidens cernua, A., Sticktight				+	+	+	+		
Bidens discoidea, A., Sticktight				+	+	+	+		
Bidens frondosa, A., Sticktight				+	+	+	+		
Chenopodium hybridum, A., Maple-leaved goosefoot				+	+	+			
Cichorium Intybus, P., Chicory				+	+	+	+		
Circium discolor, B., Field thistle				+	+	+	+		
Cirsium iowense, B., Iowa thistle				+	+	+	+		
Cirsium lanceolatum, B., Bull thistle				+	+	+	+		
Cleome serrulata, A., Stinking clover				+	+	+			
Cuscuta arvensis, A., Field dodder				+	+	+			
Digitaria humifusa, A., Smooth crab grass				+	+	+			
Dyssodia papposa, A., Fetid marigold				+	+	+	+	+	
Eragrostis pilosa, A., Pilose eragrostis				+	+				
Erechtites hieracifolia, A., Fireweed				+	+	+			
Eupatorium urticaefolium, P., White snakeroot				+	+	+	+	+	+
Gaura biennis, B., Gaura				+	+	+			
Gonolobus laevis, P., Angle-pod				+	+	+			
Helianthus annuus, A., Common sunflower				+	+	+			
Ipomoea hederacea, A., Blue wild morning-glory				+	+	+			
Iva xanthifolia, A., Poverty weed				+	+	+			
Kochia Scoparia, A., Kochia				+	+	+			
Lolium perenne, P., Rye grass				+	+				
Melilotus officinalis, A. or B., Yellow sweet clover				+	+	+	+	+	+
Mentha spicata, P., Spearmint				+	+				
Physalis subglabrata, P., Smoothish ground cherry				+	+	+			
Polygonum Convolvulus, A., Black bindweed				+	+	+			
Polygonum erectum, A., Erect knotweed				+	+	+			
Polygonum Hydropiper, A., Water pepper				+	+	+			
Polygonum Muhlenbergii, P., Tanweed				+	+	+			
Polygonum pennsylvanicum, A., Pennsylvania smartweed									
Polygonum ramosissimum, A., Branching knotweed				+	+	+			
Potentilla monspeliensis, B. or P., Five-finger				+	+	+			
Salsola Kali var. tenuifolia, A., Russian thistle				+	+	+			

Blooming Period of Common Weeds—Continued.

	Mar.	Apr.	May	June	July	Aug.	Sept.	Oct.	Nov.
Scrophularia marylandica, P., Simpson honey plant					+	+	+		
Setaria glauca, A., Yellow foxtail					+	+	+		
Setaria verticillata, A., Whorled foxtail					+	+	+		
Setaria viridis, A., Green foxtail					+	+	+		
Silene noctiflora, A., Night-flowering catchfly					+	+	+		
Solanum nigrum, A., Nightshade					+	+	+	+	
Sonchus arvensis, P., Sow thistle					+	+	+	+	
Saponaria officinalis, P., Bouncing Bet					+	+	+		
Stipa spartea, P., Needle grass				+	+				
Strophostyles helvola, A., Wild pea					+	+	+	†	
Symphoricarpos orbiculatus, P., Indian currant					+	+	+		
Tanacetum vulgare, P., Tansy					+	+	+		
Lactuca scariola, A., Prickly lettuce					+	+	+		
Hibiscus Trionum, A., Shoo-fly					+	+	+		
Urtica dioica, P., Stinging nettle					+	+	+		
Vernonia fasciculata, P., Ironweed					+	+	+		
Abutilon Theophrasti, A., velvet-leaf						+	+	+	
Amaranthus retroflexus, A., Pigweed						+	+	+	
Aristida dichotoma, A., Poverty grass						+	+	+	
Artemisia biennis, B., Wormwood						+	+	+	
Artemisia ludoviciana, P., Western mugwort						+	+	+	
Aster multiflorus, A., Many-flowered aster						+	+	+	+
Aster salicifolius, A., Willow-leaved aster						+	+	+	+
Bidens aristosa, A. or B., Stick-tight						+	+	+	
Cenchrus pauciflorus, A., Sandbur						+	+		
Chenopodium ambrosioides, A., Mexican tea						†	+	†	
Cirsium altissimum, B., Tall thistle						+	+		
Cirsium canescens, B., Woolly thistle						†	†	†	
Cyperus esculentus, P., Northern nut grass						+	+	+	
Dalea alopecuroides, A., Foxtail dalea						+	+		
Digitaria sanguinalis, A., Crab grass						+	+		
Echinochloa crusgalli, A., Barnyard grass						+	+	+	
Helianthus grosseserratus, P., Prairie sunflower						+	+	+	
Helianthus Maximiliani, P., Maximilian's sunflower						+	+	+	
Helenium antumnale, P., Sneezeweed						+	+	+	
Muhlenbergia mexicana, P., Mexican drop-seed						+	+		
Muhlenbergia racemosa, P., Dropseed grass						+	+		
Solidago canadensis, P., Canada goldenrod						+	+	+	†
Solidago rigida, P., Stiff goldenrod						+	+	+	
Solidago serotina, P., Goldenrod						+	+	+	
Panicum capillare, A., Tickle grass						+	+	+	
Sporobolus neglectus A., Small rush grass						+	+		
Sporobolus vaginiflorus, A., Sheathed rush grass						+	+		
Xanthium canadense, A., Cocklebur						+	+	+	
Xanthium spinosum, A., Spiny cocklebur						+	+	+	+
Helianthus tuberosus, P., Artichoke						+	+		

W.A.   Winter annual.

A.   Annual.

B.   Biennial.

P.   Perennial.

*In this list of plant names the group under each month is arranged alphabetically.

SEASONAL SUCCESSION OF WEEDS IN IOWA FIELDS ACCORDING TO BLOOM.

According to reports of correspondents and common observation the following weeds are most conspicuous in the fields of Iowa in early summer: Winter cress, tanweed, Mexican drop-seed, quack grass, sheep sorrel and hedge mustard.

Weeds troublesome throughout the entire summer: Mexican drop-seed, quack grass, sheep sorrel, five-finger.

Weeds coming into notice in the month of June: Wild four o'clock, smooth brome, jimson weed, poverty grass (*Aristida oligantha*), yellow trefoil, buffalo bur, buckhorn, shoo-fly, horse nettle, burdock, wild parsnip.

Weeds prominent in July: Cheat, Mexican drop-seed grass, quack grass, sheep sorrel, five-finger, downy brome, tall mustard, Canada thistle, European bindweed, yellow trefoil, buffalo bur, buckhorn, shoo-fly, horse nettle, Barnaby's thistle, bracted plantain, squirrel-tail grass, woolly thistle, chicory, western wheat grass, night-flowering catchfly, wormwood, germander, marsh cress.

Weeds continuing dominant through August: Several species of dodder, Mexican drop-seed grass, quack grass, northern nut grass, wild morning-glory, sorrel, five-finger, Canada thistle, European bindweed, horse nettle, buffalo bur, rib grass, shoo-fly, Barnaby's thistle, woolly thistle, Indian hemp, chicory, night-flowering catchfly, blue lettuce, germander, sow thistles, partridge pea.

Principal weeds in September: Buffalo bur, horse nettle, shoo-fly, Canada thistle, wild carrot.

Noticeable weeds in October: Horse nettle, chicory, branching fleabane, asters, foxtails, crab grasses.

The accompanying list of weeds represents the number of requests sent in from different parts of the state for weed identification during the season of 1924, with their distribution throughout the season.

These weeds may be regarded as the most noticeable weeds of Iowa fields and gardens.

*List of Prominent Weeds of Iowa.**

	June	May	July	August	September	October
Thlaspi arvense — wa	1					
Brassica juncea — a	1					
Cuscuta (species) — a	1			2		
Sisymbrium officinale — a	1					
Bromus secalinus — a	1	1	3			1
Muhlenbergia mexicana — p	7	4	4	4		
Baptisia bracteosa — p	1	1	1			
Equisetum arvense — p	2	1	1			
Polygonum Muhlenbergii — p	3	1			1	
Barbarea vulgaris — p	8	5				
Tragopogon pratensis — bien	1		3		1	
Agropyron repens — p	9	5	8	4	1	
Cyperus esculentus — p	2		1	2		
Convolvulus sepium — p	2	1		2		
Rumex Acetosella — p	21	3	4	2		
Potentilla monspeliensis — a	3	1	3	2	1	
Lychnis alba — p	1		1	1		
Bromus tectorum — bien	1		8			
Sisymbrium altissimum — wa	3		2			
Cynoglossum officinale — p	1		1			
Galinsoga parviflora — a	1				1	
Cirsium arvense — p			11	10	2	
Convolvulus arvensis — p	1		6	4		
Oxybaphus nyctagineus — p	2		1	1		
Bromus inermis — p	1					
Silybum Marianum — a or b	2		1			
Datura Stramonium — a	1		1			
Phytolacca decandra — p	1		1			
Aristida oligantha — a	1					
Medicago lupulina — a and b	1		9	2		
Solanum rostratum — a	2		4	7	8	
Plantago lanceolata — a	2		4	4		1
Hibiscus Trionum — a	1		3	6	1	
Solanum carolinense — p	1		7	11	9	3
Arctium minus — b	1					
Pastinaca sativa — b	1					
Lepidium Draba — p			2		1	1
Hieracium aurantiacum — p			1			
Centaurea solstitialis — a			3	3		
Hordeum pusillum — a			1			
Heracleum lanatum — p			1			
Plantago aristata — a			5	2		
Centaurea Cyanus — a			1	1		
Hordeum jubatum — b			2			
Cirsium canescens — p			2	6		
Geranium carolinianum — b. a.			1			
Hypericum maculatum — p			3			
Apocynum sp — p			1	2		

*Annuals, *a;* biennials, *b;* perennials, *p;* winter annual, *wa.*

List of Prominent Weeds of Iowa—Continued.

	May	June	July	August	September	October
Lactuca scariola var. integrata_____b or a			1			
Brassica arvensis _____a or b			1			
Asclepias tuberosa _____p			1			
Schrankia uncinata _____p			1	1		
Cichorium Intybus _____p			2	3	1	1
Lactuca pulchella_____p			1	2		
Cicuta maculata _____p			1			
Carduus nutans _____b			2			
Leonurus Cardiaca _____p			2			
Cirsium lanceolatum _____b			1	1		
Agropyron Smithii _____p			6	1	1	
Lolium temulentum _____a			2			
Lepidum campestre _____a or b			1	1		
Chenopodium ambrosioides var anthelminticum- a			4			
Psoralea esculenta _____p			1			
Euphorbia dentata _____a			1			
Silene noctiflora _____a			5	2	1	
Cirsium Hillii _____p			1			
Teucrium canadense _____p			4	6	1	
Sonchus asper _____a			1	1		
Chysanthemum Leucanthemum _____ ____p			1			
Ruellia ciliosa _____p			1			
Sonchus oleraceus _____a			1	3		
Lamium purpureum _____a or b			1			
Cassia Chamaecrista _____ _____a			1	5		
Radicula palustris _____a or b			3			
Dalea enneandra _____a			1			
Sonchus arvensis _____p			1			
Melilotus officinalis _____b			1			
Salsola Kali var. tenuifolia_____a			1	1		
Amaranthus retroflexus _____a			1			
Dioscorea villosa _____p			1			
Triosteum perfoliatum _____p			1			
Erigeron divaricatus _____a			1		1	1
Linaria vulgaris _____p			1			
Polygonum pennsylvanicum _____a			1	1		
Sonchus oleraceus _____a						
Lappula virginiana _____p				1		
Glycyrrhiza lepidota _____p				8	1	
Lygodesmia juncea _____p				1		
Daucus Carota _____b				3	2	
Abutilon Theophrasti _____a				2		
Plantago media _____p				1		
Verbascum Blattaria _____b				1		
Astragalus canadensis _____p				1		
Sorghum halepense _____p				1		
Silphium perfoliatum _____p				1		
Asclepias verticillata _____				2	1	
Euphorbia corollata _____p				1		

List of Prominent Weeds of Iowa—Continued.

	May	June	July	August	September	October
Iva xanthiifolia _____a				1		
Trifolium procumbens _____a				1		
Digitaria sanguinalis _____a				1	1	1
Silene dichotoma _____a				1		1
Centaurea solstitialis _____a					1	
Gaura biennis _____b					1	
Atriplex patula _____:						1
Verbena bracteosa _____a					1	
Lespedeza capitata _____					2	
Centaurea maculosa _____b or p					1	
Prunella vulgaris _____p					1	
Petalostemon purpureum _____p					1	
Solanum nigrum _____a					1	1
Martynia louisiana _____					1	
Dalea alopecuroides _____a					1	
Echium vulgare _____b						4
Oenothera serrulata _____						1
Carduus acanthoides _____a or b						1
Physalis Alkekengi _____ _____p						3
Eupatorium purpureum _____p				1		1
Setaria verticillata _____a				2		1
Centaurea Jacea _____						1
Sisymbrium canescens _____a or b						2
Lamium amplexicaule _____p						2
Coronilla varia _____p					1	
Verbena hastata cross _____p						1

CHAPTER V.

THE STORY OF WEED SEED DISSEMINATION.
ADA HAYDEN

AGENCIES OF WEED SEED DISSEMINATION.
L. H. PAMMEL AND CHARLOTTE M. KING.

There is a common belief that plants are anchored organisms while animals are creatures of roving habits. True it is, for instance, that trees do not walk but many of them fly with leafy wings, swim or steal rides with squirrels. And who has not seen a squirrel carry a tree in its mouth? For what is a nut but a seed case and what is a seed but a small sleeping plant sealed with some food in water proof coats, awaiting a journey. What is a bean but a thrifty plant enveloped in a papery seed coat which is left in the soil when the green plant forces its way stem foremost from the warm earth? Emerging with the food sacs (seed leaves) into light the young bud is at last able to expand into leaves by the energy of the stores of food in the seed leaves. Here is the little plant now in business for itself with root, stem and leaf all co-operating in the process of starch-making incident to growth.

Not everyone is familiar with weeds and weed activities or there would not be so many weeds nearly grown every year before the farmer is aware of the danger to his chosen crop plants.

Weeds behave like the familiar beans, acorns and wheat during the life cycle. They have a sleeping time, a growing time, a time for food storage and a fruiting time. Then, having laid away their stores of food for the coming season, they are ready for travel and all the highways are filled with the great weed families seeing the world before they settle down for a long sleep and a new period of living in a new country side.

Fall is perhaps the best time to observe these excursions for the elements then offer special opportunity for migration. In late summer and early fall the water ways are open and seeds which are lighter than water embark. Some of these such as ground cherry, wild cucumber and sedges have loose-fitting cases filled with air; some bear on their walls large knobs of cork as is the case with the sour dock and tall dock, or are lightened by papery

wings, as with sheep sorrel.   Although hosts of these plants grow
at some distance from the water temporary rivulets at the time
of rain sweep the seeds along to larger streams which run high in
flood-time; but as the level falls weed passengers are dropped on
the high, dry land or by the stream bank.

FIG. 444.   By the river's brim, a Mullein plant bearing many-seeded pods.
(Photograph by Ada Hayden.)

On sandy bars are swarms of plants which do not thrive together
at maturity; but here chance has placed them—burdock, violets,
Spanish needles, Jimson weed, buffalo bur, oaks, willows, fireweed,
cocklebur, vervain, goldenrod and buttercups.   If they can not ad-
just themselves to the conditions which surround them because
of too much water, or because their neighbors crowd them, because

Fig. 445-A.   Fig. 445-B.

FIG. 445. A and B. Common Dock *(Rumex crispus)*. Fruit scattered by the water. The wings surrounding the fruit and tubercle make **the fruit admirably adapted** to floating on the water. Section of the fruit showing wings and tubercle shown in B.

(Drawings by Ada Hayden.)

the sun shines too brightly on them or because they cannot secure their chosen food, then there will be few or no descendants. If conditions are favorable, they can live and reproduce. So the struggle goes on and to plants having the best adjustment falls the best success in life.

High over this sand bar soar aeroplane travelers. There, the dandelion fruit on a parachute, nearby the milkweed seed floating

Fig. 446-A.   Fig. 446-B.

FIG. 446. Seeds scattered by the wind. A, Achene of Red-seeded Dandelion. B. Milkweed *(Asclepias syriaca)* pod and seeds.

(Drawings by Ada Hayden.)

on shining silken threads, while the salsify, having tired of living dutifully in man's gardens, stiffly sails with a rusty, bristly parachute to other fields and roadsides. Here amid the goldenrod, fly the thistles, which clinging at first to the mother plant as puffs of white down, are caught by the current of the wind and are off in a flurry, rising high, floating off, slowly sinking to obscurity in the brown grass to find finally a resting place for the long winter.

FIG. 447. The wind piloted milkweed seeds.
(Photograph by Ada Hayden.)

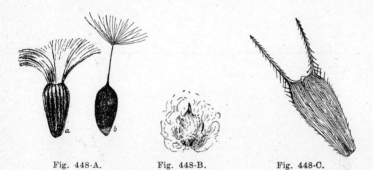

Fig. 448-A.   Fig. 448-B.   Fig. 448-C.

FIG. 448.   A and B.   Fruit scattered by the wind.   A. a, achene of Goldenrod
(*Solidago rigida*); b, Blue Flowered Lettuce (*Lactuca floridana*), the bristly hairs
called the pappus.   B. Anemone (*Anemone cylindrica*).   C.   Fruit scattered by
animals; a, an achene, commonly called a seed, of Boot-jack or Beggar-ticks
(*Bidens frondosa*); b, Spanish Needle (*Bidens bipinnata*).
(*Drawings by Charlotte M. King*).

Some seeds heavily laden with stores of food seem very nearly
to have lost their chance to travel.   There they lie in heaps on the
earth; but along comes a squirrel with an eye to business and filling his pockets undulates briskly to his storehouse.   The squirrel
through forgetfulness to re-visit all his storehouses may plant for
himself a future orchard.

Many owners of furry coats and bushy tails, when they are not
barking at the moon, furnish free rides for weedy hangers on.
Stick-tight and beggar's lice can so ride, harmless to their bene-
factors, but the porcupine grass or spear grass bears a spearlike
tip, the shaft of which twists like a screw into flesh, frequently
causing wounds.

By the wayside grow handsome poke berries and the black nightshade whose bright luscious fruits offer juicy bits to birds which
carry the seeds to distant fence-rows.   The dew-moistened or muddy
feet and feathers of web-footed creatures convey mucilaginous
coated seeds such as flax and shepherd's purse, and the plantains.
The honking geese betray this flight of voyaging seeds.

Hosts of seeds roll in the wheels of industry to new environments.   Tucked in a load of hay, seeds migrate from farm to farm.
Horse nettle or Canadian thistle seeds hidden in the straw bed-
ding of stock cars are often hurled from the running train to beds
on the gravelly roadside to flourish and compete with gorgeous

FIG. 449.   A furry-coated disseminator of many clinging seeds, coyote.
(Photograph by Ada Hayden.)

fellow travelers on the right of way. In the following summer
near the purple Canada thistle will bloom a rosy patch of primrose (Gaura) from rocky Colorado. Here the blue-green western
wheat grass with its wily twin the quack grass weaves a mottled
velvet carpet where the striped ground squirrel plays. This squirrel, too, has a part in distributing seeds of the grasses, which he
uses for food. Here the spear grass from Nebraska towers above
the Iowa rose, phlox and wind flower of fields primeval, and with
these the rovers bend and bow in the grand march by the roadside.

Some plants like Jimson weed have apparently devoted all their
energies to growing without making any provisions for travel.
The thorny pods of this weed filled to bursting with seeds, packed
with food, stand waiting on the dry bristling mother bush. Then
split goes the pod and rocked gently by the wind, the little seeds

rattle out, but only a few feet from the bushy old plants. Many
seeds fall into crevices and lie there crowded together with little
chance of growth the next season. At last snow falls and mingles
with the seeds. Then comes a whirling wind and carries the seeds
and flakes over fences, up lanes, into ditches, down hillsides, where
they lie, when the wind dies away, in great white ridges of snow,
dust and weed seeds. The next day when the sun comes out, the
drifted snow melts slightly; with the close of a day a slippery,
shining ice sheet covers the drifts. The wind blows again a wintry
blast and millions of smooth shining dustlike seeds are swirled
across the slippery snow toboggan far away to new locations.

The mighty travelers, Russian thistle, old witch grass and the
pigweeds, do not produce any means of flight; but they have slight

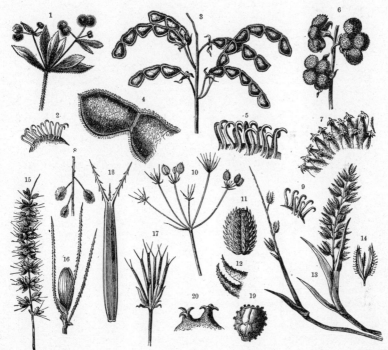

FIG. 450. Fruits furnished with hooks. 1. *Galium Aparine.* 2. Hooked bristles
of the fruit of the same. 3. *Desmodium canadense.* 4. A piece of the
lomentum of the same. 5. Hooked bristles of *Desmodium canadense.* 6.
Cynoglossum pictum. 7. Hooked prickles on the fruits of the same. 8. *Circaea
Lutetiana.* 9. Hooked bristles on the fruit of the same. 10. *Torilis Anthriscus.*
11. Single fruit of *Torilis Anthriscus.* 12. Curved prickles on this fruit. 13.
Lappago racemosa. 14. Single fruiting spike of the same. 15. *Setaria
verticillata.* 16. Fruit-bearing branchlet with involucral bristles from a spike of
Setaria verticillata. 17. *Bidens bipinnata.* 18. Single fruit of the same. 19
Fruit of *Coccinia strigosa.* 20. Hooked prickles on the fruit of *Coccinia strigosa.*
2, 4, 5, 7, 9, 11, 12, 14, 16, 18 and 20 magnified.
From The Natural History of Plants, by Kerner and Oliver, vol. II, p. 871, fig.
477.

connection with the earth and soon after the first frost will be off
with any good wind which gives them a pressing invitation. They
roll away in a cloud of dust until they have rolled their round-
ness off or until a fence row stops them. Here the empty cases
and weed stems may be seen in great piles in the fence corners and

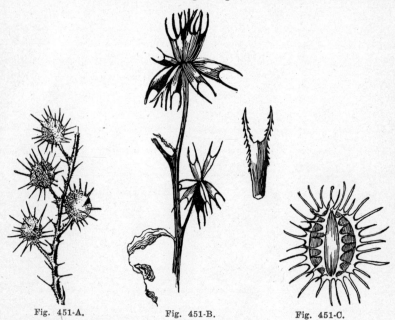

Fig. 451-A.   Fig. 451-B.   Fig. 451-C.

FIG. 451. Weeds scattered by animals. A. Buffalo Bur *(Solanum rostratum)*. B.
Pitchforks *(Bidens frondosa)*, the downwardly barbed points admirably suited for
animal dissemination. C. Carrot *(Daucus Carota)*.
(Drawings by Ada Hayden.)

Fig. 452-A.   Fig. 452-B.   Fig. 452-C.

FIG. 452. A. Cow with attached Burdock burs. B. Burdock enlarged. C. Comfrey
(Cynoglossum) enlarged.
(A, after Bailey, Macmillian & Co.: B, after Dewey, U. S. Dept. Agr.)

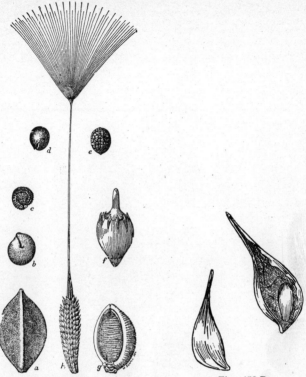

Fig. 453-A.   Fig. 453-B.

FIG. 453.   A.   Weed seeds eaten by birds.   a.   Wild buckwheat (*Polygonum Convolvulus*); b and d, Amaranth or Pigweed; c, Chickweed; e, Spotted Spurge; f, Ragweed; g, Foxtail; h, Dandelion.
B.   Seeds of sedges carried by water.
     (*A, after Dewey, U. S. Dept. of Agr.; B. drawing by Ada Hayden.*)

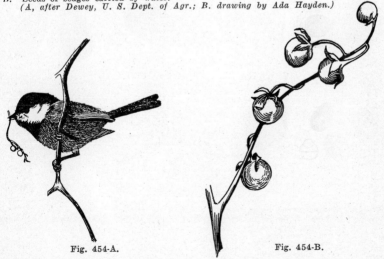

Fig. 454-A.   Fig. 454-B.

FIG. 454.   A.   Chickadee carrying fruit.   B.   Berries of Horse Nettle; carried by birds.

in the spring the path of the journey may be traced by the little red seedlings bursting through the earth.

Many weed seeds may lie buried in cultivated soil, a few seeds germinating each year for as long a period as twenty years. So one season's growth of velvet-leaf or flower-of-an-hour may mysteriously appear in a garden in which no plant of its kind has been

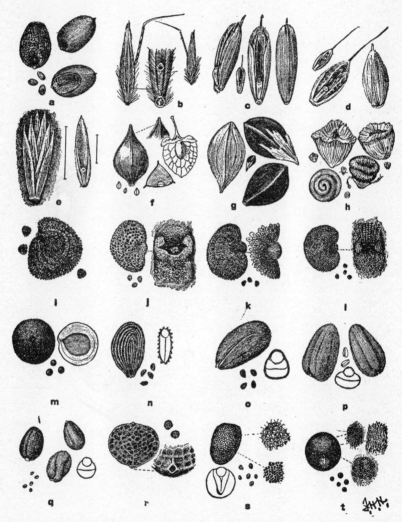

FIG. 455. Noxious weed seeds found in farm seeds (No. 1): a, sandbur; b, wild oat; c, chess; d, darnel; e, quack grass; f, dock; g, black bindweed; h, Russian thistle; i, corn cockle; j, white campion; k, bladder campion; l, night-flowering catchfly; m, cow cockle; n, pennycress; o, field peppergrass; p, large-fruited false flax; q, small-fruited false flax; r, ball mustard; s, black mustard; t, English charlock. (Enlarged and natural size.)

allowed to seed for a period of ten years. This is a provision for distributing the plant through a period of time.

Although myriads of plants travel by overland routes, the perennial types are frequently able to creep stealthily by means of underground stems in all directions, so completely filling the earth with their advancing subterranean shoots that they exclusively

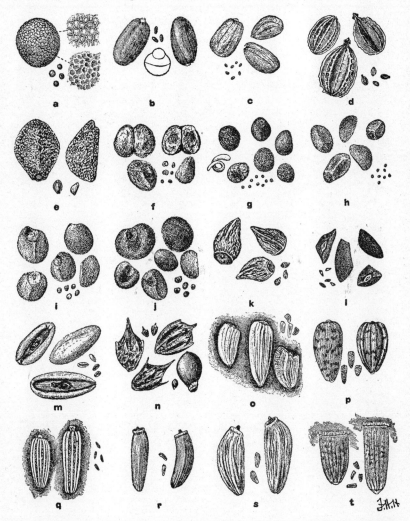

FIG. 456. Noxious weed seeds found in farm seeds (No. 2): a, Indian mustard; b, hare's-ear mustard; c, tumbling mustard; d, wild carrot: e, field bindweed; f, flax dodder; g, clover dodder; h, small-seeded alfalfa dodder; i, field dodder; j, large-seeded alfalfa dodder; k, corn gromwell; l, rat-tail plantain; m, buckhorn; n, ragweed; o, gumweed; p, wild sunflower; q, ox-eye daisy; r, Canada thistle; s, bull thistle; t, wild chicory. (Enlarged and natural size.)
(U. S. Dept. of Agrl.)

occupy a given area, smothering and crowding out their neighbors. Not until young buds shooting from the earth disclose the growing patch does the farmer realize that he has the weeds to deal with.

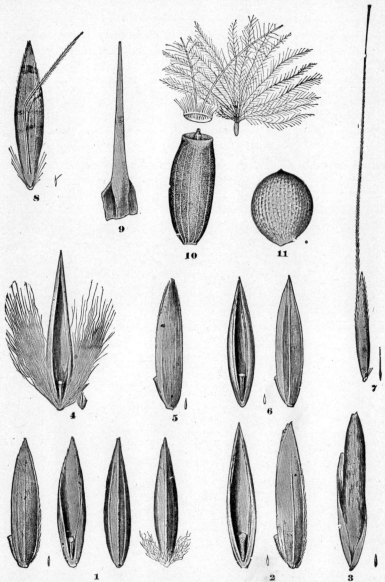

FIG. 457. Seeds of Poas with impurities. 1, Kentucky Blue Grass rubbed and un-rubbed; 2, Wood Meadow Grass (*Poa nemoralis*); 3, Ergot, a fungus; 4, Texas Blue Grass (*P. arachnifera*); 5, Canadian Blue Grass (*Poa compressa*); 6, Rough Stalked Meadow Grass (*Poa trivialis*); 7, Silky Bent Grass (*Apera spica-venti*); 8, Wood Hair Grass (*Deschampsia flexuosa*); 9, spine of Canada Thistle; 10, Canada Thistle; 11, caryopsis of Stink Grass (*Eragrostis major*).
(*U. S. Dept. Agr.*)

These are some of the ways plants travel. Not merely weeds but all plants fly, swim, float, ride, or as best they may, resort to some means of locomotion. Whether carefully provided for during

FIG. 458. The mighty traveller, Russian thistle, resting after a long roll.
(Photograph by H. I. Featherly.)

FIG. 459. Scattering of seed by wind. The Iowa Tumble-weed or Pigweed (*Amaranthus graecizans*). The weeds piled up against the fence; the Russian Thistle and other weeds are scattered in a similar way.
(After Bergen's Botany—Ginn & Co.)

the growing season, or without special provision they follow the universal law of distribution which is named dissemination.

Whether some plants will always be called weeds because man has not discovered a use for them cannot yet be foretold. The custodian of plants can better control those which he desires to cultivate if he knows the laws by which plants live. If the farmer would prevent weeds from securing the food which he desires crop plants to have he must be diligent in his preventive measures. If he does not wish weedy plants to set sail and increase their kind he must cut them before they have matured seed and are ready to sail.

Weeds have adjusted themselves by their freedom to roam to desirable environments. If man does not wish to receive his neighbor's traveling weeds nor to entertain his own he must heed the traffic laws of plants. If he would free his economic plants from all associations with the weedy fraternity, he must act in accordance with the laws by which plant life is governed.

AGENCIES OF WEED SEED DISSEMINATION.

L. H. PAMMEL AND CHARLOTTE M. KING.

Wind—Illustrations:
   a. Tumble weeds—Russian thistle, tumbling pigweed, tumbling mustard, witch grass, winged pigweed.
   b. Seeds bearing appendages—thistles, dandelion, cat-tail, goldenrod, milkweed, bedstraw.

Water.—Illustrations:
   a. Seeds with inflated seed pods—sedges, docks.
   b. Other grass seeds—wild oats.
   c. Seeds with mucilaginous seed coats—peppergrass, plantains, some mustards.
   d. In water currents—all seeds.

Snow and Wind.—Illustrations:
Many seeds borne on upright stalks—pigweeds, evening primrose, ragweeds.

Animals.—Illustrations:
   a. Edible fruits and seeds—nightshade, poison ivy, hemp, sunflower, poke-berry, foxtail grass, pigweeds, storksbill, etc.
   b. Fruits with hooks or barbs—stick-tight, beggar's lice, cocklebur, burdock, sandbur, squirrel-tail grass (in fleeces).

Burial or creeping, by special mechanisms.—Illustrations:
   a. Needle grass, various awned grasses.
   b. Hogpea (underground fruit).
Man.—Illustrations:
   a. By impure agricultural seed—dodders, buckhorn, wild carrot, quack grass, cockles and most of the common field weeds.
   b. Refuse heaps—all common weeds.
   c. Common carriers—weeds seeds from vehicles and trains.
   d. Hay and wool—buffalo bur, and fruits of various bur bearing plants.
   e. Escapes from cultivation—chicory, ox-eye daisy, salsify, butter and eggs.

Weeds are usually free-seeding plants and have by this means provided liberally for distribution. Butter-print plants have been found to produce from 1,300 to 2,200 seeds; one good-sized cocklebur plant produces 2,610 burs, or 5,220 seeds. Mr. Cratty found that a single berry of horse nettle contained 119 seeds; 137 berries on the entire plant would approximate 16,200 seeds. One plant of shoo-fly may produce 7,000 seeds. One plant of Jimson weed with 31 capsules produced 8,500 seeds; one plant of dock has been found to produce 8,500 seeds.

Notwithstanding the agencies of distribution, only a portion of the seeds produced reaches places favorable for growing. Birds alone destroy a large percentage of the seeds of some weeds.

"One of the most useful groups of native birds is the sparrow family. Their chosen fare consists largely of seeds of weeds. For the tree sparrow, for instance, one-fourth of an ounce of weed seed per day is a conservative estimate of the food of an adult. On this basis in a large agricultural state like Iowa sparrows annually eat approximately 875 tons of weed seeds."

"A ring-necked pheasant's crop contained 8,000 seeds of chickweed and a dandelion head."[*]

A single quail will contribute at least $20 annually in destruction of weed seeds.

It is also true that a certain percentage of seeds eaten by birds survive digestion and aid in the spread of weeds.

*Henshaw, H. W., Farmer's Bulletin 513. 5.

CHAPTER VI.

WEED MIGRATION.*
L. H. PAMMEL.

Geographical botany is that phase of botany which concerns it-

Fig. 460. Weed seeds commonly found in farm seeds; a, crab grass; b, witch grass; c, yellow foxtail; d, green foxtail; e, velvet grass; f, soft chess; g, sedge; h, sorrel; i, knotweed; j, pale knotweed; k, lady's thumb; l, lamb's quarters; m, wild salt-bush; n, rough amaranth; o, spreading amaranth; p, wild spurry; q and r, chickweed; s, mouse-ear chickweed; t, forked catchfly. (Enlarged and natural size.)

*This chapter has been rewritten for the most part, only a few paragraphs in the first edition have been used again. The purpose of this chapter is to show how neighboring territory influences the weeds of this state.

self with the distribution of plants over the earth's surface. The
study involves questions of geology, climatology, plant physiology,
geography, paleobotany, ethnology, history, agriculture, horticul-
ture and commerce. J. Burtt Davy says: "The facies of the
world's flora is rapidly changing, and tends to become more uniform within certain limits, under the influence of agriculture and
commerce." Before the advent of man the chief factors in weed
immigration were the wind, water, snow, animals of various kinds,
e. g., birds, mammals, reptiles and insects, and gravity. Primitive
man must have been an important factor in the distribution of
plants. Many plants were no doubt widely scattered by the Indian.
Some, like the persimmon, plum, pawpaw, maize, etc., were cultivated; but many weeds also were scattered by the Indian, finding a
congenial environment near the wigwams. Commerce and the quest
for new lands distributed many species far and wide. Lists of
weedy plants of every civilized country, as indicated by Fernald,
Davy, Gray and other botanists, show that a large percentage are
foreigners. With the rapidity of modern transportation and with

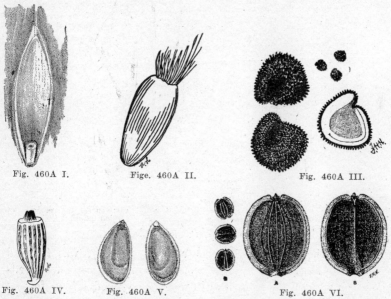

Fig. 460A I.   Fige. 460A II.   Fig. 460A III.

Fig. 460A IV.   Fig. 460A V.   Fig. 460A VI.

Fig. 460-A. Seeds scattered with commercial seed. I. Quack Grass (*Agropyron
repens*). II. Corn-flower (*Centaurea cyanus*); scattered with flower seed, a frequent escape from cultivation. III. Corn cockle (*Agrostemma Githago*); scattered
with wheat, frequent in wheat fields. IV. Chicory (*Cichorium Intybus*); seed
frequently found in alfalfa seed. It has been widely scattered in this way.
V. Peppergrass (*Lepidium apetalum*); widely scattered with timothy seed.
VI. Parsnip (*Pastinaca sativa*); a frequent escape from cultivation.
(*I and V, drawings, Charlotte M. King; II and IV, drawings, Ada Hayden; III and
VI, Hillman.*)

communication with every part of the world, weed seeds have naturally been carried with the commercial products. Without exception, wherever agriculture has advanced in Iowa, I believe weeds have followed cultivation, generally making their appear-

FIG. 461. Blue-stem (*Andropogon scoparius*). A plant common to the prairies of Iowa. a, spikelet; b, c, first and second glumes; d, third glume; f, lodicules, stamens and pistil.

(Lamson-Scribner, U. S. Dept. Agr.)

ance along the water courses where our agriculture was fostered earlier than in the interior of the state. For instance, such weeds as Jimson weed, Indian mallow, burdock, may-weed or dog fennel, cheeses, mullein, dock, black nightshade, smartweed, bull thistle, pigweed, lamb's quarters and purslane, have been known in Iowa for more than sixty years. Some of these were abundant species in cities and on farms along the Mississippi long before central and northwestern Iowa became settled. There are regions in northwestern Iowa where some of the above weeds are still unknown. The may-weed, velvet-weed and mullein were only infrequent weeds in central Iowa twenty-five years ago, though becoming more frequent from year to year. Commerce indeed has taken an important part in the migration of weeds. Wild carrot, chicory, black medick, quack grass, Canada thistle, shoo-fly and dodder are becoming more and more abundant in the fields of Iowa. Many weeds, moreover, first make their appearance in the vicinity of cultivated fields. In nearly every case wild parsnip, tansy, shoo-fly, bouncing Bet and butter and eggs show the influence of cultivation.

Every phytogeographer is confronted with the problem of placing weeds of the given area in their relation to floras.

It is interesting to note that so few of the plants of the Iowa forests and prairies have become weedy. When the sod was turned the native plants disappeared. Comparatively few of the original inhabitants thereof remain as a part of the flora. The weeds most

FIG. 462. Lamb's Quarters (*Chenopodium album*). A common foreign weed. Native to Europe.

likely to appear here are such as have been partly adjusted to the open conditions. In such places it was not uncommon in the early days to find that such weeds as the common Iowa tumble-weed (*Amaranthus graecizans*), tickle-grass (*Panicum capillare*), creeping verbena (*Verbena bracteosa*), milk spurge or milk purslane (*Euphorbia maculata* and *E. Geyeri*), evening prim-rose (*Oenothera biennis*), horse-weed (*Erigeron canadensis*), blue vervain (*Verbena stricta*), persisted for a few years, per-haps with a few other perennial weeds like flowering spurge (*Euphorbia corollata*), *Helian-thus occidentalis* and *Desmo-dium canescens*, especially in a few places where tillage was not good; but in nearly every case these perennial weeds disap-

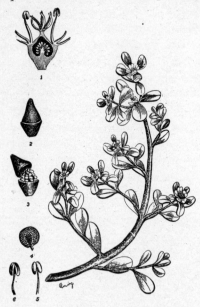

FIG. 463. Purslane (*Portulaca oleracea*). At first cultivated in the United States for greens; now appearing like an in-digenous plant.
(*Vasey, U. S. Dept. Agr.*)

Fig. 464.

Fig. 465.

FIG. 464. Shoo-fly (*Hibiscus Trionum*). This weed was widely distributed as an ornamental plant.
FIG. 465. Carrot (*Daucus Carota*). Common in the east. Probably first spread from the cultivated carrot.
(*Drawings by Charlotte M. King.*)

peared from the cultivated fields, which thereupon became occupied by a large number of native annual weeds like the greater ragweed (*Ambrosia trifida*), Spanish needles (*Bidens frondosa, B. discoidea* and *B. bipinnata*) and smartweeds (*Polygonum* sp.), a few hardy perennial weeds like milkweed (*Asclepias syriaca*), morning-glory (*Convolvulus sepium*), artichoke (*Helianthus tuberosus*) and meadow sunflower (*Helianthus grosseserratus*). Such annual or winter annual weeds as squirrel-tail grass (*Hordeum jubatum*), peppergrass (*Lepidium apetalum*) began to compete with a host of European and other exotic weeds like lamb's quarters (*Chenopodium album*), persicaria (*Polygonum persicaria*), purslane (*Portulaca oleracea*), foxtail (*Setaria glauca, S.*

FIG. 466. Tickle Grass (*Panicum capillare*). A common grass, probably originally found in clearings, has rapidly spread to cultivated ground.
(*Lamson-Scribner, U. S. Dept. Agr.*)

viridis) and, later, crab grass (*Digitaria sanguinalis* and *D. humi-fusa*). In grain fields or flax fields appeared the usual crop of weeds that are carried with grain, like corn cockle, chess, cow-herb, mustard, penny-cress and darnel. Then came the weeds which were introduced with clover seed, as buckhorn, dodder, evening catchfly, chicory, wild carrot, etc.

FIG. 467. Small Peppergrass (*Lepidium apetalum*). Rapidly occupies the virgin soil. (*Drawing by Charlotte M. King.*)

As our agriculture shifted from a wheat country to one dominating in corn, the weed flora changed slightly. Corn cockle, chess and vetch (*Vicia sativa*), so common everywhere in a small grain country, disappeared over a large section of Iowa. They are again appearing where wheat is grown. Charlock, a relic of flax culture, remained to be distributed largely with oats seed.

The fact, however, remains that a goodly number of our Iowa

FIG. 468.   Fig. 469.

FIG. 468.   Greater Ragweed (*Ambrosia trifida*).   This weed rapidly occupies culti-
vated ground.
(*Vasey, U. S. Dept. of Agr.*)
FIG. 469.   Corn Cockle (*Agrostemma Githago*).   An immigrant from western Asia.
(*After U. S. Dept. of Agr.*)

weeds are indigenous to this state. Many of these were plants
capable of enduring sunshine and so did not have to readjust
themselves to new conditions. So we have received not only from
Iowa but from the country to the west, as Nebraska and the Dakotas, such plants as the squirrel-tail grass, buffalo bur, winged
pigweed, common sunflower (*Helianthus annuus*) and stinkweed
(*Cleome serrulata*).

The same thing has occurred in states to the west where many
indigenous weeds are vying with the European weeds. To the
north in Canada a pigweed (*Monolepis Nuttalliana*) has become
extremely common, while such weeds as foxtail are troublesome
to a limited extent only. The holy grass, a curiosity in many
parts of Iowa, is a troublesome perennial weed of Manitoba.

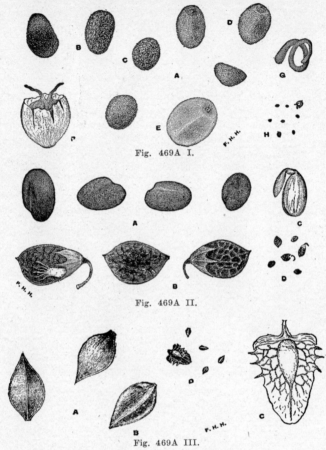

Fig. 469A I.

Fig. 469A II.

Fig. 469A III.

FIG. 469A. Seeds of weeds scattered with agricultural seeds. I. Dodder in clover and alfalfa seed. II. White Sweet Clover in alfalfa seed. III. Bitter Dock (*Rumex obtusifolius*) in red clover seed.

Why did not more of the native plants become weedy? The North American Indian cultivated maize, pumpkin, bean and a few other plants. In other words, cultivation meant that certain types of native plants became inured to cultivation. Of these, no doubt, are such plants as the following: sunflowers (*Helianthus annuus*, *H. grosseserratus* and *H. tuberosus*), greater ragweed (*Ambrosia trifida*), tickle grass (*Panicum capillare*), sprouting crab grass (*Panicum dichotomiflorum*), barnyard grass (*Echinochloa crus-galli*), marsh elder (*Iva xanthiifolia*), fetid marigold (*Dyssodia papposa*), black-eyed Susan (*Rudbeckia hirta*), winged pigweed (*Cycloloma atriplicifolium*), Iowa tumble-weed

(*Amaranthus graecizans*), poke weed (*Phytolacca decandra*), milkweed (*Asclepias syriaca*), buffalo bur (*Solanum rostratum*), cut-leaved horse nettle (*Solanum triflorum*), ground cherry (*Physalis pruinosa*), Rocky Mountain bee-plant (*Cleome serrulata*), stinkweed (*Polanisia trachysperma*), maple-leaved goosefoot (*Chenopodium hybridum*), the Canadian pigweed (*Monolepis Nuttalliana*), squirrel-tail grass (*Hordeum jubatum*). Others which we now recognize as weeds were common in the cultivated fields and around the wigwams of Indians. A few of the plants were probably cultivated by Indians. As food plants of man we may mention the marsh elder (*Iva xanthiifolia*) which Dr. Gilmore tells us was used as a food plant by the Indians of Arkansas. We know that the Indians used the common sunflower and the artichoke. In

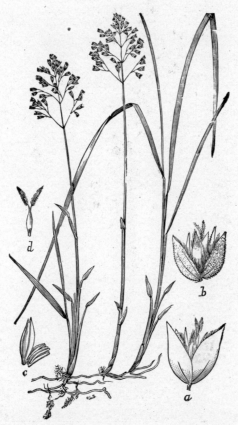

FIG. 470. Holy or Vanilla Grass (*Hierochloe odorata*). Common in the northern hemisphere, mountain regions. In northern Iowa.
(*Lamson-Scribner, U. S. Dept. Agr.*)

the list prepared by Dr. Melvin R. Gilmore of plants used by the North American Indian the following may be listed which are now recognized as weeds:

FIG. 471. Marsh Elder (*Iva xanthiifolia*). Common in the Red River Valley, spreading eastward.

Achillea Millefolium, yarrow.
Oxybaphus nyctagineus, wild four-o'clock.
Anemone canadensis, wind flower.
Arctium minus, smaller burdock.
Asclepias syriaca, milkweed.
Asclepias tuberosa, butterfly-weed.
Dyssodia papposa, fetid marigold.
Callirhoe involucrata, purple mallow.
Chenopodium album, lamb's quarters.
Cuscuta paradoxa, dodder.
Equisetum sp., horsetails.
Galium triflorum, three-flowered bed-straw.
Glycyrrhiza lepidota, wild liquorice.
Grindelia squarrosa, tarweed.
Helianthus annuus, sunflower.
Helianthus tuberosus, artichoke.
Hedeoma hispida, false penny-royal.
Heracleum lanatum, cow parsnip.
Hierochloe odorata, vanilla grass.
Lepachys columnaris, cone-flower.
Lespedeza capitata, bush clover.
Lithospermum canescens, puccoon.
Lygodesmia juncea, skeleton weed.
Melilotus alba, white sweet clover.

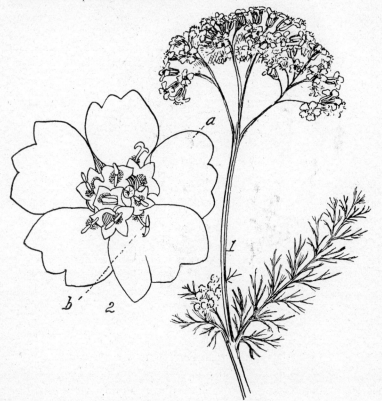

FIG. 472. Yarrow (*Achillea Millefolium*). Common in the northern hemisphere.
(*Drawing by Charlotte M. King.*)

Mentha canadensis, wild mint.
Monarda fistulosa, horsemint.
Physalis heterophylla, ground cherry.
Physalis lanceolata, ground cherry.
Phytolacca decandra, pokeberry.
Plantago major, common plantain.
Rosa pratincola, wild rose.
Rumex crispus, curled dock.
Silphium laciniatum, compass plant.
Silphium perfoliatum, cup plant.
Solidago sp., goldenrods.
Symphoricarpos occidentalis, buckbrush.
Thalictrum dasycarpum, meadow-rue.
Rhus Toxicodendron, poison ivy.
Urtica gracilis, nettle.
Verbena hastata, blue vervain.

FIG. 473. Curled Dock (*Rumex crispus*). A common European weed now occurring across the continent.
(*After Chesnut, U. S. Dept. Agr.*)

Another factor which has contributed to our native flora is that many of the plants mentioned above became inured to cultivation where they grew. Prairie dog villages, buffalo wallows, prairie squirrel holes and other places like this made possible the growth

of some plants. It was easy for such plants to adapt themselves
to cultivated ground.

It would seem to me that it is not a question of self-fertilization
or plasticity but one of tolerance of weeds for sunshine and ready
means of dissemination either by natural agencies or by man.

Kabsch, in a discussion of this problem, notes that precisely the
same things have occurred in various parts of the world where
the forests have been cleared. In Bolivia, *Pteris, Anemia,*

FIG. 474. Common Brake (*Pteris aquilina*). A troublesome weed following fires in
the northwest, also under similar conditions in some parts of northeastern Iowa.
(*Drawing by Ada Hayden.*)

Saururus, Lilicoya were followed later by small shrubs of the
Eupatoriaceae and Malvaceae. In Brazil, *Pteris caudata* and
Tristegis glutinosa make their appearance after the forest fire. In
Teneriffe, in 1815, *Pteris,* in 1820, *Erica arborea,* and in 1830,
Laurus canariensis covered the ground. Kabsch notes how sud-
denly the vegetation of a forest changes in Europe when sunshine

is admitted after a forest fire or after the clearing of the forest.
Plants like vetchling (*Orobus*), four-leaved grass (*Paris quadri-
folia*), *Arum*, lovers of the shade, soon succumb, and in their places
fireweed (*Epilobium angustifolium*), bedstraw (*Galium*), thistle
(*Cirsium*), wild marjoram (*Origanum*), foxglove (*Digitalis*) and
others appear, to be followed later by roses, brambles, hazel nut,
birches and grasses like reed bent grass (*Calamagrostis epigeios*),
meadow grass (*Poa*), sweet vernal grass (*Anthoxanthum odora-
tum*) and bear moss (*Polytrichum commune*). Later shade-loving
plants have a chance to grow.

FIG. 475. Small Ragweed (*Ambrosia artemisiifolia*). An immigrant from the southern part of the United States.
(*Vasey, U. S. Dept. of Agr.*)

As an example of the spread of American weeds in Europe several weeds may be cited. The small ragweed (*Ambrosia artemisiifolia*), which is common throughout the United States, has, according to Laubert, been widely spread with American grown
clover seed*, though known in isolated places in Germany for forty

*Landw. Jahrbucher. 35:735-737.

years. It is now on the increase, perhaps because of the recent clover importation, yet its spread is somewhat limited because it blooms late. The plants are often only pistillate. In Steglitz, Germany, it was associated with black bindweed (*Polygonum Con- volvulus*), fleabane (*Erigeron canadense*), wall barley (*Hordeum murinum*), rib grass (*Plantago lanceolata*), common plaintain (*Plantago major*), wild carrot (*Daucus Carota*), yarrow (*Achillea Millefolium*) and tumble-weed (*Corispermum hyssopifolium*).

Scherer and others record the occurrence of *Solanum rostratum* in Germany (1883) and in France. This is also reported from Australia in 1917.

In Pflanzenleben, Kabsch says, ''There are many illustrations of plant immigrations and spreading of plants in Europe, but so far as I know they have never occupied the soil to the same degree in Europe as in America. Most of our weeds of fields, like the cereals among which they grow, are of foreign origin, as star thistle (*Centaurea cyanus*), corn cockle (*Agrostemma Githago*), charlock (*Raphanus Raphanistrum*), *Myagrum,* etc.'' There are many other weeds of grain fields that are of similar origin that are not men- tioned by Kabsch. Among them are the common mustard (*Bras- sica arvensis*), common vetch (*Vicia sativa*), darnel (*Lolium temulentum*), Russian thistle (*Salsola Kali* var. *tenuifolia*), pen- nycress (*Thlaspi arvense*), false flax (*Camelina sativa*) and Berteroa (*Berteroa incana* and *B. mutabilis*). These weeds un- doubtedly were spread with the cultivation of grain. Certainly this is largely true also for America. Many, though by no means all, were brought to Europe with wheat during the early cultiva- tion of grain in Europe. The crusaders undoubtedly were re- sponsible for the spread of these small grain weeds in Europe. Other plants, of which the horseradish is an illustration, were no doubt brought into west Europe as cultivated plants.

Russian thistle was introduced by seeds from Russia into the farm lands of the Dakotas. It has now widely spread south and east. *Thlaspi arvense*, pennycress, has been widely spread with cultivation of grain.

E. W. Claypole, in speaking of the migration of weeds to Amer- ica, says:

''Underneath the great wave of human emigration from the so- called Old to the so-called New World, underneath the noisy, busy surface tide that has swept westward from the shores of Europe to those of America during the last two hundred years, there has

Fig. 476.   Russian Thistle (*Salsola Kali* var. *tenuifolia*).   Common in eastern Europe.
Introduced into the Dakotas, 1873 or 1874.   Now common in northern United
States, particularly in the west.
(Drawing by Charlotte M. King.)

existed another and a less conspicuous wave, another and a less
prominent tide of emigration.   Westward in its direction, like the
former, it has silently accomplished results that seldom strike the
superficial eye, but yet are scarcely less in magnitude than those
which have followed the advent of the white man to the shores of
America.

I allude to that slow and noiseless immigration of European
plants which has been going on for many years, and which probably commenced when the first European vessel touched our
shores.   Side by side with the displacement of the red man by the
white man has gone on the displacement of the red man's vegetable
companions by plants which accompanied the white man from his
trans-Atlantic home.   Not more completely have the children of
the pilgrim fathers made themselves at home on the banks of the
Charles and the Neponset, not more completely have the successors
of Champlain and Jacques Cartier established themselves along
the St. Lawrence, not more completely have the descendants of

the aristocratic colonists of Maryland and Virginia appropriated the shores of the Chesapeake, than have the homely weeds of England and France made themselves at home in the New World; established themselves on its soil, appropriated its fields, its gardens and its waysides. Nor have the older states alone been seized by those European invaders. The stream has flowed beyond them, and as no village or hamlet in the west is without its population of European descent, so too it is never without its plant population of European weeds."

Dr. Asa Gray, who discussed the subject of weeds from a philosophical standpoint, said:

"In the United States, and perhaps in most parts of the world, a large majority of the weeds are introduced plants, brought into the country directly or indirectly by man. Some, such as dandelion, yarrow, and probably the common plantain and the common

Fig. 477. Fig. 478.

FIG. 477. Dandelion (*Taraxacum officinale*). Common in northern hemisphere, across the continent.

FIG. 478. Poison Hemlock (*Conium maculatum*). Common in Salt Lake Basin. (*After Chesnut, U. S. Dept. Agr.*)

purslane, are importations as weeds, although the species naturally occupy some part of the country.

Why weeds are so pertinacious and aggressive is too large and loose a question; for any herb whatever when successfully aggressive becomes a weed; and the reasons of predominance may be almost as diverse as the weeds themselves. But we may inquire whether weeds have any common characteristic which may give them advantage, and why the greater part of the weeds of the United States, and probably of similar temperate countries, should be foreigners.''

THE DIRECTION OF WEED MIGRATION.

Mr. L. H. Dewey, who made a study of two hundred North American weeds and their migration, says: ''A study of the origin of weeds now in this country will impress one with the largeness of the number that have been introduced from Europe in comparison with the number of native species or of species received from other directions.'' In the list of 200 weeds of the United

Fig. 479A.   Fig. 479B.

FIG. 479. A. Charlock (*Brassica arvensis*). B. Black Mustard (*B. nigra*). Immigrants from western Asia brought to the United States by way of Europe; early colonists.

(*Dewey, U. S. Dept. Agr.*)

States published in the Year Book for 1895, 108 species are of foreign origin, while 92 are native. Of the 108 introduced species, 64 are native in Europe and 30 are ascribed to the Old World in general, only 2 Asiatic species in the list having established themselves as weeds in this country without being first distributed in Europe. Africa and Australia are not represented among our weeds, while Central and South America have contributed only 12 or 15 important species, most of which are confined to the Gulf states. A list of the plants of Michigan published in 1892 contains 1,604 indigenous species, of which 22 are recognized as injurious weeds, and 142 species introduced from Europe, of which 57 have become troublesome weeds.

A list of Kansas weeds enumerating 209 species contains 129 native species, 42 introduced from Europe, and 38 from all other sources. Eighteen species native in the states east of the Mississippi river have been introduced into Kansas in opposition to the prevailing winds and the direction of the drainage, while only 3 species are mentioned which have come from the Rocky Mountain region with both of these natural forces in their favor.

In an article on the weeds of California 110 species are mentioned as troublesome in that state. Of these, 53 are native, 43 are introduced from Europe, 5 are from the eastern United States, 3 from Central and South America, and only 2 from Asia. Even in the states bordering the Gulf of Mexico the number of weeds introduced from Europe in cultivated land equals or exceeds those from Mexico and South America. Canada thistle, bur clover, and skunkweed have been taken from California to Australia, where they quickly became naturalized and are now rapidly spreading.

Dr. Fernald has stated the case very well in the following paragraph:

"A review of the history and spread of this vagrant class of plants presents many aspects which are well worth consideration. John Josselyn, in 1672, stated that several species of European weeds had 'sprung up since the English planted and kept cattle in New England,' thus implying that these plants had come unbidden or at least were not purposely brought to this country. He records no less than 40 European weeds introduced in this manner. According to a time-honored tradition, based perhaps on fact, the first weed to spring up in the track of the pioneer is plantain, and on this account it has been called by some primitive races "Whiteman's Foot," a name of more than fanciful application; for without question the plantain and many other roadside species are spread directly by the foot of man. For some years strange and

outlandish weeds have been appearing along the river below Water-
bury, Connecticut. These plants, upon careful study, prove to be
vagrant species from geographically remote portions of the world,
and their presence along the Naugatuck river has been a mystery.
Eventually, however, the whole matter was cleared when the source
of these plants was traced to a factory which utilized old rubber
shoes. These shoes were collected from every available source, and,
before being melted for their rubber were stripped of the cloth linings which were thrown upon a rubbish heap. These linings naturally contained seeds of innumerable plants from the roadsides of
every land, and the rains and spring freshets of the Naugatuck
valley gave them every opportunity to scatter and to start life
anew in Connecticut soil. In this or similar ways many of the
plants mentioned by John Josselyn, Manasseh Cutler, and Jacob
Bigelow undoubtedly reached our shores; and these emigrants are
being reinforced by almost every person who comes to us from
foreign lands.''

Cosmopolitan Weeds.—A great many weeds, originally, had a
very wide distribution, although many of these so-called weeds
probably were introduced by man. In many cases it is almost
impossible to tell how and whence they came to the places in which
they occur.

Who can trace the immigration of such weeds as common purslane, or charlock, or barnyard grass? In the first place, these
plants immigrated when little was known about the species of
plants. What was said about them by the early botanical writers
was often very indefinite. In the second place, many of the early
writers did not take pains to leave statistics concerning the introduction of the plants. The future records, however, will be more
accurate as the adventive plants are being recorded by a host of
botanical writers the world over. The notes in such floras as Britton's Manual, Robinson and Fernald-Gray's Manual, Bentham and
Hooker's Handbook of the British Flora, Garcke's Flora of Germany, Acloque's Flora of France, Moore's Handbook of the
Flora of New South Wales, Arcangeli's Flora of Italy, Baron Ferdinand von Mueller's Systematic Census of Australian Plants,
Grisebach's Flora of the British West Indies, Millspaugh's Flora
of Yucatan, Hemsley's Botany of Central America, Urban's papers
on the Flora of the West Indies give more or less detailed information on introduced weeds.

The following weeds are more or less cosmopolitan: crab grass
(*Digitaria sanguinalis*), found in North and South America,
Europe, Asia, Africa, Australia and New Zealand; barnyard grass
(*Echinochloa crusgalli*), in Europe, Asia, Africa, North and South

Fig. 480. Fig. 481.

FIG. 480. Crab Grass (*Digitaria sanguinalis*). A cosmopolitan weed.
FIG. 481. Foxtail Grass (*Alopecurus geniculatus*). Widely distributed. Cosmopolitan grass.
(*U. S. Dept. of Agr.*)

America and Australia; green foxtail (*Setaria viridis*), in Europe, Asia, Africa, Australia, North and South America; pigeon grass (*Setaria glauca*), in Europe, Asia, Africa, North and South America; whorled millet (*Setaria verticillata*), in Europe, Asia, Africa, North and South America; Johnson grass (*Sorghum halepense*), in Europe, Asia, Australia and North America; foxtail grass (*Alopecurus geniculatus*), in Asia, New Zealand, Australia, North America; hair grass (*Agrostis hyemalis*), in Australia, New Zealand, North America; Bermuda grass (*Cynodon Dactylon*), a valuable forage plant, but, in cultivated fields, a weed, Europe, Asia, Africa, Australia, New Zealand, North and South America; southern spear grass (*Eragrostis pilosa*), Europe, Asia, Africa,

Australia, New Zealand, North and South America; crowfoot grass (*Eleusine indica*), Europe, Asia, Africa, Australia, New Zealand, North and South America; cheat (*Bromus secalinus*), Europe, Asia, North America, a weed; brome grass (*Bromus tectorum*), Europe, Asia, Africa, North America; soft chess (*Bromus arvensis*), Europe, Asia, Africa, North America. It is singular that only one species of *Bromus* is given by Moore and Ferdinand von Mueller, the *Bromus arenarius*. Reed (*Phragmites communis*), though not regarded as a weed in the United States, is a cosmopolitan plant found in Europe, Asia, Africa, Australia, New Zealand, Papua, North America (Canada, United States and Mexico).

Cress (*Barbarea vulgaris*) occurs in Europe, Asia, Australia,

FIG. 482.   Johnson Grass (*Sorghum halepense*).   An African weed.   Common in the Gulf states, and reported from southwestern Iowa
(*Lamson-Scribner, U. S. Dept. Agr.*)

FIG. 483. Awned Brome Grass (*Bromus tectorum*). Common in the Great Basin country and California, occasionally in Iowa.
(*Lamson-Scribner, U. S. Dept. Agr.*)

New Zealand and North America. None of the most common North American weeds among the remaining members of the mustard family occur in Australia or New Zealand, although shepherd's purse (*Capsella Bursa-pastoris*), common mustard (*Brassica arvensis*), the hedge mustards (*Sisymbrium officinale* and *S. altissimum*) and peppergrass (*Lepidium apetalum*) are common in Europe and Asia.

Of the pulse family the bird's-foot trefoil (*Lotus corniculatus*) occurs in Europe, Asia, Africa and Australia; the indigo plant (*Indigofera hirsuta*) in Africa, Australia, Papua and Asia. The absence of black medick (*Medicago lupulina*) and hop clover (*Trifolium agrarium*) from Australia is striking.

Of the geranium family the common European, African and

FIG. 484. Rice Cut Grass (*Leersia oryzoides*). Common in low grounds, Iowa; not, however, regarded as a weed. Common in Italy.
(*Drawn by Charlotte M. King.*)

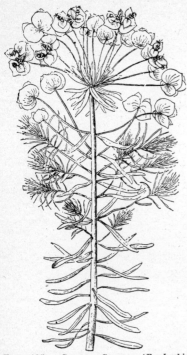

FIG. 485. Cypress Spurge (*Euphorbia Cyparissias*). Common in Europe and waste places in Iowa. In many cases started in the vicinity of cemeteries. (*After Strasburger, Noll, Schenck and Karsten.*)

Asiatic species of storksbill (*Erodium cicutarium*) are absent in Australia and New Zealand and the little flowered sorrel (*Oxalis corniculata*) is the only representative in New Zealand, Australia and Papua. This species also occurs in Europe, Asia, Africa and America. The only malvaceous weeds in Australia common also to the United States are sida (*Sida spinosa*) and butter-print (*Abutilon Theophrasti*), both of tropical origin. The former occurs in Europe, Asia, Africa, North and South America, Australia and Papua. The pigweed (*Amaranthus retroflexus*) of southern North America is common in Europe but has not reached Australia. None of our troublesome weedy species of dock, which are cosmopolitan, occurs in Australia. Of the smartweeds there are two species, the water pepper (*Polygonum Hydropiper*) (Europe, Asia, North and South America) and slender smartweed (*P. lapathifolium*) of Europe, Asia, North and South America. Silky cinquefoil (*Potentilla Anserina*), of the rose family, is common in the west and here and there in northern Iowa; it is found in Europe, Asia, Africa, Australia, New Zealand and North America. Feverfew (*Agrimonia striata*) is found in Europe, Africa and North America. None of our *Oenotheras* is cosmopolitan; however, the primrose willow (*Jussiaea suffruticosa*), a sub-tropical plant, is widely distributed in Asia, Africa, America and Papua. Very few of the Umbelliferae are cosmopolitan. Moore and Mueller record water parsnip (*Sium latifolium*) for New Zealand and Australia.

The Mexican *Ageratum conyzoides* of the sunflower family, found in Africa, Asia, Europe, North and South America, is often weedy. The Spanish needle (*Bidens bipinnata*) is found in Asia, Europe,

North and South America. The small number of plants of this family found in Australia and New Zealand is remarkable. None of our plantains is of common occurrence there. There is no morning-glory.

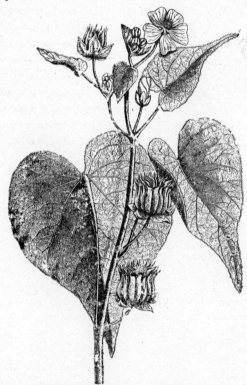

FIG. 486. Velvet-weed or Butter-print (*Abutilon Theophrasti*). A tropical weed now common in the north and spreading to Europe. (*U. S. Dept. of Agr.*)

DURATION OF WEEDS

It may be of interest to briefly compare the duration of the life of a weed with its abundance. There are two kinds of reproduction, the vegetative and seed production. We may therefore classify weeds as annual, winter annual, biennial, and perennial. When looked at in this way some of the common weeds of each class, and their abundance may be noted.

Annual.—Horseweeds (*Erigeron canadensis, E. divaricatus*), foxtails (*Setaria glauca, S. viridis, S. verticillata*), may-weed (*Anthemis Cotula, A. arvensis*), Jimson weed (*Datura Stramonium, D. Tatula*), black nightshade (*Solanum nigrum*), buffalo bur (*Solanum rostratum*), crab grasses (*Digitaria sanguinalis, D. humi-*

fusa), barnyard grass (*Echinochloa crusgalli*), purslane (*Portulaca oleracea*), mustard (*Brassica arvensis, B. nigra, B. juncea*), carpet weed (*Mollugo verticillata*), lamb's quarters (*Chenopodium album, C. hybridum, C. Boscianum*), orach (*Atriplex patula*), pigweed (*Amaranthus retroflexus, A. graecizans, A. blitoides*), small ragweed (*Ambrosia artemisiifolia, A. trifida*), sunflowers (*Helianthus annuus* and *H. petiolaris*), Spanish needle (*Bidens frondosa, B. vulgata, B. aristosa*), French weed (*Galinsoga parviflora*), tumbling mustard (*Sisymbrium altissimum*), hedge mustard (*S. officinale*), Russian thistle (*Salsola Kali* var. *tenuifolia*), the cheeses (*Malva rotundifolia*), velvet-weed (*Abutilon Theophrasti*), shoo-fly (*Hibiscus Trionum*), smartweed (*Polygonum Persicaria, P. pennsylvanicum, P. acre*, etc.), bracted plantain (*Plantago aristata*), corn cockle (*Agrostemma Githago*).

FIG. 487. Castor Oil plant. Cultivated as an ornamental plant in Iowa, but a troublesome weed in South Africa.
(*After Faguet.*)

Fig. 488.   Fig. 489.

FIG. 488.   Spiny Clotbur.   An abundant and troublesome weed in South Africa,
            occasionally a weed in southeastern Iowa.
                        (After Thurber.)
FIG. 489.   Narrow Sneezeweed (*Helenium tenuifolium*).   General aspect of plant and
                        a single head enlarged.
                   (After Chesnut, U. S. Dept. Agr.)

The above list is sufficient to show how annual weeds predominate.

Biennial.—Of the biennial weeds mention may be made of evening primrose (*Oenothera biennis*), gaura (*Gaura biennis*), field thistle (*Cirsium discolor*), bull thistle (*Cirsium lanceolatum*), mullein (*Verbascum Thapsus*), wild carrot (*Daucus Carota*), burdock (*Arctium major*).

Winter annual.—Squirrel-tail grass (*Hordeum jubatum*), peppergrass (*Lepidium apetalum, L. virginicum*), speedwell (*Veronica peregrina*), prickly lettuce (*Lactuca Scariola*), parsnip (*Pastinaca sativa*), chess (*Bromus secalinus, B. tectorum, B. arvensis*).

Perennial.—The list of the perennial weeds is somewhat larger

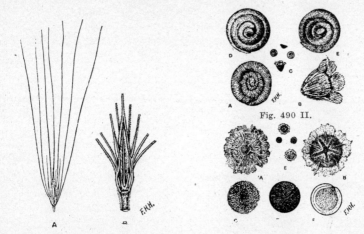

Fig. 490 I.   Fig. 490 III.

FIG. 490. Seeds of immigrant weeds. I. Squirrel-tail (*Hordeum jubatum*); widely scattered with hay and stock trains from the western plains. II. Russian Thistle (*Salsola Kali* var. *tenuifolia*); brought to Dakota with flax seed and grain seed; now scattered in Iowa with alfalfa seed. III. Winged Pigweed (*Cycloloma atriplicifolium*).

(After Hillman.)

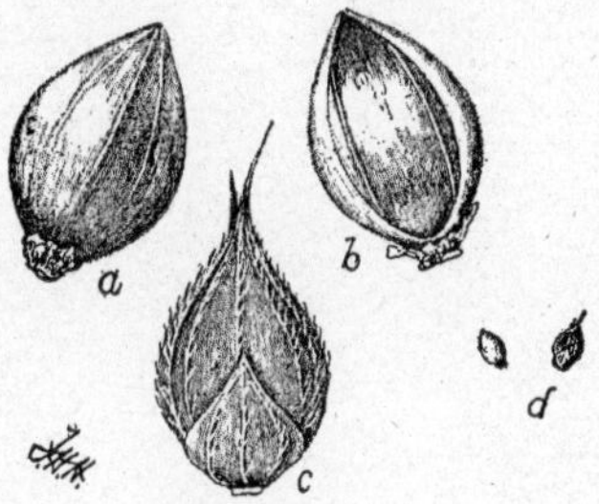

Fig. 490A I. 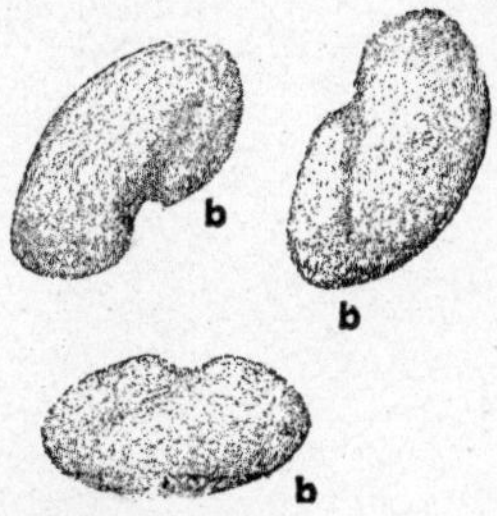   Fig. 490A II.

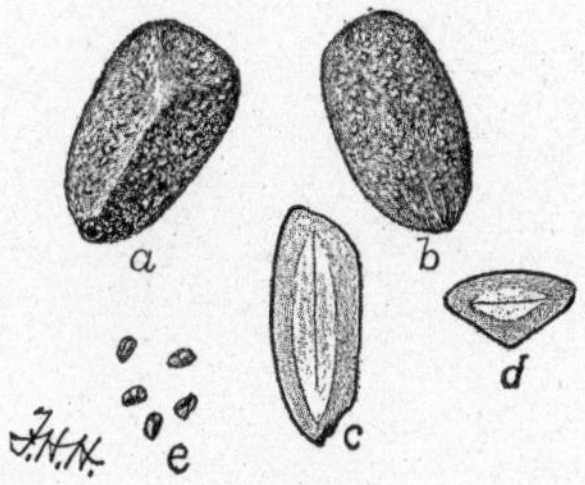

Fig. 490A III. 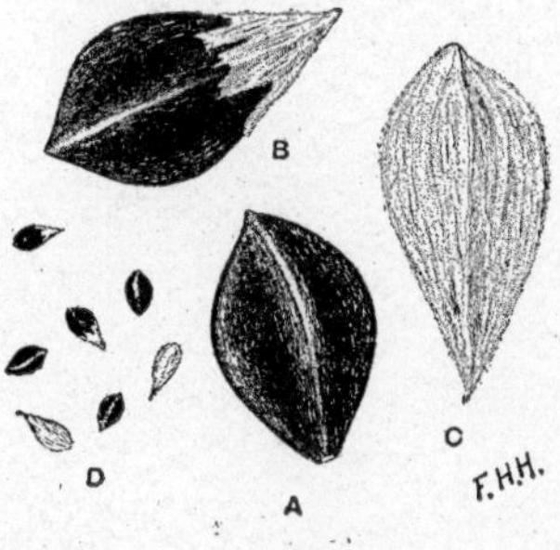   Fig. 490A IV.

FIG. 490A. Seeds scattered with agricultural seeds. I. Barnyard Grass (*Echinochloa crusgalli*). II. *Medicago denticulata*, common in alfalfa seed. II. Horehound (*Marrubium vulgare*), a weed commonly scattered with alfalfa seed. Common in the Great Basin country. IV. Wild Buckwheat or Bindweed (*Polygonum Convolvulus*), commonly scattered with grain seed.

(All after Hillman.)

and includes: quack grass (*Agropyron repens*), Canada thistle (*Cirsium arvense*), woolly thistle (*C. canescens*), plantain (*Plantago Rugelii*), buckhorn (*Plantago lanceolata*), butter and eggs (*Linaria vulgaris*), bouncing Bet (*Saponaria officinalis*), dropseed grasses (*Muhlenbergia mexicana, M. glomerata, M. Schreberi*), perennial sow thistle (*Sonchus arvensis*), perennial ragweed (*Ambrosia psilostachya*), dock (*Rumex crispus, R. altissimus*).

The list might be extended somewhat. It is evident, however, that these perennial weeds are not nearly as common as the annual. In fact the annual type is far more numerous than all other kinds put together. Has not, therefore, the adaptation to long continued cultivation had something to do with the abundance of weeds? It is also another interesting fact that many of these annual weeds come up abundantly after the crop is harvested, or "laid by."

FIG. 491. Tumbling Mustard (*Sisymbrium altissimum*). Introduced with grain in the Dakotas.
(*Dewey, U. S. Dept. Agr.*)

WEEDS IN ADJACENT STATES

What influence, if any, have the neighboring states had on the distribution of weeds? Professor Stevens, of the North Dakota Agricultural Experiment Station, tells us that the sow thistle has become abundant in parts of that state. The general range seems to cover the New England states, all of New York, Michigan, Wisconsin, Minnesota, about half of North Dakota, most of Pennsylvania, extending more or less into New Jersey, and into Delaware, the northern parts of Ohio, Indiana, Illinois, Iowa and northeastern South Dakota. Also scattered localities are represented in the Rocky Mountain region from Montana to New Mexico, and in Washington and British Columbia.

It is of interest to follow the migrations of weeds from different countries into Iowa, and especially to note how weeds migrate from adjacent states. Nearly all of our recent new weeds of Iowa have long occurred in other states. A conspicuous illustration of this migration is the sow thistle (*Sonchus arvensis*). This weed has been prevalent in Manitoba and northwestern Minnesota and northeastern Dakota for more than a quarter of a century. It has slowly worked its way southward as Dr. Stevens of North Dakota

Fig. 492. Wild Barley (*Hordeum jubatum*). Originally common along the shores of the Great Lakes, and alkali regions of the west.

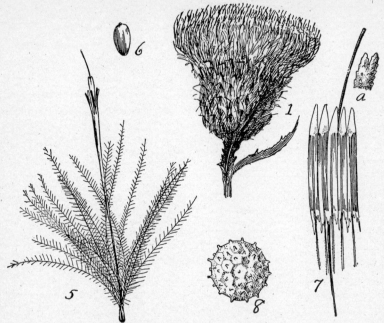

FIG. 493. Woolly Thistle (*Cirsium canescens*). Originally along the Missouri and adjacent territory. Now spreading eastward. 1, head; 5, single flower; 6, achenium; 7, stamens and style; a, stigma enlarged; 8, pollen grain.
(*Drawings by Charlotte M. King.*)

states, at the rate of twenty miles a year. It was found in north-eastern Iowa in 1924, and in northwestern Iowa a few years earlier. The progressive southward movement of quack grass (*Agropyron repens*) is another illustration. It was a part of the fields of Minnesota long before it became troublesome in Iowa. Canada thistle (*Cirsium arvense*) may be placed in the same category, though of course there were many isolated patches of Canada thistle in Iowa. The squirrel-tail grass (*Hordeum jubatum*), so common now everywhere in the meadows of Iowa, came to us from Nebraska and the Dakotas. The buffalo bur (*Solanum rostratum*) of the plains of Nebraska and Colorado is an illustration of the invasion of a weed from the west. Though it has occurred for many years in a few places in western Iowa, its general invasion is from Nebraska. This is the case also with the winged pigweed (*Cycloloma atriplicifolium*) which is one of the common plants of western Nebraska and Kansas. There are many other itinerant weeds of this class. The western sunflower (*Helianthus petiolaris*) belongs to this class. South Dakota has contributed many weeds, the most conspicuous of these being the Russian thistle (*Salsola Kali*

var. *tenuifolia*) which first became established in South Dakota
and which spread to northwestern Iowa and thence across the
state. The woolly thistle (*Cirsium canescens*) though native to
the loess soil of western Iowa is one of the common plants of the
plains of South Dakota and has come into the fields of Iowa largely
from the west. Missouri, to the south of Iowa, has contributed a
number of interesting weeds. One of the most conspicuous is the
horse nettle (*Solanum carolinense*) which in sixty years has spread
from the southern boundary of the state to the Minnesota boundary. Another Missouri contribution is the wormwood (*Chenopodium ambrosioides*) which now is not uncommon in the Keokuk
and Burlington region. The spiny amaranth (*Amaranthus spi-
nosus*) is another illustration. The little barley (*Hordeum pusillum*) is of Missouri invasion. Illinois and Wisconsin have con-

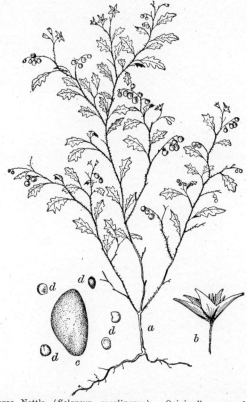

Fig. 494. Horse Nettle (*Solanum carolinense*). Originally a weed of the southern
states; rapidly spreading northward. a, general aspect of plant; b, flower; d,
seeds; c, seed enlarged.
(After Dewey, U. S. Dept. Agr.)

tributed a few, but their weeds are largely a part of the European weed flora with their general tendency to spread westward. Of these weeds we may mention the prickly lettuce (*Lactuca scariola* and the variety ·*integrata*). This weed was common in Illinois and Wisconsin long before it reached Iowa. Mullein (*Verbascum Thapsus*) was abundant on the clay hills of these states before it reached central Iowa. Bastard toadflax (*Linaria vulgaris*) was an abundant and troublesome weed in Illinois and Wisconsin before it reached Iowa. Of this same class we may mention bouncing Bet (*Saponaria officinalis*), wild carrot (*Daucus Carota*), tansy (*Tanacetum vulgare*), quack grass (*Agropyron repens*) and Canada thistle (*Cirsium arvense*).

During the past summer (1924), in August and September, one of us made a study of weeds of adjacent states. There are, of course, many other weeds than those listed. No attempt is made to give a full list but an account of the migrations of weeds as observed is as follows:

OBSERVATIONS ON WEED DISTRIBUTION, 1924.

	Ohio	Indiana	Michigan	Illinois	N. Missouri	Wis. and Minn.	Colorado	Oklahoma
Equisetum arvense	+	+	+	+	+	+		
Digitaria humifusa	+	+	+	+	+	+		
Digitaria sanguinalis	+	+	+	+	+	+	+	+
Panicum capillare	+	+	+	+	+	+		
Panicum dichotomiflorum	+	+	+	+	+		+	
Echinochloa crusgalli	+	+	+	+	+	+	+	+
Setaria glauca	+	+	+	+	+	+	+	+
Setaria verticillata	+	+	+	+	+	+		
Setaria viridis	+	+	+	+	+	+	+	+
Cenchrus pauciflorus	+	+	+	+	+	+	+	+
Phalaris canariensis	+	+	+	+	+	+		
Muhlenbergia mexicana	+	+	+	+	+	+		
Eleusine indica	+	+			+	+	+	
Eragrostis megastachya	+	+	+	+	+	+		+
Eragrostis pilosa	+	+	+			+		
Bromus secalinus	+	+	+	+	+	+		
Bromus tectorum	+	+			+	+		+
Agropyron repens	+	+	+	+	+	+		+
Hordeum jubatum	+	+	+	+	+	+		+
Cyperus esculentus	+	+			+	+		
Cannabis sativa	+	+	+	+	+	+	+	+
Urtica gracilis	+	+	+	+	+	+	+	+
Rumex crispus	+	+	+	+	+	+	+	+
Rumex altissimus	+			+		+		+

Observations on Weed Distribution—Continued

	Ohio	Indiana	Michigan	Illinois	N. Missouri	Wis. and Minn.	Oklahoma	Colorado
Rumex obtusifolius	+	+		+	+			
Rumex Acetosella	+	+	+	+	+	+		+
Polygonum aviculare	+	+	+	+	+	+		+
Polygonum erectum	+		+		+			
Polygonum lapathifolium	+	+	+	+	+	+		
Polygonum Muhlenbergii	+	+	+	+				
Polygonum pennsylvanicum	+	+	+	+	+			
Polygonum acre	+			+	+			
Polygonum Persicaria	+	+	+	+	+	+		+
Polygonum Convolvulus	+	+	+	+	+			
Cycloloma atriplicifolium				+	+			+
Chenopodium ambrosioides var. anthelminticum	+	+	+	+	+			
Chenopodium hybridum	+	+	+	+	+			
Chenopodium album	+	+		+	+		+	+
Salsola Kali var. tenuiflora	+	+	+	+	+	+	+	+
Amaranthus retroflexus	+	+	+	+	+	+	+	
Amaranthus blitoides	+	+	+	+	+			+
Oxybaphus nyctagineus	+	+	+	+	+			
Agrostemma Githago	+	+	+	+	+	+		+
Saponaria officinalis	+	+	+	+	+		+	+
Portulaca oleracea	+	+	+	+	+		+	+
Argemone intermedia							+	+
Lepidium virginicum	+	+	+	+	+			
Lepidium apetalum	+	+	+		+			+
Capsella Bursa-pastoris	+	+	+	+	+	+	+	+
Brassica arvensis	+	+		+	+			
Brassica nigra	+	+	+	+	+			
Sisymbrium officinale	+	+	+	+	+			+
Sisymbrium altissimum	+	+	+	+				+
Radicula palustris				+	+			
Polanisia trachysperma	+	+	+	+				+
Cleome serrulata					+		+	+
Geum canadense	+	+	+	+			+	
Cassia marilandica	+	+	+	+	+			
Cassia Tora					+			
Cassia Chamaecrista	+	+	+	+			+	
Melilotus officinalis	+	+	+			+		+
Melilotus alba	+	+	+	+	+			+
Medicago lupulina	+	+	+	+	+			+
Glycyrrhiza lepidota						+		+
Vicia sativa	+	+	+	+	+			+
Strophostyles helvola	+	+	+	+	+			
Strophostyles pauciflora	+	+	+	+	+	+		
Oxalis stricta	+	+	+	+	+			
Tribulus terrestris					+			+
Croton capitatus	+	+		+			+	
Croton monanthogynus	+	+		+			+	
Acalypha virginica	+	+	+	+	+			
Acalypha gracilens					+			
Euphorbia Preslii	+	+	+	+	+	+		+

Observations on Weed Distribution—Continued

	Ohio	Indiana	Michigan	Illinois	N. Missouri	Wis. and Minn.	Oklahoma	Colorado
Euphorbia maculata	+	+	+	+	+	+		+
Euphorbia corollata	+	+	+	+	+	+		
Euphorbia dentata	+	+	+	+	+			
Euphorbia heterophylla	+	+	+	+	+			
Rhus Toxicodendron	+	+	+	+	+	+	+	+
Abutilon Theophrasti	+	+	+	+	+	+	+	+
Sida spinosa	+	+	+	+	+	+	+	
Malva rotundifolia	+	+	+	+	+			+
Hibiscus Trionum	+	+	+	+	+			
Epilobium augustifolium			+				+	+
Oenothera biennis	+	+	+	+	+	+		+
Gaura biennis	+	+	+	+	+			
Pastinaca sativa	+	+	+	+	+	+	+	+
Daucus Carota	+	+	+	+	+	+		+
Anagallis arvensis					+			
Apocynum cannabinum	+	+	+	+	+	+		
Apocynum hypericifolium	+	+	+	+	+	+		
Asclepias syriaca	+	+	+	+	+	+		+
Gonobolus laevis	+	+	+	+	+			
Ipomoea hederacea	+	+	+	+	+		+	
Convolvulus sepium	+	+	+	+	+	+	+	+
Convolvulus arvensis	+	+	+	+	+	+		+
Cuscuta arvensis	+	+	+	+	+			+
Ellisia Nyctelea	+	+	+	+	+	+		
Cynoglossum officinale	+	+	+	+	+	+		
Lappula virginiana	+	+	+	+	+	+		
Verbena urticaefolia	+	+	+	+	+	+		
Verbena hastata	+	+	+	+	+	+	+	+
Verbena stricta	+	+	+	+	+	+	+	+
Teucrium canadense	+	+	+	+	+	+		
Mentha piperita	+	+	+	+	+			+
Marrubium vulgare					+			+
Nepeta Cataria	+	+	+	+	+	+	+	+
Nepeta hederacea	+	+	+	+	+	+		+
Prunella vulgaris	+	+	+	+	+	+		
Leonurus Cardiaca	+	+	+	+	+	+		
Solanum Dulcamara	+	+	+	+	+			+
Solanum nigrum	+	+	+	+	+			+
Solanum triflorum								+
Solanum carolinense	+	+	+	+	+			
Solanum eleagnifolium							+	
Solanum rostratum		+			+	+	+	+
Physalis pruinosa	+	+	+	+	+	+		
Physalis subglabrata	+	+	+	+	+			
Physalis lanceolata	+	+	+	+	+	+		
Datura Stramonium	+	+	+	+	+	+		
Datura Tatula	+	+	+	+	+	+		
Verbascum Thapsus	+	+	+	+	+	+		
Verbascum Blattaria	+	+	+	+	+			
Linaria vulgaris	+	+	+	+	+	+	+	

Observations on Weed Distribution—Continued

	Ohio	Indiana	Michigan	Illinois	N. Missouri	Wis. and Minn.	Oklahoma	Colorado
Scrophularia marilandica	+	+	+	+	+	+		
Veronica peregrina	+	+		+	+	+		
Veronica agrestis					+			
Plantago major	+	+	+	+	+	+		
Plantago Rugelii	+	+	+	+	+	+		
Plantago lanceolata	+	+	+	+	+	+		+
Plantago Purshii	+	+	+	+	+		+	
Plantago aristata	+	+	+	+	+			
Plantago virginica	+	+	+	+	+			
Diodia teres					+	+	+	
Dipsacus sylvestris	+	+			+	+		
Specularia perfoliata	+	+	+	+	+			
Vernonia novaboracensis	+	+	+	+	+		+	
Vernonia fasciculata	+	+	+	+	+	+		
Vernonia Baldwinii	+	+	+	+	+	+	+	
Eupatorium altissimum	+	+	+	+				
Eupatorium urticaefolium	+	+	+	+		+		
Grindelia squarrosa	+	+	+	+	+		+	+
Chrysopis villosa					+		+	+
Solidago canadensis	+	+	+	+	+	+	+	+
Solidago serotina	+	+	+	+	+	+		
Solidago rigida	+	+	+	+	+			
Aster multiflorus	+	+	+	+	+			+
Erigeron annuus	+	+	+	+	+	+		+
Erigeron ramosus					+	+		
Erigeron canadensis	+	+	+	+	+		+	+
Silphium perfoliatum	+	+	+	+		+		
Iva xanthiifolia	+	+	+	+				+
Ambrosia bidentata					+			+
Ambrosia trifida	+	+	+	+	+		+	+
Ambrosia artemisiifolia	+	+	+	+	+	+	+	+
Ambrosia psilostachya	+	+	+	+	+	+	+	+
Xanthium commune	+	+	+	+	+	+		+
Heliopsis scabra	+	+	+	+	+	+		
Eclipta alba	+	+	+	+	+			
Rudbeckia hirta	+	+	+	+	+	+	+	
Rudbeckia laciniata	+	+	+	+	+	+		
Helianthus annuus	+	+	+	+	+	+	+	
Helianthus petiolaris					+	+	+	+
Helianthus grosseserratus	+	+	+	+	+	+		+
Helianthus tuberosus	+	+	+	+	+	+		
Coreopsis tinctoria					+		+	
Bidens frondosa	+	+	+	+	+	+		+
Bidens vulgata	+	+	+	+		+		
Bidens bipinnata					+	+		
Bidens trichosperma					+	+	+	
Bidens trichosperma	+	+	+	+	+		+	
Galinsoga parviflora	+	+	+	+	+	+		
Helenium autumnale	+	+	+	+	+	+	+	+
Helenium tenuifolium					+	+	+	
Dyssodia papposa	+				+	+	+	

Observations on Weed Distribution—Continued

	Ohio	Indiana	Michigan	Illinois	N. Missouri	Wis. and Minn.	Oklahoma	Colorado
Achillea Millefolium	+	+	+	+	+	+	+	+
Anthemis Cotula	+	+	+		+	+	+	+
Anthemis arvensis					+			
Matricaria Chamomilla					+			
Matricaria suaveolens					+			
Chrysanthemum Leucanthemum	+	+	+	+	+	+		
Tanacetum vulgare	+	+	+	+	+	+		+
Artemisia ludoviciana	+	+	+	+	+	+		+
Artemisia biennis	+	+	+	+	+	+	+	+
Erechtites hieracifolia	+	+	+	+	+	+		+
Arctium Lappa	+	+			+		+	+
Arctium minus					+			
Cirsium lanceolatum	+	+	+	+	+	+		+
Cirsium discolor	+	+	+	+	+	+		
Cirsium arvense	+	+	+	+	+	+		+
Cichorium Intybus	+	+	+	+	+	+		
Taraxacum officinale	+	+	+	+	+	+	+	+
Taraxacum erythrospermum					+			
Sonchus oleraceus	+	+	+	+	+	+	+	+
Sonchus asper					+	+	+	
Sonchus arvensis					+	+		
Lactuca scariola	+				+	+	+	+
Lactuca scariola var. integrata		+			+	+		
Lactuca canadensis	+	+		+	+	+	+	

CHAPTER VII.

NUMBER AND KINDS OF WEEDS ON DIFFERENT SOILS.

L. H. PAMMEL.

During the season of 1912 Mr. Robert H. Birlingmair counted the weeds appearing in various fields under different conditions. A representative area 4 feet square was taken for each field and the succession of weeds noted throughout the season. The results were as follows:

FIELD 1.*

Weed	Date					
	Mar. 29	Apr. 6	Apr. 13	Apr. 20	Apr. 27	May 4
Peppergrass**	24	14	8	0	1	
Dandelion	6	3				
Tall five-finger	3	1	2			1
Small ragweed				1	31	10
Blue grass	20		51		3	24
Bracted vervain	10					
Mustard	1					
Daisy fleabane		8	1			
Pigweed				1		
Spotted spurge					282	460
Horse-weed					4	6
Pennsylvania smartweed					4	1248
Ground cherry					2	2
Green foxtail						84
			4			
						2

*On corn land that was in blue grass sod the preceding year.
**A winter annual.

FIELD 2.*

Weed	Date					
	Mar. 29	Apr. 6	Apr. 13	Apr. 20	Apr. 27	May 4
Yellow foxtail						10
Daisy fleabane						
Horse-weed**	143	65		1	34	72
Vervain			32			
Plantain				11		
Pennsylvania smartweed					1	

*On timothy meadow.
**Winter annual.

FIELD 3.*

Weed	Date					
	Mar. 29	Apr. 6	Apr. 13	Apr. 20	Apr. 27	May 4
Small ragweed				1	1	
Pennsylvania smartweed					2	1
Green foxtail						1

*On corn land that had been fall plowed. Field worked up and sowed to small grain just before April 27.

FIELD 4.*

Weed	Date					
	Mar. 29	Apr. 6	Apr. 13	Apr. 20	Apr. 27	May 4
Small ragweed			10	3	8	
Lamb's quarters					1	3
Pennsylvania smartweed			21	78	99	77
Yellow foxtail						215

*On land sowed to winter wheat.

FIELD 5.*

Weed	Date					
	Mar. 29	Apr. 6	Apr. 13	Apr. 20	Apr. 27	May 4
Yellow foxtail						599
Green foxtail						718
Daisy fleabane		1				
Bracted vervain			3			
Peppergrass			3		3	
Blue grass					4	
Pennsylvania smartweed					40	71
Spurge						47

*On old corn land. Stalks harrowed down just previous to April 20.

FIELD 6.*

Weed	Date					
	Mar. 29	Apr. 6	Apr. 13	Apr. 20	Apr. 27	May 4
Small ragweed				1	33	
Yellow foxtail						475
Green foxtail						40
Lamb's quarters						3
Pennsylvania smartweed			11	54		
Blue grass					1	
Dooryard knotweed						
Horseweed						3
Spurge						39
Hedge mustard						71

*On fall plowed oats stubble.

FIELD 7.*

Weed	Date					
	Mar. 29	Apr. 6	Apr. 13	Apr. 20	Apr. 27	May 4
Dandelion	5	11				
Veronica			1			
Lamb's quarters				1		
Small ragweed			9	6		
Yellow foxtail						16
Shepherds' purse	+75	+5	+1			
Peppergrass	+5	+4	1			
Blue grass	2	7	7	2		
Hoary vervain	2					
Pennsylvania smartweed				1		
Lady's sorrel	+3					

*On unplowed oats stubble. Field plowed previous to April 27. +Marks winter annuals.

WEED FLORA OF IOWA

FIELD 8.*

Weed	Date					
	Mar. 29	Apr. 6	Apr. 13	Apr. 20	Apr. 27	May 4
Small ragweed	--------	33	169 46	8	--------	--------
Mexican drop-seed	--------	--------	++37	++5	++16	++18
Lamb's quarters	--------	--------	10	7	--------	--------
Morning-glory	--------	--------	--------	++4	++6	++7
Spurge	--------	--------	--------	49	--------	--------
Yellow foxtail	--------	--------	--------		--------	--------
Green foxtail	--------	--------	--------	398	--------	1785
Pennsylvania smartweed	15	38	65	49	--------	--------
Mustard	23	--------	--------		--------	--------
Horse-weed	--------	--------	+26	9	10	11
Scribner's panic grass	--------	--------	++4		--------	--------
Tansy mustard	--------	--------	2		--------	--------
Nyctelea	--------	--------	--------	3	--------	--------
Yellow dock	--------	--------	--------		--------	++158
Large spotted spurge	--------	--------	--------		--------	129
Old witch grass	--------	--------	--------		--------	2
Wild four-o'clock	--------	--------	--------		--------	++2
Self-heal	--------	--------	--------		--------	+2

*In sheltered place on the south side of the railroad grade. Weeds were not all counted on April 27th, but there were hundreds of small ragweeds and smartweeds, and probably more than a thousand green foxtail plants.
+Winter annual. ++Perennial.

These tables reveal some interesting facts. The first weeds to appear in March were the winter annuals, like peppergrass and shepherd's purse, certain perennial weeds, and in one case horse-weed (*Erigeron canadensis*) in a timothy meadow. Two weeks later smartweed (*Polygonum*) was abundant. Spurge (*Euphorbia*), an annual, was abundant in the latter part of April and early May. Foxtails in some cases surpassed all other weeds in abundance early in May. The smartweeds (*Polygonum*) and spurges increased enormously. These weeds were entirely removed from the plots. Fall plowing and clean cultivation certainly reduce the number of weeds.

Long, who measured off a square yard of ground* in Great Britain, roughly grouping the plant life therein into species, found on this square yard 1,050 seedlings or 5,082,000 per acre. There were 654 buttercup seedlings, 107 of annual meadow grass, 60 of dock, 26 of goosefoot, 25 of groundsel, 15 of shepherd's purse, 14

*Trans. of Highland Agrl. Soc. Scotland, V. 23: 52.

of annual sow thistle, and 10 of chickweed, besides 139 of other species. He states that Korsmo's investigation revealed the presence of an even larger number of seeds having the power of germination, the seeds per square yard to a depth of 9.8 inches being as follows: Fallow field, 8,682 weed seeds (over 42,000,000 per acre); field for spring grain bearing the same crop for four suc-

FIG. 495. A weedy cornfield, mostly Foxtail and Smartweeds.
(Photograph by Colburn.)

cessive years, 28,213 weed seeds (over 136,000,000 per acre); fallow field, 1,474 weed seeds (over 7,000,000 per acre).

Mr. Long gives the following species of weeds found in Great Britain within an area 100 feet square:

*Convolvulus arvensis (European bindweed)
*Polygonum Convolvulus (Black bindweed)
*Polygonum aviculare (Knotgrass)
*Rumex sp. (Dock)
*Tussilago Farfara (Coltsfoot)
*Mentha arvensis (Peppermint)
*Sinapis arvensis (Common mustard)
*Sonchus arvensis (Field sow thistle)
*Stellaria media (Chickweed)
Papaver sp. (Poppy)
*Ranunculus arvensis (Corn crowfoot)
*Viola sp. (Violet)
Potentilla Anserina (Silver-weed)
Aethusa Cynapium (Fool's parsley)

Scandix Pecten Veneris (Venus' comb)
Senecio vulgaris (Groundsel)
*Galium Aparine (Cleavers)
Vicia sativa (Vetch)
*Matricaria inodora (Wild chamomile)
Plantago major (Common plantain)
Lychnis alba (White campion)
*Euphorbia exigua (Spurge)
*Alopecurus agrestis (Foxtail grass)
*Agrostis sp. (Bent grass)
Agropyron repens (Quack grass)
Poa annua (Low spear grass)
*Veronica sp. (Speedwell)
Myosotis sp. (Forget-me-not)
Alchemilla arvensis (Parsleypiert)

FIG. 496. Shepherd's Purse, a common winter annual.
(*After Vasey, U. S. Dept. Agr.*)

FIG. 497. Green Foxtail (*Setaria viridis*). Common in gardens and fields.
(*Photographed by Colburn.*)

Most of these species are troublesome weeds, and those marked with * were abundant.

For an Iowa cultivated field on June 2, 1903, the following weeds were found in one square rod.

Name of weed.	No. per sq. rod.
Smartweed (*Polygonum pennsylvanicum*)	40,324
Hedge mustard (*Sisymbrium officinale*)	3,060
Black beggar-ticks (*Bidens frondosa*)	476
Prickly lettuce (*Lactuca scariola* var. *integrata*)	204

Name of Weed	No. per sq. rd.
Pigweed *(Chenopodium album)*	340
Horseweed *(Erigeron canadensis)*	7,412
Dandelion *(Taraxacum officinale)*	68
Foxtail *(Setaria)*	136,000

WEEDS AND CONTINUOUS CROPPING.

Everyone has observed that continuous cropping increases the number of weeds; not only is this true for many parts of Iowa but it is equally true for the older sections of the United States and of Europe. A. D. Hall, who reported on the crops grown in grain land at Rothamstad,[*] said: "After continuous cropping for forty-seven years, said weeds of all descriptions occupy considerably more space than before. The relative proportion they bear to the grasses and clover has increased from year to year. Such weeds as burnet, hawkbit and black knapweed became abundant."

Mr. Long gives the following list of worst weeds, made by four expert Scotch agriculturists:

Arable Land.—Charlock, runch, chickweed, spurrey, docks, thistle, groundsel, coltsfoot, day nettle, red-shank, annual meadow grass, bulbous oat grass (pearl grass), couch grass, fine bent grass or black couch, and wild oats.

Grass Land.—Buttercups, self-heal, docks, ragwort, daisy, thistles, ribwort, plantain, creeping soft grass, common bent grass, Yorkshire fog or woolly soft grass, moss.

Many other weeds are given by him which are serious pests to the agriculturist of that country. Of the weeds of the arable land he lists buttercups, poppies, fumitory, charlock (*Brassica arvensis*), runch (*Raphanus raphanistrum*), shepherd's purse, corn cockle, spurrey, silver-weed, cleavers, thistle (Canada thistle), sow thistle, coltsfoot, groundsel, bindweeds (*Polygonum Convolvulus, Convolvulus arvensis*), dodder, buckhorn, plantain, broom rape, corn or field mint, hemp and dead nettle, smartweed, or red-shank (*Polygonum Persicaria*), knotweed, docks, goosefoot, quack grass, fine bent grass, pearl grass (*Arrenatherum avenaceum*), slender foxtail (*Alopecurus agrestis*), wild oats and horsetail. Of grass land weeds there are listed *Colchicum autumnale*, buttercups; leguminous weeds: gorse (*Ulex*) broom, rest harrow (*Ononis spinosa*), Dyer's green weed (*Genista tinctoria*), wild carrot, burdock, knapweed (*Centaurea nigra*), thistles (*Cirsium arvense, C. acaule, C. lanceolatum, C. palustris*), cotton thistle (*Onopordum Acan-*

---

[*]Jour. Roy Agr. Soc. 64:83.

FIG. 498. Needle Grass (*Stipa spartea*). In pastures.
(Photograph by Charlotte M. King.)

FIG. 499. Purple Cone Flower (*Brauneria purpurea*). In a prairie pasture.
(Photograph by Pammel.)

thium), daisy (*Bellis perennis*), ox-eye daisy, ragwort (*Senecio Jacobaea*), plantains, yellow rattle, self-heal (*Prunella vulgaris*), docks, sorrel (*Rumex Acetosa, R. Acetosella*), stinging nettle (*Urtica dioica*); grasses: bent grass (*Agrostis alba*) tussock grass (*Aira caespitosa*), Yorkshire fog (*Holcus lanatus*), creeping soft grass (*H. mollis*), quaking grass (*Briza media*), barley grass (*Hordeum pratense*); and the bracken (*Pteris aquilina*), horsetail and mosses.

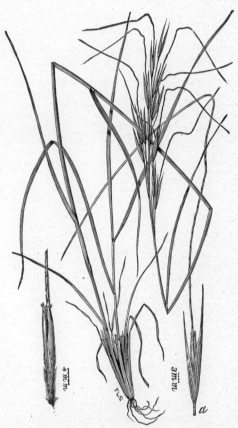

FIG. 500. Common Porcupine or Needle Grass (*Stipa spartea*). A weed native to gravel soil, soon succumbs to cropping. a, single spikelet; b, fruit with sharp pointed callus.

(Lamson-Scribner, U. S. Dept. Agr.)

CHAPTER VIII.

INJURIOUSNESS OF WEEDS.
L. H. PAMMEL.

PARASITIC FUNGI HARBORED BY WEEDS.
J. C. GILMAN.

SOME ECONOMIC INSECTS AND THEIR RELATIONS TO WEEDS.
FRED D. BUTCHER.

INJURIOUSNESS OF WEEDS.

Weeds are injurious to man in the following ways:

1.   They crowd out the growing crop.
2.   They consume the moisture necessary for a crop.
3.   They consume the mineral or other food elements essential to a crop.
4.   They pull down the crop.
5.   The seeds are difficult to remove.
6.   They harbor nematodes and insects, and shelter harmful animals.
7.   They harbor parasitic fungi.
8.   They prevent the proper cultivation of the soil.
9.   They may cause conditions which breed disease.
10.   They may poison the soil.
11.   Roots of weeds crowd roots of crop plants.
12.   Some weeds stop drains.
13.   Some weeds poison animals and man.

1. WEEDS CROWD OUT GROWING CROPS.

When weeds are abundant they crowd out growing crops. Every plant requires a certain amount of space to bring forth a bountiful crop. Two plants cannot grow together in the same place; sooner or later when plants grow too close together one plant will crowd out the other. If the weed, such as the greater ragweed, is a more vigorous grower than oats, it will prevent the oat plants from maturing a good crop. It shades the plant so that the food necessary for a crop cannot be made.

2. WEEDS CONSUME THE MOISTURE.

To mature all weeds need moisture, which should go to a more desirable crop. They transpire water just as freely as cultivated plants do. Long, in "Common Weeds of the Farm and Garden," says:

"Weeds also absorb from the soil and 'transpire,' or pass off into

FIG. 501. Ragweeds (*Ambrosia trifida*). These consume an enormous amount of moisture.

the atmosphere, large quantities of moisture which would be of great service to the growing crop. For example, a maize plant has been observed to transpire in the 16 weeks between May 22d and September 4th as much as 36 times its own weight. A large oak tree is also stated to transpire 10 to 20 gallons of water in a day; while barley, beans, and clover were found to transpire, during five months of their growth, over 200 times their dry weight of water. Experiments conducted at the agricultural experiment station of Cornell University showed that during the growth of a 60-bushel crop of maize the plants pumped from the soil, and transpired into the air through the leaves, upwards of 900 tons of water. A 25-bushel crop of wheat similarly disposed of 500 tons of water. Weeds also transpire, and if the ground be covered with weeds it is certain that much of the moisture which would be of value to the crop will be lost in the manner indicated. Weeds are especially harmful in this way in a hot summer, and the loss is most felt by the cultivated crop on light sandy soils.''

3. WEEDS CONSUME MINERAL AND FOOD ELEMENTS.

A weed needs not only the carbon dioxide of the air to make food, but the nitrogenous and mineral elements of the soil to make plant food, all of which should go to the crop. Long gives the following in his book, ''Common Weeds of the Farm and Garden:'' ''Some analyses made at Königsberg, and lately reported by Professor Stutzer and L. Seidler, show that the amounts of nitrogen, phosphoric acid, potash, and lime which are removed are deserving of serious consideration. A number of weeds without their roots were collected from oat fields, the soil of which was fairly heavy and poor in humus. In the case of the Wild Radish or White Charlock the plants had already formed many seed-pods, but the other weeds were in full bloom. The table following shows the percentage of ingredients in the dry matter. These figures indicate in a general way the amount of the chief plant foods required by weeds. The nitrogen in the Persicaria nearly equaled 20 per cent, and that in the Sow Thistle nearly 15 per cent of albuminoids in the dry matter. Phosphoric acid was taken up chiefly by Spurrey and Persicaria; potash by the Sow Thistle and Spurrey; and lime by Persicaria, Yarrow, and Cornflower.''

Percentage Contents of Dry Matter.

	Nitrogen	Phosphoric Acid	Potash	Lime	Sodium	Crude Ash
Sow thistle (*Sonchus oleraceus*)..	2.39	0.88	4.77	1.94	2.16	14.95
Corn-flower (*Centaurea Cyanus*)..	2.30	0.78	1.94	3.13	1.07	8.12
Spurrey (*Spergula arvensis*)......	2.36	1.08	4.21	1.52	1.91	10.12
Wild Radish (*Raphanus Raphanistrum*)	1.85	0.78	1.30	1.81	0.71	5.22
Persicaria or red-shank (*Polygonum Persicaria*)	3.12	1.16	3.12	4.93	2.53	10.58
Yarrow (*Achillea Millefolium*)...	2.30	0.93	3.15	3.84	1.17	9.61
Average of six weeds............	2.38	0.93	3.08	2.86	1.59	9.76

4. WEEDS PULL DOWN THE CROPS.

Weeds like morning-glory, bindweed, wild buckwheat, and others, pull down cultivated plants, thus preventing the growth of a good crop.

5. WEED SEEDS ARE REMOVED WITH DIFFICULTY FROM COMMERCIAL CROP SEED.

It is difficult in many cases to remove weed seeds from seed of various kinds. Buckhorn can be removed with difficulty from clover seed; peppergrass with difficulty from timothy seed; greater ragweed from wheat; wild oats from oats; quack grass from brome grass; cockle from wheat. These impurities occur abundantly and greatly reduce the quality of the grain or seed.

6. WEEDS HARBOR INSECTS.

F. D. Butcher on page 636 of this chapter gives an account of economic insects harbored by weeds.

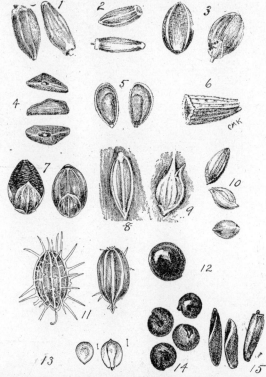

FIG. 502. Impurities found in Red Clover: 1, Bull Thistle; 2, Canada Thistle; 3, Green Foxtail (*Setaria viridis*); 4, Common Plantain (*Plantago Rugelii*); 5, Peppergrass (also found in Timothy); 6, Chicory; 7, Pigeon Grass (*Setaria glauca*); 8, Crab Grass (*Digitaria sanguinalis*); 9, Old Witch Grass; 10, Timothy; 11, Wild Carrot; 12, Pigweed (*Amaranthus retroflexus*); 13, Smartweed (*Polygonum Persicaria*); 14, Lamb's Quarters; 15, Drop-seed Grass (*Muhlenbergia*).
(*Drawings by Charlotte M. King.*)

FIG. 503. Morning-glory pulls down the corn and other crops.
(After Vasey, U. S. Dept. of Agriculture.)

7. WEEDS HARBOR PARASITIC FUNGI

Dr. J. C. Gilman on page 633 of this chapter gives an account of plant diseases carried by weeds.

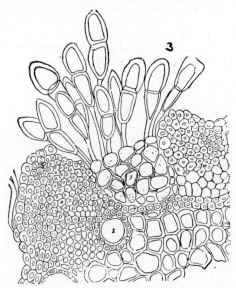

FIG. 504. Leaf Rust of Wild Barley (*Puccinia rubigo-vera*) also occurs on wheat. (*Drawing by Charlotte M. King.*)

8. WEEDS PREVENT THE PROPER CULTIVATION OF SOIL.

Weeds of certain types, particularly the perennial weeds, often make it extremely difficult to cultivate a soil. This is especially true of weeds like quack grass, which when present in the soil make it not only difficult but expensive to cultivate with plow and harrow.

9. WEEDS MAY CAUSE CONDITIONS WHICH BREED DISEASES.

Dr. Evans says that tall weeds contribute to the breeding places of mosquitos, and he thinks that in this way the mosquitos will lead to malaria. It is a well-known fact that the pollen from weeds like ragweed and goldenrod cause hay fever and for this reason these weeds should always be removed.

10. WEEDS MAY POISON THE SOIL.

There has long been a popular impression that weeds excrete poisonous substances which render the soil unfit for a succeeding crop. In regions where cockleburs are common, it is quite difficult

to get a good stand of clover. Mr. E. B. Watson found that clover
would not do as well in soil of this character, nor did the clover
seed germinate as well, as in check soils. However, this subject

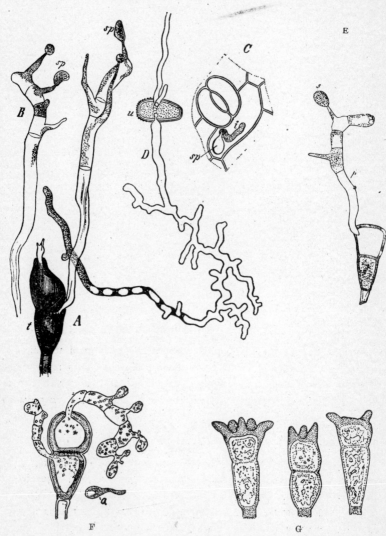

FIG. 505. Rusts of cereals also occur on weedy grasses, like Squirrel-tail Grass, Wild
Oats, etc. *Puccinia graminis*: A, "winter" or teleutospore; t, germinating.
B, germ-tube (*promycelium*) with lateral sporidia, sp. C, epidermis of under
surface of leaf of Barberry showing crescent shaped cells of stoma and the
germinating sporidium sp at i penetrating the epidermis. D, uredo spore germinating after being in water fourteen hours. E, *Puccinia rubigo-vera*, the upper
cell has germinated. C, D, E, magnified 390 times, the other somewhat more.
(*After DeBary.*) F. *Puccinia graminis* Pers.; both cells have germinated; a,
a sporidium germinating, magnified 600 times. (*After Bolley.*) G, *Puccinia
coronata* Cda.; teleutospores of rust on leaves of oats, magnified about 600 times.
(*After Bolley.*)

has been investigated but little. Particularly important is the

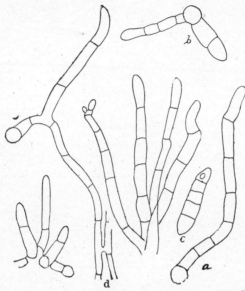

FIG. 506. Barley Blight (*Helminthosporium gramineum*) on Wild Barley. a and b, hypha; c, conidium.
(Drawing by Charlotte M. King.)

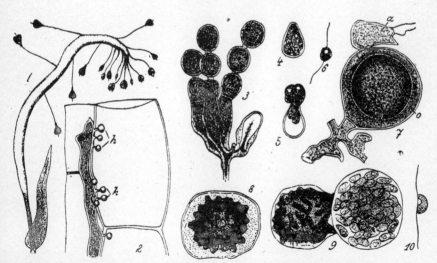

FIG. 507. White Rust (*Albugo candida*). 1. Inflorescence of Shepherd's Purse with fungus. 2. Mycelium with haustoria (b) x 390. 3. Conidiophores and conidia (spores) in chains x 400. 4 and 5. Formation of zoospores in conidia x 400. 6. Germinating zoospore. 7. Oogonium (o) and antheridium (a) attached, mycelium shown below. 8. Oospore with thick wall. 9. Germinating oospore forming a zoosporangium. 10. Zoospore 7-10 x 400.
(After DeBary.)

larger question of the actual antagonism between roots in occupied soils that should be occupied by the roots of agricultural plants.

11. WEEDS STOP DRAINS.

Drain tiles are frequently filled with a growth of the roots of weeds, causing stoppage of the drain and often much expense in removing the difficulty.

12. POISONOUS WEEDS.

There are many weeds which are injurious to man and to animals because they are poisonous. Some of the best known illustrations are the cowbane, a deadly poisonous plant, the jimson weed, and poison ivy, which is poisonous to the touch.

A large number of weeds, while not strongly poisonous, are in-

Fig. 508.   Fig. 509.

FIG. 508. Powdery Mildew of grasses (*Erysiphe graminis*). This is common on Wild Barley and occurs also on Wheat. a, mycelium and erect conidiophores; b, c, conidia. (*Drawn by C. M. King.*)

FIG. 509. Cocklebur (*Xanthium canadense*). There is a widespread belief that Cocklebur and other weeds may excrete a substance which is injurious to other crops. (*After U. S. Dept. of Agr.*)

jurious; some taint cow's milk; some are injurious because of spines, prickles and thorns. This subject has been treated in full by the writer in "A Manual of Poisonous Plants." Too little attention has been paid by the school teachers of the state to the subject of poisonous plants.

Fig. 510. Poison Ivy. Leaves are poisonous to many people when they come in contact with the plant.

PARASITIC FUNGI HARBORED BY WEEDS.

By J. C. Gilman

Weeds which harbor parasitic fungi and plant diseases may be nearly related botanically to the cultivated crop that they threaten in this manner, or there may be no apparent botanical relationship between them. The simplest condition is the harboring of a fungus on an uncultivated species which is nearly allied to the cultivated crop. Thus we find that wild grape may harbor the downy mildew, which is so harmful to cultivated varieties; wild plums are sources of infection in the brown rot, plum pocket and scab disease of the cultivated sorts. The wild grasses such as wild rye, squirrel-tail and quack grass are hosts for the black stem rust which also attacks the small grains. Wild crab apples usually carry some fire blight and apple rust, to say nothing of apple scab. Quack grass, brome grass, red top and wild rye are often infected with ergot, which is carried from these, growing as weeds in fence rows and neglected spots, to similar grasses in hay-fields and pastures, or even to grain fields such as rye.

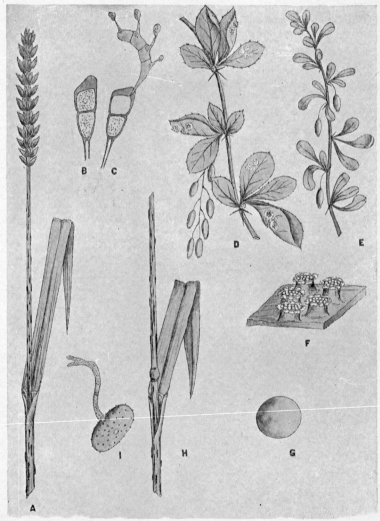

FIG. 511. A. Wheat with rust. B. Telial spores. C. Telial spore germinating.
D. Common Barberry with rust. E. Japanese barberry, does not carry rust.
F. Aecial spores. G. Aecial spore. H. Wheat stem showing uredo stripes.
I. Uredo spore germinating. *After Melhus and Durrell.*

In the second condition, the wild host may be widely separated from the cultivated crop botanically but still harbor the disease. This condition arises in two ways, either (1) the fungus may have an alternate host on which it passes a part of its life, as in the case of the European barberry, which harbors the black stem rust in the spring, or the red cedar, which carries the apple rust over winter, or (2) the disease may have a wide range of hosts that it attacks, as in the case of the mosaic disease of plants which is carried on perennial plants through unfavorable seasons which in turn become sources for infection of annual crops each year. The transfer is usually carried out by means of insects which also have both hosts in common.

A table showing some of the commoner diseases that may be harbored on weeds and then attack cultivated host crops follows:

WEED HOST	DISEASE	CAUSE	CULTIVATED HOST
Quack grass .... Western wheat grass. Slender wheat grass. Red top .... Wild oats .... Wild rye .... Orchard grass ...... Brome grass .... Wild barley	Black stem rust..	Puccinia graminis	Wheat Oats Barley
Quack grass .... Brome grass .... Red top .... Wild rye .... Western wheat grass. Timothy	Ergot	Claviceps purpurea ...	Rye Barley Oats
Red top .... Blue grass .... Wild barley	Powdery mildew..	Erysiphe graminis	Wheat
Orchard grass	Crown rust	Puccinia coronata	Oats
Wild crab	Fire blight	Bacillus amylovorus ...	Apple Pear
Wild crab	Scab	Venturia inaequalis ...	Apple
Wild crab	Cedar apple rust..	Gymnosporangium juniperi-virginianae .	Apple
Red cedar	Cedar apple rust..	Gymnosporangium juniperi-virginianae .	Apple
Barberry	Black stem rust...	Puccinia graminis	Wheat Oats Rye Barley
Buckthorn	Crown rust	Puccinia coronata	Oats
Black mustard	White rust	Cystopus candidus	Radish
Shepherd's purse .... Peppergrass	Downy mildew ...	Peronospora parasitica.	Radish
Black mustard	Club root	Plasmodiophora brassicae	Cabbage

WEED HOST	DISEASE	CAUSE	CULTIVATED HOST
Wild lettuce	Downy mildew ...	Bremia lactucae	Lettuce
Wild sunflower	Rust	Puccinia helianthi	Sunflower
Five-finger	Leaf spot	Mycosphaerella fragariae	Strawberry
Indian mallow ...... Physalis lanceolata .. Pokeweed...........	Mosaic	Unknown	Potato Cucumber Tomato
Wild plum	Plum pocket	Exoascus pruni	Plum Cherry
Wild plum	Black knot	Sclerotinia cinerea....	Plum Cherry Peach
Wild plum .... Choke cherry	Powdery mildew..	Podosphaera oxycanthae	Plum Cherry
Wild plum	Black knot	Plowrightia morbosa ..	Plum
Wild plum	Scab	Cladosporium carpophyllum	Plum Cherry Peach
Wild grape	Downy mildew ...	Plasmopara viticola ...	Grape
Wild grape	Black rot	Guignardia bidwellii ..	Grape
Sedge	Rust	Puccinia fraxinata	Ash
Wild gooseberry	Blister rust	Cronartium ribicola ...	White pine
Clammy ground cherry Prairie ground cherry Horse nettle .... Black nightshade ...	Leaf spot	Septoria lycopersici ..	Tomato
Annual morning-glory	Black rot	Sphaeronema fimbriata.	Sweet potato

SOME ECONOMIC INSECTS AND THEIR RELATIONS TO WEEDS.

By FRED D. BUTCHER

Grasshoppers, cut worms and army worms breed in large numbers on weeds or grasses and then attack our farm crops. This is well illustrated by the alfalfa which is lost each year along the edges of the field where a heavy mass of blue grass or weeds has harbored grasshoppers throughout the season. Army worms are found migrating from the areas in which they bred early in the spring out into the field crops in the summer. The garden webworm, the sod webworm and the corn bill bug all attack our crops which are put on sod inasmuch as the plowing of the sod has destroyed their natural food plant and they are compelled to attack the corn or other crops for food. In a similar way, wire worms and grub worms are found attacking corn or potatoes and other crops when the roots of their natural food plants have been destroyed by plowing or cultivation.

The wheat stem maggots breed during the latter part of the season on grasses and then attack the wheat, causing injury just before harvest. The rose chafers feed on the roots of common grasses and the adult beetles feed on roses and other of our cultivated plants, often causing severe injury.

The tarnished plant bugs hibernate during the winter months on grasses and feed in the early spring on miscellaneous grasses and weeds and then attack our cultivated crops, such as truck crops or fruits, during the mid-summer.

The corn root aphis is carried by ants to the small smartweed and grasses which are present in the corn field before the corn breaks through the ground, and successfully feeds and breeds until the corn is large enough to sustain it, at which time it starts sucking the juices from the corn roots, often causing the weakening of enough corn to very seriously reduce the yield.

Chinch bugs winter over in grass areas or in sedges and migrate from these areas early in the spring for oviposition. If they do not have small grains or similar crops on which to feed, they can successfully feed on grasses. The common stalk borer attacks the giant ragweed or dock early in the spring and as these weeds harden in June and July, migrates from them to corn, oats, potatoes or other plants for more succulent feed. In a similar way the smartweed borer feeds upon the smartweed and in cases where the smartweed is not present in large enough quantities the insect will be found attacking corn.

Squash vine borers are found breeding in large numbers on our wild cucumbers. Thus an infestation is maintained in areas where squashes are not grown. The potato stalk borer feeds on different species of nightshade, thus maintaining an infestation as in the case of the squash vine borer. The adults of the corn root worm depend on the pollen of various weeds for food and can usually be found causing the most injury in a corn field which is near a weed patch where there is a good deal of pollen produced. The cabbage curculios and the cabbage aphis breed on different species of mustard and later attack our cultivated cabbage. The rhubarb curculios breed in the early spring on curly dock and later attack the rhubarb plant. Seldom, if ever, is a rhubarb plantation attacked by this insect unless the dock is nearby. In a similar way the potato leaf hopper attacks the dock early in the spring and later migrates to the potatoes to feed the rest of the season.

The parsnip butterfly feeds as readily on the wild parsnip as it does on the tame parsnip, carrot or celery. In a similar way the painted lady butterfly will feed on hollyhocks if thistles are not present for food. The tree cricket will oviposit in nearly any woody stemmed weed as readily as it will oviposit in raspberry and blackberry canes. The buffalo treehopper is a detriment to orchards which have a heavy growth of weeds to furnish their young with something on which to feed. The European corn borer feeds on a large number of our common weeds, in this way maintaining an infestation and making control very difficult. The brown plum aphis breeds on weeds and in the summer migratory stage migrates to the plum. The rosy apple aphis breeds in the early spring on apples and in mud-summer goes to plantain. The melon aphis is found attacking morning-glory and other weeds as readily as it attacks the melons or other cucurbits. The green bug attacks grasses as well as wheat and thus maintains an infestation. The European grain aphis is found feeding on apples in the early spring and on oats and grasses in mid-summer.

Table Showing Weed Hosts and Crop Plant Hosts of Various Insects.

INSECT	WEED HOSTS	CROP HOSTS
Grasshoppers (Locustidae)	Grasses and some weeds	Hay, grain and other crops
Cut worms (Noctuidae, Agrotinae)	Grasses	Corn and other crops
Army worms (Noctuidae, Hadeninae)	Grasses	Corn, grain and other crops
Garden Webworm (Loxostege similalis Gn.)	Grasses	Corn, hay, grain and garden crops
Corn bill bug (Sphenophorus spp)	Sedges	Corn
Wheat stem maggot (Meromyza americana Fitch)	Grasses	Wheat
Rose chafer (Macrodactylus subspinosus Fab.)	Grasses	Roses and other plants
Sod webworm (Crambus spp)	Grasses	Corn and other crops
Wireworm (Elateridae)	Grasses and sedges	Corn, potatoes and other crops
Grub worm (Lachnosterna spp)	Grasses	Corn, potatoes and other crops
Chinch bug (Blissus leucopterus Say)	Grasses and sedges	Grain, hay, corn and sorghums
Tarnished plant bug (Lygus pratensis Linn.)	Grasses (rubbish)	Truck crops and fruit trees
Corn root aphis (Aphis maidi-radicis Forbes)	Smartweed and grasses	Corn
Common stalk borer (Papaipema nitela Guen.)	Ragweed and dock	Grain, corn, potatoes and other plants
Smartweed borer (Pyrausta ainsliei Heinr.)	Smartweed	Corn
Squash vine borer (Melittia satyriniformis Hbn.)	Wild cucumbers	Squashes
Potato stalk borers (Trichobaris trinotata Say)	Nightshade (spp)	Potatoes
Blister beetle (Meloidae)	Various weeds	Potatoes and other crops
Corn root worm (Diabrotica spp.)	Various weeds	Corn, cucurbits
Cabbage curculio (Ceutorhyncus rapae Ayll.)	Mustard, peppergrass	Cabbage
Rhubarb curculio (Lixus concavus Say)	Dock (curly)	Rhubarb
Potato leafhopper (Empoasca mali Leb.)	Dock (curly)	Potatoes
Parsnip butterfly (Papilio polyxenes Fab.)	Wild parsnips	Parsnips, carrots, celery
Painted lady butterfly (Pyrameis cardui)	Thistles	Hollyhock
Tree cricket (Oecanthus spp)	Woody stemmed weeds	Raspberry, blackberry
Buffalo treehopper (Ceresa bubalus Fab.)	Various weeds	Fruit trees
European corn borer (Pyrausta nubilalis Hubner)	Nearly all large-stemmed weeds	Corn and other crops
Brown plum aphis (Aphis setariae Thos.)	Grasses	Plum
Rosy apple aphis (Aphis sorbi Kahl.)	Plantain	Apple
Melon aphis (Aphis gossypii Glov.)	Morning-glory and others	Cucurbits
Green bug (Toxoptera graminum Rond.)	Grasses	Wheat
Cabbage aphis (Aphis brassicae Linn.)	Mustard	Cabbage, rape
European grain aphis (Siphocoryne avenae Fab.)	Grasses	Apple, oats

CHAPTER IX.

WEED ERADICATION.
DONALD PORTER

EFFECT OF DRYING ON ROOT-STOCKS OF WEEDS.
R. ROTHACKER.

WEED ERADICATION.

The various methods of weed eradication are based largely upon the class to which the particular weed in question belongs. It is readily conceivable that the methods which apply to the eradication of annual weeds would not be efficient in the control of perennials. For this reason it is of prime importance that the nature of each weed be thoroughly understood, in order that the most practical, economical and efficient eradication methods be employed.

There are four main classes of weeds, each class characterized by the length of time required for the weed to produce its seed. The four classes are:

1. Annuals.
2. Winter annuals.
3. Biennials.
4. Perennials.

ANNUAL WEEDS.

Annual weeds are those which grow from seed only, requiring but one growing season to produce seed. The seed germinates in the spring, the plant produces seed in the fall and then the entire plant dies down. Hence the plant is absolutely dependent upon the production and maturing of its seed for its propagation.

Some of the most troublesome of the annual weeds in Iowa are shoo-fly, velvet-weed, smaller ragweed, greater ragweed or king-head, buffalo bur, cocklebur, horseweed, smartweed, crab grass and foxtail.

Eradication of most annual weeds is comparatively simple. Any method which will prevent the production of seed will in time destroy them. However, it is known that the seeds of some of our annual weeds will live many years in the soil and still germinate.

Hence it is necessary to destroy each year's crop before seed is formed. The most outstanding example of this type of annual weed is the velvet-weed (*Abutilon Theophrasti*), sometimes known as button weed, butter-print, velvet-leaf, Indian mallow, stinkweed and skunkweed. It is a very common weed in southern Iowa, but is widespread over the state. Its seed will probably live in the soil and maintain the power of germination as long as the seed of any other annual weed. In one instance, a farmer near Davenport tore down an old country church which had been built forty years. After the foundation was removed, a vigorous crop of velvet-weeds sprung up. In other cases farmers have stated that they have seen this weed come up where it never before appeared, after they had plowed up sixty year old blue grass pastures. The weed will also come up at any time during the growing season, often in September and October, grow to a height of several inches and produce seed before frost. Hence it is very important that every plant be prevented from forming seed if the weed is to be killed out.

Cocklebur is another quite troublesome annual weed. The bur contains two "seeds," one of which may germinate the first year and the other the year following.

Observations made throughout the state indicate that the chief reason why annual weeds persist is the fact that so many of them go to seed, even though they are kept down for a time, and the seed is then scattered to adjoining fields by the wind, animals, man, etc.

WINTER ANNUALS.

The winter annual weeds are very similar in habit to the annuals. They differ, however, in one characteristic. The seed of winter annual weeds germinates in the fall, the plant grows for a time, then dies down to the ground with frost and the root remains alive through the winter. The following spring the root sends up another plant which produces seed. Thus the winter annual plant requires a season and a half to produce its seed.

Wild lettuce (*Lactuca scariola*), wild barley (*Hordeum jubatum*) and shepherd's purse (*Capsella Bursa-pastoris*) are examples of winter annual weeds in Iowa. They are much like cultivated winter wheat and rye in habit of growth.

In order to kill a winter annual weed the first year it is necessary to remove the crown of the root before winter. This will prevent the appearance of the plant the following season. The second

year, if new plants come up, simply prevent seed formation as with
the annuals.

BIENNIALS.

Biennial weeds are two year plants. They grow from seed in
the spring, produce no seed, only vegetative growth the first season,
die down to the ground with frost, and the following season new
growth comes up which is capable of producing seed. Thus a biennial weed requires two full growing seasons to produce its seed.
In order to eradicate a biennial weed the first year, cut it off two
or three inches below the surface of the ground and pour gasoline
or kerosene on the cut. A handful of common salt thrown on each
plant after it is cut off also will be effective. The second season
it is only necessary to prevent seed formation in order to destroy
the plant. Plowing, cutting or pulling will be effective if practiced before seed has formed.

Burdock, mullein, bull thistle, wild carrot and wild parsnip are
examples of serious biennial weeds found in Iowa.

It is thus apparent that the eradication of annuals, winter annuals and biennials depends chiefly upon the prevention of seed
formation. Use any method which accomplishes this result.

PERENNIALS.

Ordinarily the annual, winter annual and biennial weeds are
eradicated with comparative ease. The fourth class of weeds,
namely the perennials, are much harder to kill. Perennials are
capable of living many years even though they are never allowed
to produce seed. They grow each year from roots and sometimes
from seeds. The point is, however, that the existence of perennial
weeds is not dependent upon seed production, as is the case with
the first three classes. Hence it is much harder to eradicate a
perennial weed than an annual, winter annual or biennial.

Canada thistle, perennial sow thistle, quack grass, morning-
glory, horse nettle, milkweed, nimble will, sour dock, smooth dock
and devil's shoestring are probably Iowa's worst perennial weeds.

The methods of eradication which apply to one perennial weed
will usually apply to another. During the past three years quite
definite experiments have been conducted throughout the state in
an effort to determine the most practical, efficient and economical
methods which will eradicate Canada thistle and quack grass.
Considerable information relative to the eradication of horse nettle
and morning-glory also has been accumulated.

During the past three years a specialist from the Extension

Service of the Agricultural College has coöperated with over sixty county farm bureaus in conducting weed eradication demonstrations. The meetings are arranged by the local county agent and the extension specialist assists in conducting the demonstration.

In the main these demonstrations have been held in Canada thistle patches. In some cases they were held in patches of horse nettle, quack grass or morning-glory. The specialist discussed with the farmers the subject of weeds in general and took up methods of eradication. The past summer each farmer was asked to sign a card and answer the following questions:

1. Do you have Canada thistle on your farm?
2. Have you had experience in eradicating it?
3. Have you succeeded?
4. What method did you follow?

The following summary table shows that 63 per cent of the farmers who came to the demonstrations in 1924 had Canada thistles on their farms. Forty-one per cent of this number had tried to eradicate the weed, and only 20 per cent of these had succeeded.

The outstanding feature of this table shows that a high percentage of the farms in Iowa are infested with Canada thistle. In some cases every farmer who came to the meeting said his farm was infested. It has been stated that in certain townships hardly a farm is free of this weed.

COUNTY	PER CENT OF FARMS WITH CANADA THISTLES	PER CENT ATTEMPTING ERADICATION	PER CENT SUCCEEDING	ATTENDANCE
Allamakee	80	37	20	35
Boone	40	38	31	13
Butler	33	16	5	18
Calhoun	66	48	32	26
Cerro Gordo	80	30	30	29
Chickasaw	60	20	6	57
Clayton	84	71	57	7
Hamilton	83	62	20	24
Hancock	75	50	30	37
Humboldt	50	38	14	21
Ida	90	60	15	18
Iowa	66	50	35	23
Louisa	50	45	20	31
Marshall	55	33	16	53
Mills	50	15	7	14
Mitchell	98	71	22	59
O'Brien	88	63	27	48
Plymouth	50	40	23	43
Shelby	65	45	22	9
Warren	66	33	..	15

PRINCIPLES IN CANADA THISTLE ERADICATION.

In order successfully to eradicate Canada thistle it is necessary to bear in mind the habit of growth and development of the plant.

1. The leaves of the plant make the food used by the plant. If these parts are kept from appearing above the surface for two seasons the plant starves.

2. The roots act as storehouses for the plant food formed in the leaves, so that new growth can be started each year. The roots enlarge, lengthen and start new shoots from the joints or nodes of the root-stocks. They store away the greatest amount of plant food during the latter part of the summer after the plants have blossomed. Constant disturbance of the roots during this storage period greatly weakens the plants.

3. A plant is in its weakest condition when it is producing seed; that is, when the roots are supplying the flower with food for seed production. Hence, if the thistles are first cut during flowering time, in July or August, the task of eradication will not be as long and tedious as would be the case if they were cut in early spring.

Canada thistles cannot be eradicated in a week or a month by the ordinary practices. Experience has proven that the reason for failure to successfully eradicate this pest was the fact that persistence was lacking. It is not an easy job; there is no known easy control; but, unless the public soon realizes the seriousness of the situation, our Iowa farms will be over-run with this weed. It is not only a problem for each farmer, it is a community project, and since the wind blown seeds serve to start new patches, every effort should be made at least to cut the plants before they seed.

Not all plants, of course, produce seed. Many patches never do so, but some do in Iowa, especially in recent years.

Persistence, then, is the keynote to the successful eradication of Canada thistle, the worst weed now growing in Iowa.

METHODS OF ERADICATION.

The method followed for ridding a field of the thistle will vary with the size and location of the patch, the type of soil, climatic conditions, and machinery available. The following recommendations are based chiefly upon the experience of up-to-date Iowa farmers, supported by experimental evidence.

SMALL PATCHES.

For small patches any of the following methods have proven successful:

1. Dig out all plants and as many of the roots as possible and destroy them. As more shoots appear dig them out by the roots.

2. Keep all sprouts cut off below the surface of the ground for one season. Watch carefully the second season and cut when necessary. It is often necessary to cut the shoots every four or five days.

3. Smothering has been successful in some cases. This is practical only for small patches a few yards square. Tar paper, weighted down at the edges by dirt, is recommended. The edges of the tar paper should be lapped at least six inches in order to keep light from the weeds.

4. Salt has been used successfully in pastures where there are plenty of cattle. The tramping of the cattle, together with action of the salt, seems to kill out the weed. It is not best to use salt on a large area because of its injury to the soil. Gasoline mixed with used oil from automobiles or tractors will kill the plants, but new shoots come up from the roots in a short time. Several applications are necessary to be successful.

LARGE PATCHES.

For larger patches either of the following methods may be practical:

1. Plow deeply in July or August. If possible follow with a spring tooth harrow or some other implement which will rake many of the roots to the surface where they may be gathered and burned. Disc to smooth the ground. Cultivate at least once a week until freezing weather with either a surface cultivator, a disc set at a sharp angle, or an ordinary heavy road-drag. This practice will serve to keep down any new shoots, prevent the formation of leaves, and thus weaken the roots. The following spring plow again, disc, and cultivate the same as before. If the land is then to be used for a crop, it should be cultivated once a week until late June and then sown to some heavy smother crop such as millet, sudan grass or sorghum. The third year if the work has been thoroughly done, no plants should appear.

2. As soon as growth starts in the spring, plow to the ordinary depth, disc, harrow and cultivate with corn cultivator or an ordinary road-drag, which will cut off the plants as soon as they sprout. If this practice is followed every week for the first season and as often as necessary during the second season the weed may be killed out.

QUACK GRASS.

Quack grass is one of the European grasses introduced into Iowa and is now well established in most of the northern and a few of the southern counties. The plants grow from one to three feet high, from a jointed, creeping root-stock. The leaves are from four to twelve inches long, smooth on the lower side but in some cases rough on the upper. In the early part of the season the color of the leaves is sometimes a bluish green. Each stem bears one head or spike, three to ten inches long, thinner than a wheat head but similar in shape and structure.

The spikelets are 4 to 8-flowered, the outer glumes acute or awn pointed and the flowering glumes either awnless or with short awns. An abundance of seed is produced each season and new patches are started in this way.

The root-stocks of quack grass seldom run deeper than four inches. It is from these that new growth starts each spring before other weeds begin growing. When once established they form such a strong dense sod that nothing else can grow and often it is nearly impossible to pull a plow through it. The shallowness of the roots permits them to be pulled out by a harrow or shovel cultivator and in this way they become scattered into various parts of the field. It is contended by some that quack grass is a good fertilizer and therefore is beneficial. There is no doubt but that it adds considerable green manure when plowed under, but its ability to crowd out and starve other grasses and grains outweighs any advantage that it may have as a fertilizer.

METHODS OF ERADICATION.

The spreading habits of quack grass make it very desirable to isolate all patches and work them separately. If this is not done, a new patch may start while another is being cleaned out. The following methods are recommended:

A. For small patches in the garden or field.—Dig out all plants and roots with a fork and destroy them. Repeat the operation as new growth appears.

B. For patches one-fourth acre to one acre in size.—1. In cultivated fields plow in the spring and cultivate every week with a spring tooth harrow until the latter part of June. If the month of June is hot and fairly dry, the roots will be dragged to the surface and many will die. Sow millet, buckwheat, sudan grass or sorghum and cut when ripe. All of the above plants grow rapidly and act as smother crops. The next year the ground can be planted to corn or other cultivated crop.

2. If quack grass has started in the pasture or meadow plow about four inches deep in July or August and cultivate with a spring tooth harrow the remainder of the season.

C. In large fields either partly or wholly infested.—Plow in August after harvest and cultivate the infested areas once a week until late fall. Cultivate the following spring as soon as growth starts and plant to corn. If possible blind plow and harrow, then cultivate often during the summer. During the fall and spring it is best to clean the harrow before going from one patch to another to prevent spreading.

THE EFFECT OF DRYING UPON ROOT-STOCKS AND ROOTS OF WEEDS.

By R. R. ROTHACKER

The subject of weeds and their extermination is one of much importance to the Iowa farmer. It is strange how little is known concerning the underground vegetative organs of weeds. The longevity of the roots of many weeds after removal from soil, especially annual and biennial weeds, is very short, while there is much variation with reference to perennial weeds.

This latter group, the perennial weeds, contains those weeds which live from year to year by means of their underground roots or root-stocks, from which new shoots appear above ground every year. However, the most troublesome to the farmer are the ones which "sprout" or produce new plants from pieces of the root or stem when it is broken. Quack grass, Canada thistle and others are able to grow from these small pieces; hence plowing and ordinary cultivation help to spread the "patch."

The great amount of work necessary to eradicate weeds of this type has given rise to many and diverse methods of controlling them but perhaps the most common way is to expose the roots and allow them to dry. Likewise, many and rather far-stretched tales of the remarkable ability of some of these seeds to withstand unfavorable conditions have resulted. The familiar saying, "Hang it on the fence for a month and if given half a chance it will grow," seemed to need authentic proof or disproof. With this object in view, a drying experiment on some of the roots of perennial weeds was undertaken.

A brief description of the experiment will give an idea of the method used. Sufficient roots or root-stocks of twenty-nine perennial weeds were dug in order to make six bundles of five each or a total of thirty roots of each weed. The roots were not washed but shaken free of soil and the tops were cut off before the roots were bundled.

The part of root or root-stock used varied with the type of root system. In such plants as Indian hemp, curled dock, smooth dock, burdock, sheep sorrel, ox-eye daisy, sunflower, nettle, dandelion, goldenrod, cypress spurge, germander, buckhorn, catnip, hoary vervain, drop-seed grass and artichoke, the entire crown was included. In such plants as horseradish, devil's shoestring, flowering spurge, quack grass, hedge nettle, swamp milkweed, American morning-glory, European morning-glory, horse nettle, bouncing Bet and field milkweed, a six inch piece of root or root-stock was used. The bundles were made as nearly alike as possible as to age and size of the roots or root-stocks.

The bundling of the material required more time than anticipated so that the initial or fresh weight of each bundle was not obtained. However, the five day weight of all bundles was made. The bundles of roots were air-dried as follows: bundle No. 1 for 5 days, No. 2 for 10 days, No. 3 for 15 days, No. 4 for 20 days, No. 5 for 25 days, No. 6 for 30 days. The manner of drying was very simple. The bundles of roots or root-stocks were placed spread out in containers in a well ventilated shed and then weighed at the proper intervals.

All bundles were weighed at the end of the first period of five days as the fresh weight was not obtained. Bundle No. 1 of each weed was then placed in a greenhouse bench, properly labeled and lightly covered with sand. Proper growing conditions of moisture, light, and heat were provided. Bundles No. 2 were placed in the sand after weighing at the end of ten days drying. Bundles Nos. 3, 4, 5 and 6 at the end of 15, 20, 25 and 30 days respectively were treated in the same manner. The experiment began on August 7, 1924, and observations were completed by October 17, 1924.

The record charts of the different weeds follow and for the most part are self explanatory:

Record Charts

Curled Dock *(Rumex crispus)*

Bundle No.	1	2	3	4	5	6
Days air-dried	5	10	15	20	25	30
*Per cent H_2O lost	0	10.52	26.58	31.03	41.56	35.37
Total shoots after 40 days in sand	10	3	7	1	0	0

Smooth Dock *(Rumex altissimus)*

Bundle No.	1	2	3	4	5	6
Days air-dried	5	10	15	20	25	30
*Per cent H_2O lost	0	18.75	34.24	37.5	50	41.86
Total shoots after 40 days in sand	12	2	0	0	0	0

Dandelion *(Taraxacum officinale)*

Bundle No.	1	2	3	4	5	6
Days air-dried	5	10	15	20	25	30
*Per cent H_2O lost	0	35.38	54.28	58.97	66.66	56.9
Total shoots after 40 days in sand	10	7	0	0	0	0

Quack Grass *(Agropyron repens)*

Bundle No.	1	2	3	4	5	6
Days air-dried	5	10	15	20	25	30
*Per cent H_2O lost	0	11.42	12.92	16.21	14.	15.7
Total shoots after 40 days in sand	8	2	0	0	0	0

Bouncing Bet *(Saponaria officinalis)*

Bundle No.	1	2	3	4	5	6
Days air-dried	5	10	15	20	25	30
*Per cent H_2O lost	0	11.81	19.35	21.05	22.72	25.71
Total shoots after 40 days in sand	10	2	0	0	0	0

Meadow Sunflower *(Helianthus grosseserratus)*

Bundle No.	1	2	3	4	5	6
Days air-dried	5	10	15	20	25	30
*Per cent H_2O lost	0	16.66	32.72	36.11	46.87	36.5
Total shoots after 40 days in sand	13	0	0	0	0	0

Field Milkweed *(Asclepias syriaca)*

Bundle No.	1	2	3	4	5	6
Days air-dried	5	10	15	20	25	30
*Per cent H_2O lost	0	24.24	34.09	52.94	49.3	47.76
Total shoots after 40 days in sand	10	0	0	0	0	0

Cypress Spurge *(Euphorbia Cyparissias)*

Bundle No.	1	2	3	4	5	6
Days air-dried	5	10	15	20	25	30
*Per cent H_2O lost	0	1.44	12.47	17.37	22.43	
Total shoots after 40 days in sand	**22	0	0	0	0	

*Based on weight of bundle after 5 days drying. Fresh weight not obtained.
**2 periods of shoots—9 first (died), 13 second.

Record Charts

Indian Hemp (Apocynum cannabinum)

	1	2	3	4	5	6
Bundle No.	1	2	3	4	5	6
Days air-dried	5	10	15	20	25	30
*Per cent H_2O lost	0	18.75	34.24	37.5	50	41.86
Total shoots after 40 days in sand	8	0	0	0	0	0

Burdock (Arctium Lappa)

Bundle No.	1	2	3	4	5	6
Days air-dried	5	10	15	20	25	30
*Per cent H_2O lost	0	39.64	37.75	60	71.87	36.15
Total shoots after 40 days in sand	5	0	0	0	0	0

Goldenrod (Solidago rigida)

Bundle No.	1	2	3	4	5	6
Days air-dried	5	10	15	20	25	30
*Per cent H_2O lost	0	16.28	22.61	22.2	25	10.97
Total shoots after 40 days in sand	4	0	0	0	0	0

Swamp Milkweed (Asclepias verticillata)

Bundle No.	1	2	3	4	5	6
Days air-dried	5	10	15	20	25	30
*Per cent H_2O lost	0	16.9	13.38	20.48	22.16	12.48
Total shoots after 40 days in sand	4	0	0	0	0	0

Flowering Spurge (Euphorbia corollata)

Bundle No.	1	2	3	4	5	6
Days air-dried	5	10	15	20	25	30
*Per cent H_2O lost	0	19.37	23.25	35.61	58.08	42.65
Total shoots after 40 days in sand	2	0	0	0	0	0

Horseradish (Radicula Armoracia)

Bundle No.	1	2	3	4	5	6
Days air-dried	5	10	15	20	25	30
*Per cent H_2O lost	0	22.8	35.69	39.85	24.68	37.
Total shoots after 40 days in sand	2	0	0	0	0	0

Germander (Teucrium canadense)

Bundle No.	1	2	3	4	5	6
Days air-dried	5	10	15	20	25	30
*Per cent H_2O lost	0	20.32	28.5	22.87	19.36	15.71
Total shoots after 40 days in sand	2	0	0	0	0	0

European Morning-glory (Convolvulus arvensis)

Bundle No.	1	2	3	4	5	6
Days air-dried	5	10	15	20	25	30
*Per cent H_2O lost	0	9.61	12.12	12.5	9.86	16.
Total shoots after 40 days in sand	1	0	0	0	0	0

Sheep Sorrel (Rumex Acetosella)

Bundle No.	1	2	3	4	5	6
Days air-dried	5	10	15	20	25	30
*Per cent H_2O lost	0	22.2	33.38	33.19	32.93	35.65
Total shoots after 40 days in sand	1	0	0	0	0	0

*Based on weight of each bundle after 5 days drying. Fresh weight not obtained.

The following weeds were treated similarly to the preceding ones but were completely killed by being dried for five days:

NAME	GROWTH
Nettle *(Urtica gracilis)*	None
Horse Nettle *(Solanum carolinense)*	None
Hedge Nettle *(Stachys palustris)*	None
Canada Thistle *(Cirsium arvense)*	None
Ox-eye Daisy *(Chrysanthemum Leucanthemum)*	None
Buckhorn *(Plantago lanceolata)*	None
Catnip *(Nepeta Cataria)*	None
Drop-seed Grass *(Muhlenbergia mexicana)*	None
Hoary Vervain *(Verbena stricta)*	None
Artichoke *(Helianthus tuberosus)*	None
Devil's Shoestring *(Polygonum Muhlenbergii)*	None
American Morning-glory *(Convolvulus sepium)*	None

Growth Summary, Number of Shoots.

Days in Sand	5	10	15	20	25	30
Bundle*	1 2 3	1 2 3	1 2 3	1 2 3	1 2 3	1 2 3
Curled dock	1	8 1	10 1	10 1 2	10 1 6	11 3 7
Smooth dock	2	10 1	10 1	11 2	12 2	12 2
Dandelion	3 2	10 5	10 6	10 6	10 7	10 7
Quack grass	1	8	8 1	8 2	8 2	8 2
Bouncing Bet		1	1	7	7 2	8 2
Sunflower	7	9	11	13	13	13
Field milkweed	1	2	10	10	10	10
Cypress spurge			1	9	9	14
Indian hemp			3	6	8	8
Burdock	1	3	4	4	4	5
Goldenrod		1	4	4	4	4
Swamp milkweed			3	3	3	4
Flowering spurge			1	2	2	2
Horseradish				2	2	2
Germander			1	1	1	2
Morning-glory		1	1	1	1	1
Sheep sorrel						1

*Bundles Nos. 4, 5, and 6 not recorded as no shoots appeared. The weeds not producing shoots are tabulated in preceding list.

By referring to the record charts the weeds will be found to be arranged in the order of their ability to withstand drying as found in this experiment. Curled dock leads the list by growing after air drying for a period of twenty days. It was the only weed that put out growth after more than ten days of drying and persisted ten days longer than any of the others.

Among those which were able to grow after drying ten days are found smooth dock, dandelion, quack grass and bouncing Bet.

In the five day group are found meadow sunflower, field milkweed, cypress spurge, Indian hemp, burdock, goldenrod, swamp milkweed, flowering spurge, horseradish, germander, European morning-glory, and sheep sorrel.

Of those giving no growth after drying five days are found nettle, horse nettle, hedge nettle, Canada thistle, ox-eye daisy, American morning-glory, buckhorn, catnip, drop-seed grass, hoary vervain, artichoke, and devil's shoestring.

A noticeable decrease in moisture loss is found in the case of
bundles No. 6 and is explained by the fact of a heavy rain between the 25th and 30th days of drying. From this it is easy to
see that the more moisture in the air the less will be the loss of
moisture from the weeds. Weed roots exposed to drying in wet
weather will be able to survive longer than those exposed to drier
conditions. Roots covered with dirt do not dry out as readily as
those from which the soil is removed, because of the protective
covering. Weeds in piles should be turned occasionally to allow
the lower ones to dry out.

The ability of weed roots to withstand drouth may be one of
the factors in determining their ecological distribution. However,
a more general correlation seems to exist between a rather hard
coated fleshy root more or less taplike in nature and its power to
recover after drying, than in the case of fine fibrous roots, which
succumb quickly to drying. The age of the root used and the conditions under which the root is grown are factors which must be
considered in an experiment of this kind.

Fig. 512. The effect of drying roots and root-stocks of weeds. Photograph taken
January 6, 1925. Curled dock withstood drying for 20 days. Quack grass,
smooth dock, and bouncing Bet for 10 days. Several others
for 5 days. See tables.
(Photograph by Richardson, Iowa Agr. Exp. Sta.)

DRYING TESTS WITH QUACK GRASS ROOT-STOCKS.

Conducted by Botany Department Iowa State College.

Date, August, 1924

		6	7	8	9	10	11	12	13	14	15	20
						Number of shoots produced						
Row 1.	Exposed to sun 24 hours in field	0	0	0	0	0	0	0	0	0	0	0
Row 2.	Check. Fresh plants from field	75	75	75	75	75	75	75	75	75	75	75
Row 3.	Exposed on ground 10 days	4	4	4	4	4	4	4	4	4	4	4
Row 4.	Dried in laboratory 48 hours	0	0	0	0	0	0	0	0	0	0	0
Row 5.	Check to 6. Fresh from field	12	12	12	12	12	12	12	12	12	12	12
Row 6.	Dried 24 hours in field	0	0	0	0	0	0	0	0	0	0	0
Row 7.	Dried 3½ days in field	0	0	0	0	0	0	0	0	0	0	0
Row 8.	Check to 7. Fresh from field	44	44	44	44	44	44	44	44	44	44	44
Row 9.	Exposed in field 5 days	0	0	0	0	0	0	0	0	0	0	0
Row 10.	Check to 9. Fresh roots	2	7	22	30	36	43	46	48	48	48	50
Row 11.	Dried 6½ hours in laboratory	0	0	1	4	10	14	20	23	25	27	28
Row 12.	Dried 24 hours in field	0	0	0	1	2	4	9	20	27	27	27

For each of the twelve plantings the quantity of rhizomes used was about equal in amount, being twenty-five fragments four to six inches long. The test shows that drying retards and may prevent the growth of quack grass root-stocks.

CHAPTER X.

WEED LAW AND SEED LAW OF IOWA.

This chapter presents the present weed law and seed law of Iowa.

CODE OF IOWA, 1924, CHAPTER 246.—WEEDS.

4817. *Duty to Enforce.*—The provisions of this chapter shall be enforced:

1. By the board of supervisors as to all county and primary roads.

2. By the councils and commissioners of all cities and towns, irrespective of their local form of government, as to all roads, streets, and other lands within said cities and towns.

3. By the township trustees as to all township roads and as to all other lands, including railroad lands, within the township not embraced in paragraphs one and two hereof.

4818. *Noxious Weeds.*—The following weeds are hereby declared to be noxious weeds, namely: quack grass (*Agropyron repens*), Canada thistle (*Cirsium arvense*), cocklebur (*Xanthium canadense*), wild mustard (*Brassica arvensis*), sour or curled dock (*Rumex crispus*), smooth dock (*Rumex altissimus*), buckhorn or ribbed plaintain (*Plantago lanceolata*), wild parsnip (*Pastinaca sativa*), horse nettle (*Solanum carolinense*), velvet-weed or button-weed (*Abutilon Theophrasti*), burdock (*Arctium Lappa*), shoo-fly (*Hibiscus Trionum*), wild carrot (*Daucus Carota*), sow thistle (*Sonchus arvensis*), and Russian thistle (*Salsola Kali* L. var. *tenuiflora*). Wild sunflower was added; Acts 41st General Assembly, Chapter 64.

4819. *Duty to Destroy.*—Each owner and each person in the possession or control of any lands, including railroad lands, shall:

1. Cut, burn, or otherwise destroy, all noxious weeds thereon, as defined in this chapter, at such times in each year and in such manner as shall prevent said weeds from blooming or coming to maturity, and keep said lands free from such growth of other weeds as shall render the streets or highways adjoining said lands unsafe for public travel, or shall interfere in any manner with the proper construction or repair of said streets or highways.

2. Cause all weeds on the streets or highways adjoining said lands to be cut or destroyed in the manner and at the time prescribed by the board of supervisors. Nothing herein shall prevent the landowner from harvesting, in proper season, the grass grown on the road along his land.

4820. *Extent of Duty.*—The duty of one who owns, controls, or occupies land to destroy weeds within a public highway shall only extend to the line in the highway to which the abutting land would extend in case no highway existed.

4821. *Order for Destruction.*—The board of supervisors of each county shall, at their April meeting of each year, by resolution make an order fixing the time for destruction of noxious weeds and may fix different times for the destruction of different varieties of weeds.

4822. *Notice of Order.*—Notice of aforesaid order shall be given by one publication in the official newspapers of the county and shall be directed to all property owners. Said notice shall state:

1. Time for destruction.

2. Manner of destruction if other than cutting above the surface of the ground.

3. That unless said order is complied with the trustees (or council or commissioners as the case may be) will cause said weeds to be destroyed and the cost thereof to be taxed to the owner of the property.

4823. *Destruction.*—The trustees, council, commissioners, or board of supervisors, as the case may be, shall forthwith, in case of a substantial failure to comply with said order, cause said weeds to be destroyed. The expense of such destruction, including costs of serving said notice and the costs, if any, of any special meetings, may be advanced from the township road fund, or from the town or city general fund, or from the county road fund, as the case may be.

4824. *Assessments of Costs.*—The trustees, council, commissioners, or board of supervisors shall assess all of said costs against the said land and the owner thereof by a special tax which shall be certified to the county treasurer by the clerk of the governing body, placed upon the tax books and collected, together with interest and penalty after due, in the same manner as other unpaid taxes. When collected, said funds shall be paid into the fund upon which said warrants were drawn.

4825. *Notice of Assessment.*—Before making said assessment, thirty days' notice shall be given such owner of the time and place of meeting of the trustees, council, commissioners, or board of supervisors, which notice shall also contain a statement of the work done and the expense thereof with costs, and shall be given by posting a copy thereof on the premises affected and by mailing a copy thereof by registered mail to the last known address of the person owning or controlling the same. At such time and place such owner may appear with the same rights given by law before boards of review upon increase in assessments.

4826. *Duty to Make Complaint.*—It shall be the duty of all officers directly responsible for the care of public highways to make complaint to the proper township trustees or town councils or commissioners or board of supervisors, as the case may be, whenever it shall appear that the provisions of section 4819 hereof may not be complied with in time to prevent the blooming and maturity of noxious weeds or the unlawful growth of weeds, whether in the streets or highways for which they are responsible or upon lands adjacent to the same.

4827. *Report—To Whom Made.*—It shall be the duty of the township clerk, between the fifteenth and thirtieth days of October of each year, to make report to the board of supervisors of the county in which his township is situated as to the presence and location of noxious weeds that have been reported or found within the township and the steps taken to bring about the destruction thereof, a copy of which report shall be forwarded by them to the secretary of agriculture not later than the first day of December following.

4828. *Duty of County Attorney.*—It shall be the duty of the county attorney, upon complaint of any citizen that any officer charged with the enforcement of the provisions of this chapter has neglected or failed to perform his duty, to enforce the performance of such duty.

4829. *Penalty.*—Any officer referred to in this chapter who neglects or fails to perform the duties incumbent upon him under the provisions of this chapter shall be punished by a fine not exceeding one hundred dollars.

CODE OF IOWA, 1924, CHAPTER 153.—AGRICULTURAL SEEDS.

3127. *Definitions and Rules of Construction.*—For the purpose of this chapter:

1. "Agricultural seed" shall mean the seeds of Canada or Kentucky blue grass, brome grass, fescues, millet, tall meadow oat-grass, orchard grass, red top, Italian, perennial, or western rye grass, Kaffir corn, sorghum or cane, Sudan grass, timothy, alfalfa, alsike, crimson, mammoth or sapling, red, sweet, or white clover, Canada field peas, cowpeas, soy beans, vetches, and other grasses and forage plants, buckwheat, flax, rape, barley, field corn, oats, rye, wheat, and other cereals.

2. "Weed seed" shall mean the seeds of noxious weeds listed herein, and all seeds not listed above as agricultural seed.

3. "Noxious weeds" shall mean common wild mustard or char-lock, Indian mustard, perennial sow thistle, sour, curled, or smooth dock, wild oats, corn cockle, sheep or horse sorrel, and such other plants as may be declared to be noxious weeds as provided in the next succeeding section.

4. "Purity" of agricultural seed shall mean freedom from inert matter, and from other agricultural or weed seed distinguishable by their appearance.

3128. *Additional Noxious Weeds—Hearing—Determination.*—Whenever it shall appear to the department that any plant, other than those specifically enumerated in the last preceding section, has become, or threatens to become, a menace to the agricultural industry of this state the secretary of agriculture shall call a committee of three experts in plant life, one of whom shall be the botanist of the State College of Agriculture and Mechanic Arts. If the said committee shall find that such plant has become, or threatens to become, a menace to the agricultural industry it shall so report to the department, which shall then declare the same to be a noxious weed. Notice of such declaration shall be given by posting same at the courthouse in each county of the state and the provisions of this chapter shall apply to such plant from and after thirty days from the posting of said notice.

3129. *Labeling Agricultural Seed.*—All agricultural seed offered or exposed for sale, or sold in package or wrapped form, for seeding purposes shall be labeled on the package or container as provided in sections 3037 and 3038, and in addition thereto shall have printed on the label prescribed in said sections:

1. Variety of seed.

2. The approximate percentage by weight of the purity of the seed.

3. The approximate total percentage by weight of weed seed.

4. The name of each kind of seed or bulblet of noxious weeds which is present.

5. The approximate percentage of germination of such agricultural seed, together with the month and year said seed was tested, and year grown, and, if corn, the county and state where grown, and if clover of any variety or alfalfa, the state or country where grown.

3130. *Labeling of Certain Mixed Seed.*—Mixtures of alsike and timothy, alsike and white clover, red top and timothy, alsike and red clover, offered or exposed for sale, or sold as mixtures in package or wrapped form, for seeding purposes and in lots of ten pounds or more shall be labeled on the package or container as to the quantity, percentage of weed seed present, and name of vendor, in the manner prescribed for pure agricultural seed, and in addition the label shall contain the following specific items:

1. The statement that such seed is a mixture.

2. The name and appropriate percentage by weight of each kind of agricultural seed present in such mixture in excess of five per cent by weight of the total mixture.

3. The name of each kind of seed or bulblet of noxious weeds which is present singly or collectively in excess of one seed or bulblet in each fifteen grams (approximately three-fifths ounce) of such mixture.

4. The approximate percentage of germination of each kind of agricultural seed present in such mixture in excess of five per cent by weight, together with the month and year said seed was tested, and year grown.

3131. *Labeling Other Mixtures of Seed.*—Special mixtures of agricultural seed except as provided in the preceding section, offered or exposed for sale, or sold in package or wrapped form for seeding purposes, and in quantities of eight ounces or more, shall be labeled on the package or container as prescribed in the preceding section, except that the percentage of germination need not be stated, but the label shall contain a statement showing the approximate percentage by weight of inert matter.

3132. *Written Labels.*—The label on a package or container of agricultural seed may be written instead of being printed, but when written, the writing must be plain and legible.

3133. *Sales from Bulk.*—In case agricultural seed or mixtures of the same are offered or exposed for sale in bulk, or sold from bulk, there shall be conspicuously displayed in connection therewith a placard containing the items required on the label of such seed when offered or exposed for sale, or sold in package or wrapped form, or in lieu of this requirement the vendor may furnish the vendee with a printed or written statement containing the said items.

3134. *Presumption of Freedom from Weed Seed.*—In every sale of agricultural seed or mixture of the same it shall be presumed that the said seed is free from weed seed unless the label on the package or container specifies the presence of such weed seed or the purchaser is informed of the presence of the same in the manner provided in the preceding section.

3135. *Analyses of Seed for Personal Use—Fee.*—Any person purchasing any agricultural seed in this state for his own use may submit fair samples of said seed to the department of agriculture, accompanied by an analysis fee of fifty cents for each sample and a proper analysis of the same shall be made and furnished.

3136. *Exemptions.*—Agricultural seed or mixtures of same shall be exempt from the provisions of this title:

1. When possessed, exposed or offered for sale, or sold for food purposes only.

2. When sold or in store for the purpose of recleaning.

3. When sold by one farmer to another and delivered upon the vendor's premises; but if such seed is advertised for sale or is delivered through a common carrier, then the seed shall be subject to all the requirements of this title, but this exemption shall in no event be construed as permitting the sale of agricultural seed containing the seeds or bulblets of Canada thistle, quack grass, buckhorn, wild carrot, horse nettle, or dodder (clover, alfalfa, or field) in violation of the next succeeding section.

3137. *Certain Sales Prohibited.*—No person shall sell, offer or expose for sale, or distribute, for seeding purposes, any agricultural seed if the seeds or bulblets of Canada thistle, quack grass, buckhorn, wild carrot, horse nettle, or dodder (clover, alfalfa, or field) are present, single or collectively, as follows:

1. In excess of one seed or bulblet in each five grams of timothy, red top, tall meadow oatgrass, orchard grass, crested dog's-tail, Canada or Kentucky blue grass, fescues, brome grass, Italian, perennial or western rye grass, crimson, mammoth or sapling, red, white, alsike, or sweet clover, alfalfa, or any other grass or clover not otherwise classified.

2.   One in twenty-five grams of millet, rape, flax, or other agricultural seed not specified in subsections 1 or 3 of this section.

3.   One in one hundred grams of wheat, oats, rye, barley, buckwheat, vetches, or other agricultural seed as large as or larger than wheat.

BIBLIOGRAPHY.

L. H. PAMMEL AND CHARLOTTE M. KING

Perhaps the best known of the modern German treatises on the subject of weeds is that of Thaer of the University of Giessen on the Agricultural Weeds, in which some twenty-seven species are described with colored figures, methods of extermination being given. Many of the weeds here described, as the sheep sorrel, corn cockle, Canada thistle, quack grass, and horsetail, are common to North America. This work passed through several editions, the first appearing in 1881 and the last in 1905.

L. Danger in 1887 published a treatise on the subject of Weeds and Plant Parasites. This work discussed the more important weeds of Germany, frequently giving methods of extermination, and numerous notes on the origin of weeds, including also, under the head of geographical botany, a list of weeds found in different soils.

Sorauer and Frank discuss the weeds of Germany. Stebler and Schroeter discuss, in an extended way, in a work appearing in 1891, the weeds of Switzerland, giving many colored illustrations and good descriptions. Numerous other papers also have appeared in German technical agricultural journals and in the transactions of societies.

William Darlington of West Chester, Pennsylvania, wrote a work on agricultural botany, an enumeration and description of "useful plants and weeds, which merit the notice or require the attention of American agriculturists."

Mr. Thomas Shaw in 1893 published a small book in which he discussed the prevalence of weeds, the evils which arise from the presence of weeds, the possibility of destroying weeds, the agencies concerned in the distribution and propagation of noxious weeds, methods and principles generally applicable in the destruction of weeds and finally specific modes of eradicating certain troublesome weeds, which should generally be adopted to keep a field free from weeds.

In 1911 Orange Judd & Co. published a book on Weeds of the Farm and Garden, which was written by L. H. Pammel. This book contains, in addition to a number of half tone plates, figures of a great many weeds of North America, discusses their geographical distribution and the best methods of extermination, and the most important noxious weeds with their distribution.

Prof. H. L. Bolley also published an extensive treatise on "Weeds of North Dakota," particularly with reference to the treatment with iron sulphate.

W. S. Blatchley, in the "Indiana Weed Book," 1912, describes one hundred and fifty common weedy plants, including an account of their nature and habits, as well as suggestions for eradication. Of the weeds considered, it is interesting to note that seventy-seven are natives of Indiana, while seventy-three are introduced species.

Of the more important treatises on weeds the recent bulletin by W. J. Beal, who was formerly botanist of the Michigan Agricultural College, should be mentioned. This book of 167 pages describes and figures the important weeds of Michigan. This is a most helpful treatise, and with the excellent figures one will be able to recognize any of the common weeds of that state. Another good book is the Ohio weed manual by Professor Selby. This excellent manual describes and gives the distribution of Ohio weeds as well as hints on extermination of the common weeds of that state. The discussions on weeds by Crozier, Dewey and other botanists of the United States Department of Agriculture are most helpful as regards the more common weeds of eastern North America.

The most recent extensive account of weeds in Canada is a book by Clark and Fletcher. This work describes many families of weeds, one or more species of each genus being illustrated with colored figures.

The most recent English publication is a book by H. C. Long and John Percival, "Common Weeds of the Farm and Garden." This book of 451 pages contains many half tone illustrations and figures of weeds that are common to the British Isles.

The earliest account of Russian thistle was made by J. N. Rose in 1891, followed by a more extensive bulletin on the same weed by Dewey in 1893 and another paper by the same author in 1894. Papers were also published by Bessey of Nebraska, Goff of Wisconsin, Pammel and Wilson of Iowa, Hays of Minnesota, Bolley of North Dakota, Williams of South Dakota, Clinton of Illinois, Selby of Ohio, and Wooten of New Mexico.

The Canada thistle has been discussed by numerous writers both in Europe and in the United States. Mention of this weed is made by Linnaeus in his Flora Lapponica, by Ratzeburg in 1859, and by Darlington in 1853. More recently the weed has received attention from such botanists as H. L. Bolley of North Dakota, T. J. Burrill of Illinois, E. S. Goff of Wisconsin, Fletcher and Clark of Canada, L. F. Henderson of Idaho, L. H. Dewey of Washington, D. C., Professor Howitt of Canada, and L. H. Pammel.

Another weed that attracted much attention a few years ago was squirrel-tail grass or wild barley. This was discussed by C. S. Crandall of Colorado, Hillman of Nevada, Nelson of Wyoming, Wooten of New Mexico, and Pammel of Iowa.

Prickly lettuce has been discussed by Arthur of Indiana, Weed of Ohio, Dewey of Washington, D. C., Morrow of Illinois, Pammel of Iowa, and Fernald of Massachusetts.

Buffalo bur has been discussed by Henry of Wisconsin, Halsted and Pammel of Iowa, Clinton of Illinois, and Harvey of Maine.

Mustards of various kinds have been discussed by Dewey of Washington, D. C., Clark and Fletcher of Canada, Hitchcock of Kansas, Howitt of Canada, and Pammel of Iowa.

The perennial sow thistle has been discussed by the agricultural press of Canada and in special treatises by Howitt and Fletcher and Clark of the Dominion of Canada, and Stevens of North Dakota.

Much has been published on the subject of weed seeds. Among the more important contributions are the following:

European work.—The importance of this work has long been recognized in Europe. The pioneer work in this line was carried on first in Germany, a station for testing commercial seeds having been organized in 1867 in connection with an academy located in Tharandt. Dr. Nobbe was its first director. Early in his work he saw the importance of making careful examination for the impurities of various grass and clover seeds. In 1876 appeared his classical book, Handbuch der Samenkunde. In addition to this work he was the author of many important papers on viability of seeds and other physiological seed problems.

Among other important contributions along this line, we may mention the papers and work of Kraft, Luhn and Harz.

The work of Burchard on the adulteration of seed with special reference to their origin is particularly noteworthy. In his book he has published statistical records showing the origin of clover seed and the weed seeds found in the same from Middle Europe, Eastern Europe, Southern Europe and North and South America.

The work of Settegast treats extensively the subject of agricultural seeds and seed testing, especially with reference to vitality and seed production.

Vandevelde's work treats of the morphology and physiology of germination and includes a splendid bibliography.

Attention should be called to the excellent contributions of Wollny whose reports of his splendid work on seeds and the care of agricultural crops often give considerable detail on the germination and viability of various agricultural seeds.

Determinations on the germination of the cocklebur have been worked out by Wm. Crocker.

Samek carried on an experiment, testing seeds for a period of eleven years, showing the results of germination after the first and eleventh years.

H. von Guttenberg gives the description of five species of *Cuscuta* and a key for their identification.

RECENT PUBLICATIONS ON WEEDS AND SEEDS.*

Adams, J.   The use of chemical sprays for combating weeds. (Ann. Rept. Quebec Soc. Protect. Plants (etc.), 10 (1917-18), pp. 70-78).

Arthur, J. C.   Weeds.   (Indiana Sta. Rep't., 1915, p. 31, 32.)

Aslander, A.   Weed control through spraying.   (Lantmannen, 6 (1923), No. 19, pp. 319-321, fig. 1.)

Atherton, L. G.   Weeds.   (Normal Teacher (Madison, S. Dak.) 5 (1915), No. 6, pp. 31, figs. 13.)

Atkinson, A., and Whitlock, B. W.   Seed testing.   (Mont. Sta. Circ. 38 (1914), pp. 11, figs. 4.)

Beal, W. J.   Michigan Weeds.   (Mich. Sta. Bul. 262, 2nd ed. (1915), pp. 181, figs. 248.)

Bedford, S. A., Walton, G., Brown, H. B.   Report of weeds commission.   (Manitoba Dep't. Agr. and Immig. Ann. Rep't., 1919, pp. 48-53, figs. 4.)

Bedford, S. A., Walton, G., Brown, H. B. (Manitoba Dept. Agr. and Immigr.   Ann. Rept., 1920, pp. 33-36, fig. 1.)

Blake, S. F.   Two New Western Weeds.   (Science, 55 (1922), No. 1426, pp. 455, 456.)   *Bassia hyssopifolia and Centaurea picris.*

Blakely, W. F.   Newly recorded weeds.   (Agr. Gaz. N. S. Wales, 33 (1922), No. 1, p. 6.)

Bolin, P.   Investigation of the frequency and relative importance

*Earlier bibliography may be found in the first edition of *Weed Flora of Iowa*.

of the more common weed species in Sweden. (Meddel Centralanst. Forsoksv. Jordbruksomradet, No. 239 (1922), pp. 36, pls. 39.)

Bolley, H. L., and Stevens, O. A. North Dakota pure seed law —Interpretations and suggestions. (North Dakota Sta. Circ. 20 (1923), pp. 8.)

Bornemann, F. The important agricultural weeds. (Die Wichtigsten Landwirtschaftlichen Unkrauter, pp. 146, figs. 40.)

Breakwell, E. Weed seeds and impurities in imported seed. (Agr. Gaz. N. S. Wales, 28 (1917), No. 6, pp. 405-408).

Breakwell, E. Weed seeds and impurities in New South Wales, (Agr. Gaz. N. S. Wales, 29 (1918), No. 9, pp. 633-638.)

Brenchley, W. E. Eradication of weeds by sprays and manures. (Jour. Bd. Agr. (London), 25 (1919), No. 12, pp. 1474-1482.)

Brenchley, W. E. Buried Weed Seeds, (Jour. Agr. Sci. (England), 9 (1918), No. 1, pp. 1-31.)

Brenchley, W. E. Useful farm weeds. (Jour. Bd. Agr. (London), 25 (1918), No. 8, pp. 949-958.)

Brenchley, W. E. Weeds of farm land, 1920, pp. X+ 239, pls. 2, figs. 38.

Burgess, J. L. Farm weeds of North Carolina and methods for their control. (Bul. N. C. Dept. Agr. 37 (1916), No. 8, pp. 20, figs. 17.)

Burgess, J. L., and Waldron, C. H. Farm weeds of North Carolina and methods for their control. II. (Bul. N. C. Dep't. Agr. 40 (1919), No. 8, pp. 53, figs. 25.)

Burgess, J. L. Rep't. of seed tests for 1913. (Bul. N. C. Dep't. Agr. 34 (1913), No. 9, pp. 48, figs. 2.)

Burns, G. P., and Pietersen, A. K. Agricultural seed—concerning weeds and weed seeds. (Vermont Sta. Bul. 200 (1916), pp. 3-79, figs. 52.)

California, weeds of, and methods of control. (Calif. Dep't. Agr. Mo. Bul., 11 (1922), No. 2-3, pp. xxii + 74-360, figs. 125.)

Call, L. E., and Getty, R. E. The eradication of bindweed (Convolvulus arvensis). (Kansas Sta., Circ. 101 (1923), pp. 18, fig. 10.)

Call, L. E., and Sewell, M. C. The relation of weed growth to nitric nitrogen accumulation in the soil. (Jour. Amer. Soc. Agron. 10 (1918), No. 1, pp. 35-44.)

Campbell, E. G. What is a weed? (Science, 58 (1923), No. 1490, p. 50.)

Cates, H. R. The weed problem in American agriculture. (U. S. Dep't. Agr. Yearbook, 1917, pp. 205-215, pl. 5.)

Clark, G. H.　Weeds and weed seeds.　(Canada Dep't. Agr. Seed Branch Bul. S-8 (1920), rev., pp. 68, figs. 174.)

Coe, H. S.　Weeds.　(S. Dak. Sta. Bul. 150 (1914), pp. 380-453, fig. 39.)

Coleman, F. F.　Weeds in Sudan grass.　(Queensland Agr. Jour., 17 (1922), No. 1, p. 19.)

Cox, H. R.　Weeds: How to control them.　(U. S. Dep't. Agr. Farmer's Bul. 660 (1915), pp. 29, figs. 27.)

Crocker, Wm., Role of Seed Coats in Delayed Germination. Bot. Gaz. 42, 265.

Cumming, M., et al.　Weed control measures (in Canada) (Agr. Gaz. Canada, 7 (1920), No. 6, pp. 484-488, fig. 6.)

Darlington, H. T.　Weed immigration into Michigan.　(Ann. Rep't. Mich. Acad. Sci. 20 (1918), pp. 261-267.)

De Rosa, A.　Control of *Cuscuta*, Coltivatore, 66 (1920), No. 24, pp. 594-597.

Dymond, J. R.　Grain screenings with results of feeding experiments.　(Can. Dep't. Agr., (Pub.) 1915, June, pp. 44.)

Eastman, M. G.　Results of seed tests for 1921.　(New Hampshire Sta. Bul. 202 (1921), pp. 24.)

Eastman, M. G.　Results of seeds tests for 1923.　(New Hampshire Sta. Bul. 211 (1923), pp. 16.)

Egginton, G. E.　Colorado weed seeds.　(Colorado Sta. Bul. 260 (1921), pp. 91, figs. 164.)

Ferdinandsen, C. Danish weed growth.　(Nord. Jordsbrugsforsk., 1920, No. 2, pp. 49-67.)

Fiske, J. G.　Common weeds and their control.　(New Jersey Circ. 125 (1921), pp. 19, figs. 14.)

French, G. T.　Seed inspection in Virginia, 1920-21.　(Va. Dep't. Agr. and Immigr., Ann. Rep't. Comm'r., 1921, pp. 47-66.)

Fron, G.　(Plants detrimental to agriculture: Botanical characteristics and methods of control.)　Plantes nuisibles a l'agriculture; Caracteres Botaniques et Agricoles Methodes de Destruction.　Paris, 1917.　Pp. 346, figs. 151.

Garman, H.　Some Kentucky Weeds and Poisonous Plants. (Ken. Sta. Bul. 183 (1914), pp. 255-339, pls. 43.)

Georgia, Ada M.　A Manual of Weeds.　(New York, 1914, pp. xi + 593, figs. 387.)

Goss, W. L.　Germination of seed buried ten years.　(Proc. Ass'n. of Official Seed Analysts of North America, 1914.)

Gray, G. P. Tests of chemical means for the control of weeds. (Univ. Cal. Pubs. Agr. Sci. 4 (1919), No. 2, pp. 67-97, fig. 11.)

Groh, H. A Preliminary Weed Survey of the Province of Ontario. (Coöperative experiments with field crops in Ontario) (Ontario Dept. Agr., Agr. and Exp. Union Ann. Rept., 44 (1922), pp. 9-24, 29-38.)

Hall, F. H. Purity of farm seeds. (N. Y. State Sta. Bull. 378, popular ed., (1914), pp. 2-4.)

Hansen, A. A. Nineteen noxious weeds of Indiana. (Indiana Sta. Circ. 106 (1922), pp. 32, figs. 20.)

Hansen, A. A. Recent Pennsylvania Weeds. (Penn. Sta. Rep't., 1917, pp. 317-328, pl. 6.)

Hansen, A. A. Lawn pennywort, a new weed. (U. S. Dep't. Agr. Cir. 165 (1921), pp. 6, figs. 3.)

Hansen, A. A. The Toll of Weeds in Indiana. (Ind. Acad. Sci. Proc., 1921, pp. 105-109.)

Hansen, A. A. Recent Indiana weeds. (Ind. Acad. Sci. Proc., 38 (1922), pp. 293-295.)

Hansen, A. A. Wild corn (*Andropogon sorghum drummondii*), a serious weed in Indiana. (Ind. Acad. Sci. Proc., 38 (1922), pp. 295, 296.)

(Hawaii, the use of bagasse paper in weed eradication.) (La Planter, 66 (1921), No. 15, p. 236.)

Howitt, J. E. Coöperative experiments in weed eradication. (Ann. Rep't. Ontario Agr. Col. and Exp't. Farm, 39 (1913), pp. 46, 47.)

Howitt, J. E. Summary of coöperative experiments in weed eradication, 1912-1917. (Ann. Rep't. Ontario Agr. and Expt. Union, 39 (1917), pp. 10-14.)

Howitt, J. E. Experiments in spraying to destroy dandelions. (Ann. Rep't. Ontario Agr. Col. and Exp't. Farm, 39 (1913), pp. 43, 44.)

Helyar, J. P. Weed Control. (New Jersey Sta. Cir. 60 (1916), pp. 3-12.)

Hutcheson, T. B., and Wolfe, T. K. Eradication of field hawkweed. (Virginia Sta. Rep't., 1918, pp. 31-38, fig. 5.)

Ince, J. W. Fertility and Weeds. (North Dak. Sta. Bul. 112 (1915), pp. 233-247, fig. 6.)

Ince, J. W. The use of sodium arsenite for killing weeds. (North Dakota Sta. Spec. Bul. 3 (1914), No. 9, pp. 146, 147.)

Indiana (report of the department of botany for 1921.) (Indiana Sta. Rep't., 1921, pp. 14-19, fig. 2.)   Mosaic transferred from weeds.

Iowa, report of field crops work in, 1918.   Germination of buried seed.   Iowa Sta. Rep't., 1918, pp. 10-12, 24, 25, 26.

Iowa, report of field crops work in, 1919.   (Iowa Sta. Rep't., 1919, pp. 10-14, 25, 26, 35.)   Buried seeds.

Jones, J. W.   Rice (Weed Control) Experiments at the Biggs Rice Field Station in California.   (U. S. Dep't. Agr. Bul. 1155 (1923), pp. 60, figs. 14.)

Juhlin-Dannfelt, H.   Review of weed laws in (different) coun-tries.   (K. Lantbr. Akad. Handl. och Lidskr., 58 (1919), No. 3, pp. 166-174.)

Kellogg, J. W., and Gensler, H. E.   Seed Report, 1915.   (Penn. Dep't. Agr. Bul. 276 (1916), pp. 35, figs. 5.)

Kennedy, P. B.   Observations on some rice weeds in California. (California Sta. Bul. 356 (1923), pp. 465-494, fig. 26.)

Kephart, L. W.   Quack grass, (U. S. Dep't. Agr., Farmer's Bul. 1307 (1923), pp. 32, figs. 15.)

Kitchin, P. C.   Preliminary report on chemical weed control in coniferous nurseries.   (Jour. Forestry, 18 (1920), No. 2, pp. 157-159.)

Korsmo, E.   The control of weeds in field crops (Tidsskr. Norske Landbr., 26 (1919), No. 5, pp. 193-227, fig. 20.)

Larson, A. H., Gilbert, H. C., and Ure, R.   Seed and Weed Studies at the Minnesota Station.   (Minnesota Sta. Rep't., 1922, pp. 100, 101.)

Levy, E. B.   Seed testing (in New Zealand.)   (Jour. Agr. (New Zealand), 18 (1919), No. 3, pp. 129-139, fig. 9.)

Lund S., and Rostrup, E. *Cirsium arvense* En monograf. D. Kyl. Danske, Vidensk Naturvid. v. Math., Part III, 1901.

Maiden, J. H.   Newly recorded weeds. (Agr. Gaz. N. S. Wales, 32 (1921), No. 8, p. 580.)

Munn, M. T.   The New York seed law and seed testing.   (New York State Sta. Bul. 476 (1920), pp. 3-28, fig. 4.)

Munn, M. T.   Spraying lawns with iron sulphate to eradicate dandelions.   (New York State Sta. Bul. 466 (1919), pp. 21-59, pl. 6, fig. 2.)

Munn, M. T., and Hopkins, E. F.   Work of the seed testing laboratory (New York) from 1918 to 1923.

Naumann, A.   Field weeds in their relation to forage: Determination of their fruit and seed. (Arch. Wiss. w. Prakt. Tier-heilk., 44 (1918), Sup., pp. 310-356, pl. 1, fig. 20.)

Newman, L. F., and Newman, R. W. Some records of the seasonal flora of arable land under cultivation. (Jour. Ecology, 6 (1918), No. 3-4, pp. 178-188.)

Osborn, T. G. B. *Solanum rostratum.* A new weed plant. (Jour. Dep't. Agr. So. Aust., 20 (1917), No. 10, pp. 783, 184, fig. 1.)

Oswald, W. L., and Boss, A. Minnesota Weeds. (Minn. Sta. Bul. 139 (1914), pp. 47, figs. 25.)

Oswald, W. L., and Boss, A. Minnesota Weeds, III. (Minn. Sta. Bul. 176 (1918), pp. 5-43, fig. 25.)

Palmer, E. L. A seed key to some common weeds and plants. (Proc. Iowa Acad. Sci. 23 (1916), pp. 335-394, fig. 41.)

Pammel, L. H., and King, C. M. Seed analysis, 1913 to 1921. (Iowa Sta. Bul. 203 (1921), pp. 27-43.)

Pammel, L. H. Squirrel-tail grass or wild barley. (Iowa. Sta. Circ. 52 (1918), pp. 2, fig. 1.)

Pammel, L. H. A Comparative Study of the Weeds of Central Iowa, Northern Minnesota and Wisconsin. (Proc. Iowa Acad. Sci. 22 (1915), pp. 57-59.)

Pammel, L. H., and King, Charlotte M. Unlawful Iowa weeds and their extermination. (Iowa Sta. Circ. 5 (1912), pp. 3-18, figs. 15.)

Pammel, L. H., and King, Charlotte M. The weed content in some commercial seeds. (Proc. Ass'n. of Official Seed Analysts of North America, 1914.)

Parish, S. B. Plants introduced into a desert valley as a result of irrigation. (Plant World, 16 (1913), No. 10, pp. 275-280.)

Porter, J. The spraying of cornfield weeds with sulphate of ammonia. (Jour. Min. Agr., (London), 28 (1922), No. 12, pp. 1109-1116.)

Roberts, H. F. Farm seeds and weeds. (Bien. Rep't. Kans. Bd. Agr., 21 (1917-1918), pp. 228-303, fig. 30.)

Roberts, H. F. Principal noxious weeds of Kansas. (Kansas Sta. Circ. 84 (1920), pp. 19, figs. 10.)

Robbins, W. W., and Boyack, B. The identification and control of Colorado weeds. (Colorado Sta. Bul. 251 (1919), pp. 126, figs. 77.)

Robbins, W. W., and Egginton, G. E. Alfalfa Dodder in Colorado. (Colorado Sta. Bul. 248 (1918), pp. 15, figs. 8.)

Robbins, W. W., and Egginton, G. E. Third annual report of

the Colorado seed laboratory. (Colorado Sta., Seed. Lab. Bul., 2 (1919), No. 2, pp. 5-27, fig. 5.)

Robbins, W. W., and Egginton, G. E. Irrigation water as a factor in the dissemination of weed seeds. (Colorado Sta. Bul. 253 (1920), pp. 25, figs. 7.)

Rudolphs, W. Experiments with common rock salt. II. Eradication of weeds and cleaning of roadsides with salt, (pp. 457-470.)

Saunders, C. B. Dodder and its removal from clover seed. (Jour. Min. Agr. (Gt. Brit.), 30 (1924), No. 10, pp. 928-931).

Selby, A. D. Handling the Weed Situation. (Mo. Bul. Ohio Sta. 1 (1916), No. 8, pp. 225-256, fig. 6.)

Shevelev, I. N. Varieties of self-sowing weeds and their distribution in the soil. ((Trudy Ekaterinoslav. Oblastn. Selsk. Khoz. Optyn. Sta., No. 5 (1922), pp. 29, figs. 3.)

Smith, W. G. Common weeds. (Scot. Jour. Agr., 4 (1921), Nos. 1, 2, 3, 4, 5 (1922) ; 5-(1922) No. 1.)

Stapleton, R. G. The condition of permanent meadows. (Jour. Min. Agr. (London), 28 (1921), No. 3, pp. 207-215.)

Stevens, O. A. North Dakota Weeds. (North Dakota Sta. Bul. 162 (1922), pp. 3-44, fig. 45.)

Stone, A. L. How to rid our farms of weeds. (Wis. Sta. Circ. 48 (1914), pp. 3-24, fig. 14.)

Stone, A. L. Seed and weed control in Wisconsin, 1918-1920. (Wis. Dep't. Agr. Bul. 33 (1920), pp. 81-102, fig. 9.)

Stone, A. L. The weed content of seeds. (Proc. Ass'n. of Official Seed Analysts of North America, 1914.)

Stone, A. L. State seed inspection and weed control, 1914. (Wis. Sta. Bul. 254 (1915), pp. 3-39, fig. 28.)

Stone, G. E. Some recent publications on weeds and weed seeds. Weed extermination (in lawns). (Mass. Agr. Exp. Sta. Rep't., 1912, pt. 2, pp. 35-40, pl. 3.)

Stone, G. E. Some variable results of seed testing. (Mass. Sta. Rep't., 1912, pt. 2, pp. 22-30.)

Swingle, D. B., Morris, H. E., and Jahnke, E. W. Fifty important weeds of Montana. Mont. Agr. Col. Ext. (Pub.), No. 45 (1920), pp. 126, figs. 108.

Talbot, P. R., and Cooper, J. C. Weeds poisonous to live stock. (Alberta Dept. Agr., Prov. Schools Agr. Bul. (191), pp. 40, pls. 4, figs. 15.)

Thompson, R. B., and Sifton, H. H. A guide to the poisonous

plants and weed seeds of Canada and the northern United States. (Toronto Univ., Toronto Press, 1922, pp. 169, figs. 40.)

Tovey, J. R. The introduced (weed) flora of Victoria (Journ. Dept. Agr. Victoria, 19 (1921), No. 10, pp. 614-618, fig. 6.)

True, G. H., et al. Germination tests. (Nev. Sta. Rep't., 1913, pp. 23, 24.)

Ullrich, F. T. Suggestions for the study of weeds in agriculture in the elementary schools. (Bul. State Norm. School, Platteville, Wis., 15 (1919), No. 4, pp. 22, figs. 12.)

Von Petery, W. Alfalfa seed in Argentine. (Rev. de Revistas (Buenos Aires), 4 (1921), Nos. 38, pp. 15-17, figs. 13, 39; pp. 12, 13, fig. 4.)

Weed eradication, coöperative experiments in. (Ann. Rep't. Ontario Agr. Col. and Exp't. Farm, 41 (1915), pp. 16, 17; Rep't. Min. Agr. Ontario, 1915, pp. 18, 19.)

Wehsarg, O. The distribution and control of field weeds in Germany. I. Biologic studies and general control. (Arb. Deut. Landw. Gesell., No. 294 (1918), pp. 21-496, fig. 44, pl. 5.)

Wenger, P. Pure seed law and the weed control act. (Idaho Sta. Circ. 8 (1919), pp. 12.)

Wisconsin (report of field crops work in, 1921-22.) (Wisconsin Sta., Bul. 352 (1923), pp. 28, 29, 40-46, 47, 48, 50-52, fig. 4.) Control methods for Canada thistle, quack grass, field-cress and white campion.

GLOSSARY.

HARRIETTE S. KELLOGG, J. N. MARTIN AND
CHARLOTTE M. KING

Acaulescent. Apparently stemless, or with stem subterranean.

Achene. A dry, hard, 1-celled, 1-seeded, indehiscent fruit.

Acumbent. Lying against, as when the edges of the cotyledon lie against the caulicle or radicle.

Acuminate. Tapering gradually to a point.

Acute. Ending in a sharp angle, not prolonged.

Adventitious. Not in order, or in chance arrangement.

Aerial roots. Those appearing on the stem above ground; may be brace roots as in corn, or clinging roots as in ivy.

Albumen. Nutritive material in seeds accompanying the embryo.

Aleurone grains. Protein grains filling the cells of the aleurone layer.

Aleurone layer. Outermost layer of the endosperm especially well defined. Outermost layers of the endosperm of grass seeds.

Alternate (leaves). One at a node, not opposite; (flowers) parts of one whorl opposite to intervals of next.

Alveolate. Honey-combed.

Anatropous. Inverted and straight.

Angiosperms. Higher seed plants.

Angium. Case for pollen grains.

Annual. A plant that performs its life cycle from germination to matured seed in one season.

Annual (Winter). A plant that germinates in the fall, grows until frost; but blooms and matures seed the following spring.

Anther. The part of the stamen which contains the pollen.

Antheridium. The male sexual organ in cryptogams.

Apetalous. Without petals.

Apex. Is opposite to point of attachment.

Appressed. Lying flat against.

Arachnoid. Cobwebby; covered with tangled hairs, fewer and longer than when tomentose.

Arrow-shaped. See Sagittate.

Ascending. Rising obliquely or curving upward.

Auricle. An ear-shaped appendage.

Awn. An appendage consisting of a bristle.

Axil. The upper angle formed between the leaf and stem.

Axis. The central line of any organ or support of a group of organs.

Axillary. In the axil.

Barbed. With ridged points or short awns usually reflexed.

Base. The part of an organ nearest its point of support.

Bast. A vegetable tissue composed of thick-walled, strengthening fibers or cells.

Beard. Awns of grasses; a tuft of hairs, generally stiff and long.

Biennial. Of two years duration; a plant germinating one season and maturing seed the next.

Bract. A modified leaf subtending a flower or flower branch.

Bracteate. Furnished with bracts.

Bracteolate. Having secondary bracts.

Bristle. A short stiff hair.

Bulb. A leaf bud with fleshy scales; usually subterranean.

Bulbiferous. Bulb-bearing.

Callus. A hard protuberance or callosity.

Calyx. The outer part of the perianth.

Canescent. Hoary with gray or white pubescence.

Capillary. Hairlike.

Capitate. With a globose head. Collected into a head or dense cluster.

Capsule. A dry dehiscent fruit composed of more than one carpel.

Carpel. A simple pistil or one element of a compound pistil.

Caryopsis. A dry one-seeded indehiscent fruit with a thin, adherent pericarp as in the "seeds" of grasses.

Caulicle. The first internode of the stem above the true root.

Cauline. On the stem.

Cellulose. Primary cell wall substance. A carbohydrate having the general formula ($C_6H_{10}O_5$).

Chaff. A small thin scale or bract becoming dry or membranous as in the glume of grasses or bracts on head of compositæ.

Chalaza. The end of the ovule opposite the micropyle.

Chlorenchyma. An assimilating tissue usually composed of parenchyma cells.

Chlorophyll. Green coloring matter of plants.

Chromatophore. A granule of protoplasm bearing a pigment of color.

Ciliate. Having hairs or bristles on margin.

Circumscissile. Dividing by a transverse circular line as in capsule of purslane.

Clavate. Club-shaped; gradually thickened away from the point of attachment.

Cleft. Having narrow sinuses extending about half-way to base; as cleft leaf.

Cleistogamous. Fertilized in bud; closed flowers.

Climbing. Rising by laying hold of other objects without twining.

Coma. A silky tuft of hairs.

Compound. Composed of two or more similar, subordinate parts.

Conduplicate. Folded upon itself lengthwise.

Conidia. In fungi, propagation cells or spores borne upon special branches of the plant body or thallus.

Conidiophore. In fungi, a branch of the mycelium that bears conidia.

Cordate. Heart-shaped with point upward.

Coriaceous. Leathery.

Corolla. Inner part of the perianth.

Corymb. A convex or flat-topped, indefinite inflorescence, like a raceme with lower pedicels elongated.

Cosmopolitan. Widely distributed.

Cotyledons. The first leaves of a plant as found in the embryo.

Creeping. Running along above ground or beneath the surface, and rooting.

Cremocarp. Fruit of Umbelliferæ.

Crenate. Dentate with rounded teeth.

Crested. Having a crest or elevated appendage.

Crystalloids. Protein bodies in the form of crystals.

Culm. The stem of grasses.

Cuneate. Wedge-shaped.

Cut. Having divisions deeper than when dentate.

Cyme. A somewhat flat-topped, determinate inflorescence, resembling a corymb.

Decumbent. Reclining but with end rising.

Dehiscent. Opening in a regular manner by valves or slits to discharge seeds or pollen grains.

Dentate. Toothed, usually with teeth directed outward.

Denticulate. Finely dentate.

Determinate inflorescence, in which flowers arise from terminal bud and check growth of axis.

Diadelphous (stamens). Collected in two sets.

Dicotyledonous. Plants producing two cotyledons.

Diffuse. Spreading loosely and irregularly.

Digitate. Compound with parts radiating from apex of support.

Dioecious. Having stamens and pistils in separate flowers upon different plants.

Divided. Having incisions extending to base or midrib.

Dorsal. Pertaining to the back or outer surface of organ.

Downy. Having a dense covering of short weak hairs.

Echinate. Beset with prickles.

Ellipsoid. Having an elliptical outline.

Elliptical. Oblong and rounded at ends.

Emarginate. Notched at end.

Embryo. Rudimentary plantlet within the seed.

Endosperm. Albumen of seed in embryo-sac as distinguished from perisperm.

Ephemeral. Lasting only a day.

Epicarp. Outer layer of pericarp.

Epiderm. External layer of cells in any organ.

Epigynous. Apparently rising from top of ovary.

Erect. Perpendicular, or nearly so, to the surface to which attachment is made.

Exserted. Protuding beyond margin of envelope as stamens from corolla.

Falcate. Scythe-shaped.

Fertile. Capable of producing fruit.

Fibro-vascular Bundle. A bundle of conductive stringlike, woody, fibro-vascular tissue, containing xylem and phloem.

Fibrous. Composed of fibers.

Filiform. Thread-shaped.

Floccose. Covered with mats or flocks of soft woolly hairs.

Foliate. Leaved, as trifoliate (three-leaved).

Follicle. A fruit consisting of a single carpel opening by the ventral suture.

Fruit. The mature ovary and its contents with any closely adhering part.

Funicle. The stalk of a seed or ovule.

Fusiform. Enlarged in the middle and tapering toward each end.

Gamopetalous. Having petals more or less united.

Gibbous. Swollen or protuberant on one side.

Glabrous. Smooth.

Gland. A secreting surface or structure.

Glandular. Bearing glands or glandlike.

Glaucous. Covered with a whitish bloom, as on cabbage.

Globoids. Granules of calcium-magnesium-phosphate found in grains of aleurone.

Globose. Spherical or nearly so.

Glomerate. Compactly clustered in a head.

Glume. One of the outer floral envelopes of grasses.

Glutinous. Viscid, sticky.

Hadrome. Tissue which conducts water and mineral substances in the plant.

Hairy. Covered with hairs longer and coarser than when pubescent.

Halberd-shaped. See hastate.

Hastate. Describing leaves which have spreading lobes at the base.

Haustoria. Suckers or roots by which certain parasitic plants attach themselves to their hosts.

Heart-shaped. See cordate.

Herb. A soft, tender plant with but little wood in the stem.

Herbaceous. Having the characters of an herb.

Hermaphrodite. Perfect, having both stamens and pistils in the same flower.

Hilum. The scar of the seed; its place of attachment.

Hirsute. Clothed with rather coarse or stiff hairs.

Hispid. Beset with erect stiff hairs or with bristles.

Hypoderm. Beneath the epiderm.

Hypogynous. With parts situated on the receptacle below the pistil.

Imbricated. Overlapping either vertically or spirally, as in case of shingles on a roof. In aestivation, one piece is wholly external and one wholly internal.

Imperfect. Applied to a flower lacking either stamens or pistils.

Included. Opposed to exserted; not protruding from the envelope.

Incumbent. Applied to cotyledons when the radicle is folded back against one of them.

Indehiscent. Not opening by valves or slits.

Indeterminate inflorescence. Flowers arise laterally and successively as floral axis elongates.

Indurated. Hardened.

Inflexed. Bent abruptly inward.

Inflorescence. The flowering part of a plant.

Inserted. Attached to or growing out of.

Integuments. Coats of ovule.

Internode. The part of a stem situated between two nodes.

Interrupted. Applied to surface or series the continuity of which is broken.

Involucre. A circle or series of bracts immediately subtending a flower or inflorescence.

Isodiametric. Equal in three dimensions.

Jassid. A leaf-feeding insect of the group hemiptera, or bugs.

Joint. A node.

Keel. A ridge somewhat resembling the keel of a boat; applied especially to the two anterior united petals of a papilionaceous flower.

Lamella. A thin plate.

Lamina. Blade or expanded part of leaf.

Lanceolate. Lance-shaped; tapering abruptly toward the base and gradually toward the apex.

Lenticular. Lentil-shaped; in the shape of a double convex lens.

Leptome. The tissue which conducts the food of the plant.

Ligneous, lignose, lignified. Woody in texture.

Ligulate. Refers to the strap-shaped corolla of composite flowers, as in dandelions.

Ligule. A strap-shaped corolla, as in the ray flowers of composites, like the sunflower. A membranous projection on inner side of leaf at top of sheath of some grasses.

Linear. Long and narrow with nearly parallel margins.

Lobe. A rounded portion or segment of any organ.

Locule. Cavity within ovule.

Lodicule. A small scale between the stamens in the flowers of grasses.

Lomentum. A legume with constrictions between the seeds.

Lumen. Internal space or cavity of a cell.

Lyrate. Lyre-shaped.

Membranaceous or membranous. Thin, soft, and generally translucent.

Malpighian cells. Cells forming the outer layer of certain seeds and having one or more light lines.

Mesocarp. Middle layer of pericarp.

Mesophyll. All the soft tissues between the lower epidermis and upper epidermis of leaves.

Micropilar process. The point upon the seed marking the location of the micropyle.

Micropyle. Opening through which pollen tube passes.

Monadelphous. Stamens united in one set.

Monocotyledon. One cotyledon.

Monoecious. With stamens and pistils in separate flowers on the same plant.

Mother cells. Cells that produce the pollen grains in the anthers and the eggs in the ovules.

Mucronate. Tipped with a short stiff point.

Multiple. Compound.

Muricate. Beset with short and hard or prickly points.

Mycelium. The vegetative portion of a fungus.

Nerve. A vein on the floral envelopes of grasses.

Node. The place on a stem where one or more leaves are attached; the joint.

Nucellus. Interior portion of an ovule.

Oblanceolate. Lanceolate with the broadest part toward the apex.

Oblong. Widely linear.

Obovate. Inverted ovate.

Obtuse. Blunt or rounded at the apex.

Oogonium. The female reproductive organ in some cryptogams. A sac within which oospheres are developed.

Orbicular. Circular.

Osteosclerids. Cells immediately beneath the Malpighian cells in Leguminosæ. They vary in shape and length, sometimes marked by longitudinal canals.

Ovary. Seed case of pistil.

Ovate. Outline like that of an egg, with larger part downward.

Ovoid. A solid having an oval outline.

Ovule. Unripe seeds in ovary.

Palet. Upper bract of the flower in grasses.

Palisade cells. Elongated cells perpendicular to epidermis on upper side of leaf.

Palmate. Radiately lobed or divided.

Panicle. Loosely, irregularly branched inflorescence.

Papilionaceous. Butterfly-shaped, like the corolla of the pea, etc.

Papilla. A soft elongated projection.

Papillate, papillose. Having papillæ.

Pappus. The modified limb of the calyx in corn, in Compositæ, especially, when the summit is developed in a feathery or plumose manner.

Parenchyma. All tissue composed of cells not having tapering extremities; soft cellular tissue like that of pith.

Parted. Cleft nearly or quite to the base.

Pedicel. A branch of inflorescence supporting one or more flowers.

Peduncle. A flower-stalk.

Pellucid. Clear, transparent.

Perennial. Living more than two years.

Perfect. Having both pistil and stamens.

Perianth. The floral envelope including calyx and corolla (or calyx alone when corolla is absent) whatever their form.

Pericarp. The matured ovary.

Perigynia. The bodies around the pistil.

Perigynium. The inflated sac enclosing the ovary in sedges.

Perigynous. Arranged around pistil.

Persistent. Remaining longer than usual, as calyx upon fruit, or leaves which die but remain on trees through the winter.

Perisperm. The albumen of a seed.

Petal. A division of the corolla.

Petiole. The stalk of a leaf.

Phloem. Portion of fibrovascular bundle containing the bast and sieve tissues.

Photosynthesis. Process by which sugar and starch are produced in a plant by means of the chlorophyll grain.

Pilose. Covered with long soft hairs.

Pinnate leaf. Compound with leaflets arranged on each side of a common petiole.

Pinnatifid. Pinnately cleft.

Pistil. The central seed-bearing organ of the flower consisting of ovary, style and stigma.

Pistillate. Provided with pistils; properly, without stamens.

Placenta. The part of the ovary to which the ovules are attached.

Plumose. Like a feather, having fine hairs on each side, as in the pappus-bristles of thistles.

Pod. Any dry, dehiscent fruit.

Pollen. The fertilizing powder produced in the anthers.

Pollination. Transferring pollen from anther to stigma.

Polygamous. Plants bearing both perfect flowers and flowers of either sex, or of both, as in the soft maple.

Pore-canal. Passage through a pit between adjoining cells.

Prickles. Short, stiff, spine-like growths from the epidermis, as in the rose.

Procambium. Fibro-vascular tissue of an organ formed before it is differentiated into xylem and phloem.

Procumbent. Trailing or lying on the ground.

Promycelium. A filament produced by a germinating spore on which are formed cells called sporidia.

Prostrate. Lying flat on the ground.

Protein. A plant food manufactured in the plant from starch or sugar by the addition of one of the compounds of nitrogen, phosphorus, potassium or other similar substances.

Protogynous or proterogynous. Having pistils ready for fertilization before anthers are matured.

Puberulent. Minutely pubescent.

Pubescent. Covered with fine, soft, short hairs.

Raceme. A simple indeterminate infloresence of pediceled flowers arranged along a rather long, common axis.

Rachilla. Axis of spikelet in grasses.

Rachis. The axis of a spike or other body.

Radical. Proceeding from the root or base of stem.

Raphe. The continuation of the seed-stalk along the side of an anatropous ovule or seed.

Raphe. The continuation of the seed-stalk along the side of an anatropous ovule or seed.

Receptacle. Summit of flower-stalk.

Reflexed. Abruptly bent or turned downward.

Repand. Having a slightly undulating margin.

Respiration. Process of oxidizing food by cells to release energy which is used by the cell in its chemical processes.

Reticulated. Net-veined.

Retrose. Directed backward or downward.

Rhizome. Any subterranean stem, usually rooting at the nodes and rising at the apex.

Rib. A primary or prominent vein in a leaf.

Root. The descending axis of the plant, which supplies it with nourishment.

Root-stock. See Rhizome.

Rugose. Covered with wrinkles. Corrugated.

Runcinate. Sharply toothed, the teeth directed backward.

Runner. A slender stolon that roots and forms new plants at intervals.

Sagittate (leaves). Arrow-shaped, lobes with acute lobes and apex.

Scabrous. Having a rough surface.

Scale. Any thin appendage, morphologically a modified, degenerated leaf.

Scape. A peduncle rising from the root, without proper foliage.

Scapose. Resembling a scape.

Scarious. Dry and membranous.

Sclerenchyma. Lignified tissue as applied to thick-walled fibers.

Sclerotic. Consisting of sclerenchyma.

Seed. The ripened ovule, enclosing a rudimentary plant and the food necessary for its germination.

Sepal. A division of the calyx.

Serrate. Having sharp teeth pointing forward.

Serrulate. Finely serrate.

Sessile. Without a stalk; thus a leaf is sessile when the blade is seated directly upon the stem.

Sheath. A tubular envelope as the sheath of grasses.

Shrub. A woody perennial smaller than a tree and usually having several stems.

Sieve tube. A vegetable cell having sieve-like perforations.

Silique. A narrow 2-valved pod.

Simple. Without subdivisions, opposed to compound; leaves, as oak, dock, etc.

Sinuate. Having strongly wavy margin.

Sinuous. Wavy, curving back and forth.

Sinus. The cleft between two lobes or divisions.

Spatulate. Shaped like a druggist's spatula, rounded at the summit and gradually narrowed downward.

Spicate. Arranged in a spike.

Spike. An inflorescence like a raceme, except that the flowers are sessile.

Spikelet. The characteristic inflorescence of grasses, secondary spike.

Spindle-shaped. See Fusiform.

Spine. A sharp, rigid process growing from the stem.

Sporangium. Spore case.

Spore. Pollen grain; reproductive body of flowerless plants.

Sporidium. A minute spore borne on a promycelium.

Spreading. Applied to branches that bend outward at less than a right angle.

Stamen. A pollen-bearing organ of a flower.

Staminate. Applied to a flower or plant which has stamens, but no pistils.

Stellate. Star-shaped.

Stereome. The supporting and protecting cells of the plant.

Sterile. Unfruitful, as a flower without a pistil or antherless stamen, or with abortive pollen grains.

Stigma. That part of the pistil which receives the pollen.

Stipules. Leaf-like appendages arranged in a pair at the base of the leaf stalk.

Stolon, or stole. A trailing or reclining and rooting shoot.

Stoma. Opening in the epidermis by which air enters and moisture escapes.

Striate. Marked with parallel lines or ridges.

Style. The slender part of a pistil supporting the stigma.

Sub-. A prefix meaning somewhat or slightly.

Subcuneate. Somewhat wedge-shaped.

Subulate. Awl-shaped.

Succulent. Juicy, fleshy.

Sulcate. Grooved or furrowed.

Suspensor. Filament of cells in ovary.

Tapetal Cells. Cells surrounding mother cells in anthers and containing food material for pollen.

Teleutospore. The winter spore of the rust fungus.

Telial. Pertaining to winter spores of the rust fungus.

Terete. Long and round.

Terminal. Attached to or pertaining to the extremity or apex, as the terminal bud.

Testa. Outer seed coat. Sometimes both coats are spoken of as the testa.

Tomentose. Densely pubescent with matted wool.

Tomentum. Matted, woolly hairs.

Toothed. See Dentate.

Trailing. Prostrate on the ground but not rooting.

Transpiration. Process by which leaves lose moisture.

Trichome. A plant hair of any kind.

Truncate. Ending abruptly as if cut off transversely.

Tuber. A short thickened subterranean branch.

Tubercle. A small tuber-like body.

Turbinate. Top-shaped.

Turgid. Thickened like a tuber, or distended with a liquid (never with air).

Umbel. Any indeterminate inflorescence in which the peduncles or pedicels of a cluster seem to rise from the same point.

Umbellate. Like an umbel.

Undulate. Having a wavy surface.

Uredo spore. A non-sexual spore in the rust fungus.

Urticating. Stinging. A term applied especially to the plant hairs of members of the Urticaceae, some of which are poisonous.

Utricle. A small inflated membranous 1-seeded fruit.

Valve. 1. One of the parts of a dehiscent fruit. 2. Applied also to the top of a pitcher in the Sarracenia.

Vascular. Pertaining to ducts or vessels for conveyance of sap.

Vein. A bundle of threads of fibro-vascular tissue in a leaf or other organ.

Verticillate. Whorled.

Villous. Bearing long, soft, straight hairs.

Viscid. Sticky, glutinous.

Wavy. Margin forms wavy line bending inward and outward in succession.

Wedge-shaped. See Cuneate.

Whorl. An arrangement of organs in a circle around a stem.

Wing. 1. Any thin or membranous expansion attached to or bordering an organ. 2. The lateral petal of a papilionaceous flower.

Winter annual. See Annual.

Xylem. Woody part of fibro-vascular bundle containing larger continuous air-containing vessels; the water-conducting tissue.

Zoosporangium. A sporangium producing zoospores or motile spores.

INDEX

ABBREVIATIONS

f.—figure.
m.—map.
sp.—species.

Absinth 323
Abutilon Theophrasti 214-216, 641, *f. 214, 215, 602*
  Distribution 216, 601, *m. 215*
  Extermination 216
  Seed 473, *f. 474*
  Number of seeds per plant 575
  Common names 641
  Southern weed 601
  Longevity of seed 641
  An ornamental, "Davis weed" 216
Acalypha virginica 202-203, *f. 203*
  Distribution 202, *m. 202*
  Extermination 203
  Seed 472, *f. 472*
Achenial hairs 489, 490, 491, 497, 498, 499, *f. 499, 500*
Achillea Millefolium 376-377, *f. 376, 587*
  Distribution 377, *m. 377*
  Extermination 377
  Seed 501, *f. 501*
Acnida tamariscina 118
  tuberculata 118-120, *f. 119*
  Distribution 118, *m. 119*
  Extermination 120
  Seed 454, *f. 454*
Adventitious buds 547
Aerial roots 542
Agastache scrophulariaefolia, seed 483-484, *f. 483*
Agencies of weed seed dissemination 561, 574, 575
Agricultural seeds in Iowa 656
Agoseris cuspidata, seed 510, *f. 510*
Agropyron repens 49-54, *f. 50*
  Distribution 50-51, 608, 610, 646, *m. 51*
  Extermination 51-52, 169, 546, 646
  Chemical composition 53-54
  Root-stocks 540, *f. 540*
  Roots, crowns 550
  Drying tests with roots 649, 653, *f. 652*
  Seed 443, *f. 443, 570, 577*
  Serious perennial 642
  Infested with ergot 634
  Smithii *f. 52*
  Distribution *m. 53*
  Seed 442, *f. 442*
  tenerum 49-53
  Distribution *m. 53*
  Seed *f. 443*
Agrostemma Githago 125-127, *f. 126, 583*
  Distribution 127, *m. 127*
  Extermination 127
  Seed 454-455, *f. 454, 570, 577, 583*
Agrostis alba, seed 436, *f. 436*
Alfalfa Dodder, Large-seeded, *Cuscuta* sp. *f. 571*
  Small-seeded *f. 571*
Alfilaria (Stork's bill)
Alkanet 258
Allium canadense 63-64, *f. 63*
  Distribution 63, *m. 64*
  Extermination 63-64
  Development of seed 538
  vineale 63
Alopecurus geniculatus *f. 597*
Alsike Clover, *Trifolium hybridum*, seed 467, *f. 467*
Alyssum, Hoary (Hoary Alyssum)

Amaranth, Green, see Rough Pigweed
  Spreading, see Prostrate Pigweed
Amaranthaceae 1, 113-120
  Seeds 453-454
Amaranthus blitoides 117-119, *f. 118*
  Distribution 117, *m. 117*
  Extermination 117
  Seed, 453, *f. 453*
  graecizans 115-117, *f. 116, 117, 573*
  Distribution 115, *m. 116*
  Seed 453, *f. 453*
  retroflexus 113-115, *f. 113, 114*
  Distribution 113, 601, *m. 115*
  Extermination 113-114
  Chemical composition 115
  Seed 453, *f. 453, 576*
  Trichome *f. 115*
Ambrosia artemisiifolia 345-349, *f. 346, 347, 348, 590*
  Distribution 345, *m. 348*
  Extermination 345-349
  Trichome *f. 348*
  Seed 495, *f. 494*
  bidentata, seed 493, *f. 494*
  psilostachya 349-350, *f. 349*
  Distribution 350
  Extermination 350
  Propagation 548
  Seed 495, *f. 494*
  Roots 548
  trifida 343-345, *f. 344, 583, 625*
  Distribution 344, *m. 345*
  Extermination 344
  Seed 493-495, *f. 494*
American Germander, *Teucrium canadense* 272-275, *f. 273, 274*
  Distribution 272, *m. 275*
  Extermination 272-274
  Seed 483, *f. 483*
  Gromwell, *Lithospermum latifolium*, seed 480, *f. 481*
  weeds in Europe 590
Anacardiaceae 2, 212-214
Andropogon scoparius *f. 578*
Anemone, Long-fruited, see below
Anemone cylindrica, seed 457-458, *f. 457, 565*
Angiospermae 1, 4-429
Angiosperms, embryo 537
Animals, dissemination by 574
Annual Brome Grass (Soft Chess)
  Morning Glory, *Ipomoea purpurea* 246-248, *f. 247*
  Distribution 248, *m. 247*
  Extermination 248
  Seed 477, *f. 478*
  Endosperm 539
  Sow Thistle, *Sonchus oleraceus* 416-418, *f. 417*
  Distribution 416-418, *m. 418*
  Extermination 418
  Seed 508, *f. 508*
  weeds 542, 602, 640
Annuals 546
Anthemis Cotula 377-379, *f. 378, 379*
  Distribution 377-379, *m. 379*
  Extermination 379
  Seed 501-502, *f. 501*
Anther 532, *f. 532*
Antheridium *f. 631*
Apera spica-venti, seed *f. 572*

Berry 539
Berteroa incana 142-143, *f. 143*
 Distribution 142, *m. 143*
 Extermination 142
Bessey, C. E. 297
Bibliography 661-671
Bidens, achenial hairs 499
 aristosa 371-372, *f. 372*
 Distribution 371-372, *m. 371*
 Extermination 372
 bipinnata
  Seed 499-500, *f. 500, 567*
 cernua 370-371, *f. 371*
  Distribution 370
  Extermination 370
 connata 369-370, *f. 370*
  Distribution 369
  Extermination 370
 discoidea, seed 499, *f. 500*
 frondosa 366-368, *f. 367*
  Distribution 368, *m. 367*
  Extermination 368
  Fruit 539
  Seed 499, *f. 500*
  sp., fruit 539
 vulgata 368-369, *f. 369*
  Distribution 368, *m. 368*
  Extermination 368
Biennial root *f. 546*
 Weeds 604, 642
 Wormwood, *Artemisia biennis* 385-387,
  f. 386
  Distribution 385-386, *m. 386*
  Extermination 387
  Seed 502, *f. 502*
Biennials 544, 546, 640
Bindweed, Black, Wild Buckwheat, *Poly-
 gonum Convolvulus* 96-98, *f. 97, 98*
 Distribution 96, *m. 96*
 Extermination 96
 Seed 450, *f. 450, 570, 605*
 European or Small, Morning-glory,
  Convolvulus arvensis 250-253, 548,
  f. 251. 252. 253, 549
  Distribution 250, *m. 252*
  Extermination 250-253
  Drying of root-stock 650
  Seed 478, *f. 478, 571*
  Flowers, *f. 528*
 Hedge (Wild Morning-glory)
 Field (European Bindweed)
 Small (European Bindweed)
Birlingmair, Robert H. 615
Bi-sexual flower 525
Bishop, J. J. 351
Bitter or Red-veined, Broad-leaved Dock,
 Rumex obtusifolius 75-76, *f. 76*
 Distribution 75, *m. 76*
 Extermination 75
 Seed 447, *f. 447, 584*
Black Bindweed, Wild Buckwheat, *Poly-
 gonum Convolvulus* 96-98, *f. 97, 98*
 Distribution 96, *m. 96*
 Extermination 96
 Seed 450, *f. 450, 570, 605*
Henbane 289
Medic, Yellow Trefoil, *Medicago lupulina*
 189-190, *f. 189*
 Distribution 190, *m. 189*
 Extermination 190
 Chemical composition 190
 Seed 469, *f. 469*
Mustard, *Brassica nigra*, 158-159,
 f. 159, 594
 Distribution 158, *m. 159*
 Extermination 158
 Flower, essential organs *f. 523*
 Seed 462, *f. 463, 570*
Nightshade (Common Nightshade)
 Stem rust 634
Black-eyed Susan, Nigger-head, Cone-
 flower, *Rudbeckia hirta* 357, *f. 356*
 Distribution 357, *m. 357*

Extermination 357
 Seed 497, *f. 497*
Bladder Campion, *Silene latifolia*
 Seed 455-456, *f. 456, 570*
 Ketmia (Shoo-fly)
Blazing Star, *Liatris punctata*, seed 490,
 f. 490
 Achenial hairs, *f. 490*
Blatchley, W. S. 662
Blooming time of weeds, 551-560
 cosmopolitan weeds 552
 grasses 551
Blue Field or Wild Blue Morning Glory,
 Ipomoea hederacea 245-246, *f. 246*
 Distribution 245, *m. 246*
 Extermination 245
 Seed 477-478
 Flowered Lettuce, *Lactuca floridana*,
  seed 510, *f. 509, 565*
 Grass 4. 6
 Canadian, seed *f. 572*
 Lettuce, *Lactuca pulchella* 426-427,
  f. 427
  Distribution 426, *m. 427*
  Extermination 426
 Sage (Lance-leaved Salvia)
 Stem, *Andropogon scoparius f. 578*
 Vervain, *Verbena hastata* 267-269,
  f. 267, 268
  Distribution 268, *m. 269*
  Extermination 269
  Seed 482, *f. 482*
Bokhara Clover (White Sweet Clover)
Bolley, H. L. 662
Boneset, White Snakeroot, *Eupatorium
 urticaefolium* 326-327, *f. 326, 327*
 Distribution 327, *m. 327*
 Extermination 327
 Seed 489, *f. 489*
 False (False Boneset)
Boot-jack (Stick-tight, Spanish Needles,
 Pitchforks)
Borage, flower *f. 526*
 Family, Boraginaceae 2, 258-264
 Seeds 479-481
Boraginaceae 2, 258-264
 Seeds 479-481
Bouncing Bet, Soapwort, *Saponaria offici-
 nalis* 132-135, *f. 132, 133, 134*
 Distribution 132-134, 610, *m. 135*
 Extermination 135
 Drying up of roots 649, *f. 652*
Bracted Plantain, *Plantago aristata* 319-
 320, *f. 319*
 Distribution 320, *m. 320*
 Extermination 320
 Seed 487-488, *f. 488*
Brake, common, *Pteris aquilina f. 589*
Brassica alba
 Floral arrangement 528
 Seed 461, *f. 461*
 arvensis 155-158, *f. 157, 594*
  Distribution 156, *m. 158*
  Extermination 156
  Chemical composition 157-158
  Seed 462, *f. 461, 570*
 campestris, seed 462, *f. 463*
 juncea 158
  Distribution 158
  Extermination 158
  Seed 462, *f. 462, 571*
 Napus, seed 463, *f. 463*
 nigra 158-159, *f. 159, 594*
  Distribution 158, *m. 159*
  Extermination 158
  Flower, essential organs *f. 523*
  Seed 462, *f. 463, 570*
Brauneria purpurea *f. 622*
Brazil, vegetation succeeding forest fires
 589
Bristly Foxtail, Whorled Millet, *Setaria
 verticillata* 18-19, *f. 18*
 Distribution 18-19, *m. 19*
 Seed 434, *f. 434, 567*

712

INDEX

Veronica arvensis, rare 309
peregrina 309-310, *f. 310*
  Distribution 309, *m. 310*
  Extermination 309-310
  Seed 486, *f. 486*
Vervain, Blue, *Verbena hastata,* 267-269,
f. 267, 268
  Distribution 268, *m. 269*
  Extermination 269
  Seed 482, *f. 482*
  Family 264-272
  Seeds 481-482
Hoary, *Verbena stricta* 269-271, *f. 269, 270*
  Distribution 270-271, *m. 271*
  Extermination 271
  Seed 482, *f. 482*
Large-bracted, Common Prostrate,
Verbena bracteosa 271-272, *f. 272*
  Distribution 272, *m. 272*
  Extermination 272
  Seed 482, *f. 482*
White, *verbena urticaefolia* 264-267, *f 265, 266*
  Distribution 265, *m. 267*
  Extermination 265
  Seed 481-482, *f. 482*
  Offshoots 550
Vetch, Common, *Vicia sativa* 195, 196, *f. 195*
  Distribution 196, *m. 196*
  Extermination 196
  Chemical composition 196
  Seed 470, *f. 470*
Hairy, *Vicia villosa,* seed 471, *f. 470*
Lathyrus aphaca, leaf *f. 513*
Vicia sativa 195-196, *f. 195*
  Distribution 196, *m. 196*
  Extermination 196
  Chemical composition 196
  Seed 470, *f. 470*
villosa, seed 471, *f. 470*
Viper's Bugloss, *Echium vulgare,* seed 481, *f. 481*
Virginia Ground Cherry, *Physalis lanceolata* 298-300, *f. 298*
  Distribution 299
  Extermination 299-300
Physalis virginiana 299
  Distribution 299, *m. 299*
  Extermination 299-300
Creeper, *Psedera quinquefolia,* leaf 212
Von Guttenberg, H. V. 664
Wallace's Farmer 79, 86, 112, 121, 216, 240, 249, 250, 252, 254, 257, 320, 323, 335, 346, 352, 353, 402
Water, seed dissemination by 561, 574
Hemlock, Cowbane, *Cicuta maculata,* 225-227
  Seed 475, *f. 475*
Hemp, *Acnida tuberculata* 118-120, *f. 119*
  Distribution 118, *m. 119*
  Extermination 120
  Seed 454, *f. 454*
Pepper, Mild, Water Smartweed, *Polygonum hydropiperoides* 93-95, *f. 94*
  Distribution 93-94, *m. 93*
  Extermination 94
  Leaf 515
  Seed 450
Smartweed, *Polygonum acre* 94-95, *f. 95*
  Seed 448, *f. 448*
Smartweed, Water Pepper, *Polygonum Hydropiper* 91, *f. 91*
  Distribution 91, 601
  Extermination 91
  Leaf 515
  Seed 449, *f. 449*
Waterleaf Family, Hydrophyllaceae 257-258

Watson, E. B. 350, 630
Wavy-leaved Thistle, Pasture Thistle, *Cirsium undulatum,* creeping roots 548
  Seed 504, *f. 504*
Weed hosts of fungi 635, 636
  hosts of insects 639
  law of Iowa 654-656
Seeds, dissemination 561-575
  Story of dissemination 561-574
  Agencies of dissemination 574-575
Weeds, of arable lands 621
  consume mineral and food elements 626
  and continuous cropping 621
  distribution, 1924, 610-614
  drying of roots 649
  eradication 640-647
  following fires 589
  frequency in fields 618, 619
  hosts for insects 639
  hosts for fungi 635-636
  injuriousness of 624-639
    effect on crop plants 627
    effect on soil cultivation 629
    harbor plant diseases 633-636
    harbor insect pests 624, 636-639
    stoppage of drains 632
  life cycle 561
  migration, from foreign countries 595
    from adjacent states 607-610
    from east to west 610
  morphology 512
  prominent, of Iowa 558-560
  roots 540
  seasonal succession 551
Weekly Register 273
Weems, J. B., 10, 15, 17, 44, 45, 53, 56
Weinhold 80
Western Ironweed, *Vernonia fasciculata* 323-325, *f. 324*
  Distribution 323, *m. 324*
  Extermination 323, 325
  Seed 489, *f. 488*
Mugwort, White Wormwood, *Artemisia ludoviciana* 384-385, *f. 385*
  Distribution 384, *m. 385*
  Extermination 385
Ragweed (Perennial Ragweed)
Sunflower (Prairie Sunflower)
Tumble Weed (Winged Pigweed)
Wheat Grass, *Agropyron Smithii, f. 52*
  Distribution *m. 53*
  Seed 442, *f. 442*
Westgate, J. M. 187
Wheat 4, 6
  with rust 635, *f. 634*
White or Many-flowered Aster, *Aster multiflorus* 333-334, *f. 334*
  Distribution 333, *m. 334*
  Extermination 333
  Achenial hairs 493, *f. 492*
Avens (Stickweed)
Clover, *Trifolium repens,* seed 467, *f. 467*
Campion, White Cockle, Evening Catchfly, *Lychnis alba,* 127-129, *f. 128*
  Distribution 128, *m. 128*
  Extermination 129
  Seed 455, *f. 455, 570*
Dwarf Plantain (Dwarf Plantain)
Mustard, *Brassica alba,* floral arrangement 528
  Seed 461, *f. 461*
Plantain (Dwarf Plantain)
Snakeroot (Boneset)
Sweet Clover, *Melilotus alba* 186-188, *f. 187, 188*
  Distribution 186-187, *m. 186*
  Extermination 187-188
  Chemical composition 188
  Roots *f. 541*
  Seed 467-468, *f. 468, 584*

The Amaranths   By E. E. Stanford

SOME people call th ... ... stamens and pistils are borne in
the farmers don't ... ... wers. These tiny blossoms are
properly amarant ... ... ch but a seed apiece—tiny, brown
Greek; it means ... ... and hard-shelled, in a thin-papery
applied by the ol ... ... hich readily bursts and lets it out.
fort to this grou ... ... owever, is quite enough. The
flower parts d ... ... eriment Station, seed-counting
been a favo ... ... n weeds a few years
were not ... ... species ... ...
Milton ...
... ...